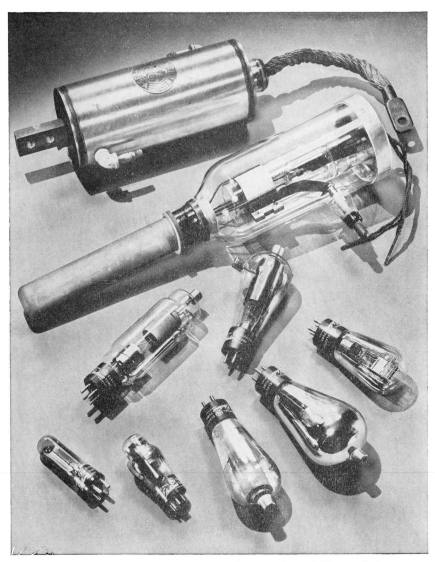

Group of industrial electron tubes. (Courtesy General Electric Co.)

# ELECTRONICS

## PRINCIPLES AND
## APPLICATIONS

BY

### RALPH R. WRIGHT

ASSOCIATE PROFESSOR OF ELECTRICAL ENGINEERING
VIRGINIA POLYTECHNIC INSTITUTE

THE RONALD PRESS COMPANY ⋎ NEW YORK

4

Library of Congress Catalog Card Number : 50–7004

PRINTED IN THE UNITED STATES OF AMERICA

To
KAYE

"Electronics is that branch of science and technology which relates to the conduction of electricity through gases or in vacuo."

—*American Standard Definitions of Electrical Terms*, New York: American Institute of Electrical Engineers, 1941, p. 231.

# PREFACE

This book is specifically designed to give a broad coverage of the basic applications of electron tubes in the fields of industrial control, power, and communications. Both the arrangement and the presentation of material are planned so as to make it a suitable text for use either in a basic electronics course for students in various nonelectrical engineering curricula, or in an introductory course in electronics for electrical engineering students or physics majors. The material presented herein has been used successfully with each of these groups.

With the conscious objective of making the text both flexible and suited to the various college curricula which include a basic course in electronics, more material has been offered than will usually be covered in the average one-quarter or even one-semester course. This will allow the instructor to choose from the later chapters those topics which he believes most valuable for the class at hand.

The make-up and arrangement of the book is as follows: Chapters 1 through 3 present basic electronic principles; Chapter 4 is a brief review of dc and ac circuits; and Chapters 5 through 12 deal with basic applications of electron tubes. Chapter 4 has been introduced to adapt the text to students of various backgrounds. Although one or more elementary courses in electrical engineering are ordinarily prerequisites for electronics, nonelectrical students may require a brief review of basic circuit theory, as presented in this chapter, before taking up analysis of electronic circuits. If the instructor prefers to leave the responsibility of review to the student, omission of Chapter 4 will not affect the continuity of the text.

Chapters 5 through 12, devoted to electronic circuits, have also been planned with flexibility in mind. They are arranged in the book in an order which the author considers a logical one, though it is by no means the only desirable order of coverage. Each of these chapters is a more or less complete unit in itself; thus the actual order of use may be any that seems most suitable.

Every effort has been made to present the material in a clear and coherent manner slanted to meet the requirements of a basic or introductory course. Ordinarily most students do not require an extensive knowledge of electronic circuits. Rather, they need a good grounding in basic principles of electronics and an understanding of how these principles can be applied to control or facilitate various industrial processes. In consequence, a highly mathematical approach has been deemed undesirable. Wherever possible topics are presented from a qualitative rather than a quantitative point of view. Only basic equations have been included. In most instances these are not derived; they are simply stated with the terms in each equation explained sufficiently to enable the student to use them intelligently. For the most part, only elementary mathematics is used, with employment of simple calculus in a few places to analyze phenomena that cannot be readily analyzed in any other way. In Chapter 12, which deals with control circuits, no attempt has been made to describe specific control equipment. Instead, various types of basic circuits illustrating the principles of electronic control circuits are explained.

The author wishes to express his appreciation to Professor W. A. Murray, Head of the Department of Electrical Engineering, and to Dr. F. L. Robeson, Head of the Department of Physics, both of the Virginia Polytechnic Institute, for their assistance; to the many manufacturing companies who supplied illustrations, for their courtesy and cooperation; and to Mrs. Kathleen M. Wright, his wife, for the encouragement given in the writing of this book and for her assistance in typing the manuscript.

RALPH R. WRIGHT

Blacksburg, Virginia
March, 1950

# CONTENTS

# CHAPTER 1

## ELECTRON BEHAVIOR

**1–1. Introduction.** In 1883 Thomas A. Edison performed the famous experiment which gave evidence of the possibility of passing a current through vacuum.* In the early days of his development of the incandescent lamp, Edison was faced with the somewhat baffling problem of preventing the lamp from losing its effectiveness because of the formation of a black deposit on the inside of the bulb. In the course of studying this problem, he had occasion to place a metallic electrode within the evacuated chamber near the filament and to connect it electrically through a galvanometer to the filament, as indicated by Figs. 1–1 and 1–2. He discovered

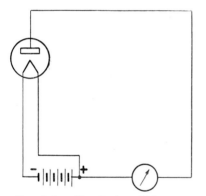

Fig. 1–1. Circuit in which current will exist between filament and anode.

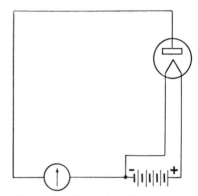

Fig. 1–2. Circuit in which no current will exist between filament and anode.

that when the electrode is connected through the galvanometer to the positive side of the dc filament supply, as shown in Fig. 1–1, the galvanometer deflects; but that when it is connected to the negative side of the filament supply, as shown in Fig. 1–2, no deflection is to be observed.† As this experiment did not result in a solution of Edison's problem, he attributed little practical importance to this discovery and did not pursue further study of it.

Other scientists, however, became interested in Edison's discovery and took up study of it. Preece was among the first to make an extended study

* A. E. Kennelly, Biographical Memoir of Thomas Alva Edison, *Proc. nat. Acad. Sci. Wash.*, 1933, **15**.
† E. J. Houston, Notes on Phenomena in Incandescent Lamps, *A.I.E.E. Trans.*, 1884, **I**, 1.

of the *Edison effect*, as it came to be called. After a quantitative investigation which extended over a period of approximately two years, Preece, in 1885, presented a paper in which he discussed his observations concerning the Edison effect. He found the magnitude of the anode current to be a function of the spacing between filament and anode, the temperature of the filament, and the difference of potential between anode and filament.

Although these observations were sound, Preece was unable to offer a satisfactory explanation of the phenomenon. He suggested that the current was the result of particles ejected from the filament towards the anode, but he was unable to identify the type of particles involved.

During approximately the same period Elster and Geitel, employing a very crude arrangement of what might be classified as a two-electrode tube, observed the unilateral conducting property of the diode. However, they failed to recognize its greatest field of usefulness — rectification.

In 1897 * J. J. Thomson and his associates, after several years of investigation of the so-called cathode rays, proved cathode rays to be streams of small negatively charged particles, termed electrons.† Thomson measured the ratio of charge $e$ to mass $m$ of these electrons and advanced the concept that this ratio is fixed. Subsequent investigation has revealed that each electron is identical to all other electrons, carries a negative charge of $1.60199 \times 10^{-19}$ coulomb and possesses a mass of $9.1055 \times 10^{-31}$ kilogram. E. Goldstein in 1886 observed so-called canal rays in a discharge tube. These later proved to be streams of positively charged particles, now termed protons. In 1898 W. Wien determined the ratio of charge to mass for protons and established the fact that this ratio is the same regardless of the type of gas used in the discharge tube. Protons carry a positive charge equal in magnitude to the negative charge of an electron and possess a mass of $1.67248 \times 10^{-27}$ kilogram. In 1932 J. Chadwick discovered particles with a slightly greater mass than protons ($1.67472 \times 10^{-27}$ kilogram) and which possess zero electric charge. These particles are known as neutrons. Particles which are identical to electrons in mass and magnitude of charge but of opposite sign were discovered by C. D. Andersen in 1932. These particles, which are termed positrons, are commonly emitted in nuclear reactions.

A group of negatively charged electrons surrounding a positively charged nucleus comprised of neutrons and protons constitutes what is known as an atom. The number and arrangement of electrons surrounding the nucleus determine the chemical characteristics of the element comprised of a particular kind of atom. For a further discussion of atomic structure the reader is referred to any standard text on physics or chemistry. Present recommended values for several of the more commonly used atomic constants are given in Table 1–1.

---

* J. J. Thomson, Cathode Rays, *Annual Report Smithsonian Inst.*, 1897, 157.
† The term electron was first used by G. J. Stoney in 1891.

TABLE 1–1*

| Constant | Recommended Value |
|---|---|
| Electronic charge $e$ .............. | $(1.60199 \pm 0.00016) \times 10^{-19}$ coulomb |
| Electronic mass $m$ .............. | $(9.1055 \pm 0.0012) \times 10^{-31}$ kilogram |
| Specific electronic charge $e/m$ ...... | $(1.75936 \pm 0.00018) \times 10^{11}$ coulomb/kilogram |
| Planck's constant $h$ ............. | $(6.6234 \pm 0.0011) \times 10^{-34}$ joule-second |
| Velocity of light $c$ .............. | $(2.99776 \pm 0.00004) \times 10^{8}$ meters/second |

* J. W. M. Dumond and E. R. Cohen, Our Knowledge of the Atomic Constants $F$, $N$, $m$ and $h$ in 1947 and of Other Constants Derivable Therefrom, *Rev. Mod. Phys.*, 1948, **20**, 85.

Electrons in all materials drift at random within the material of which they are a part. However, since their motion is random, the net drift in any one direction cancels out and the passage of charge in any one direction is zero. If a sufficiently strong electric field is applied, an oriented drift will be superimposed on the random drift. This results in a net passage of charge in the direction of the field. The electrons which take part in the oriented drift are known as *free electrons* and the charge conveyed by these electrons as they move through the circuit gives rise to what is termed *electric current*. Materials such as mica, rubber, porcelain, glass, etc., have very few free electrons per unit volume, therefore are poor conductors of electricity. On the other hand, metals in general have a relatively large number of free electrons per unit volume, thus are good conductors. Silver, copper, gold and aluminum are among the best metallic conductors.

Let it be assumed that two resistors $R_1$ and $R_2$ of equal length and cross-section differ in resistance by a factor of ten but that $R_2 = 10R_1$ due to difference in material. Now assume that a difference of potential of $E_1$ volts

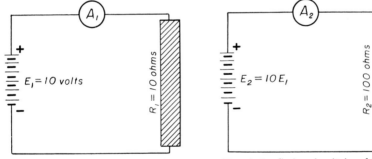

FIG. 1–3. Series circuit in which rate of flow of charge is one coulomb per second.

FIG. 1–4. Series circuit in which rate of flow of charge is one coulomb per second.

is applied through an ammeter to $R_1$ and a difference of potential of $10E_1$ volts is applied through an ammeter to the terminals of $R_2$. These arrangements are indicated by Figs. 1–3 and 1–4, respectively. If $E_1$ is equal to ten volts and $R_1$ is ten ohms, then ammeter $A_1$ will indicate one ampere.

This means that charge is being transferred through $R_1$ at the rate of one coulomb per second. Now since the charge possessed by an electron is $1.60199 \times 10^{-19}$ coulomb, and since the charge is being transferred by the so-called free electrons, free electrons must drift through any given cross-section of $R_1$ at the rate of $6.24 \times 10^{18}$ per second. Now if $R_2$ is 100 ohms and $E_2$ is 100 volts, then ammeter $A_2$ also indicates one ampere; but since $R_2$, though of the same length and cross section as $R_1$, is of ten times the ohmic value, there will be only one tenth as many so-called free electrons per unit volume in $R_2$ as in $R_1$. It is for this reason that the voltage necessary to produce the same rate of electron flow, and therefore the same current, is ten times as great for $R_2$ as it is for $R_1$. Therefore, since $E_2 = 10E_1$ and $I_2 = I_1$, the heat dissipation $P_2 = E_2I_2$ in $R_2$ will be ten times greater than that in $R_1$ — namely, $P_1 = E_1I_1$.

In 1904 J. A. Fleming took out a patent in Great Britain on a two-electrode vacuum tube (hence the long-used term of "Fleming valve" to designate a diode). He obtained a patent on the same tube in the United State in 1905.* While this tube was of limited application, it paved the way for a new field in engineering by serving as the forerunner of all modern vacuum tubes.

Later, Lee DeForest introduced a grid structure between the filament and anode of the two-electrode tube, thus obtaining a triode. This invention was one of the greatest single advances in the development of the modern vacuum tube. DeForest obtained a patent on this tube in January, 1907.† It is interesting to note that he encountered considerable difficulty in obtaining a patent on his tube. It was argued that the triode was covered by Fleming's patent. The triode makes possible amplification, which is utilized in many different types of electronic apparatus. At present vacuum tubes are being manufactured that incorporate many active electrodes; however, most such tubes are modifications of the simple triode.

## Electron Emission

**1–2. Nature of Emission.** In electrical devices that do not incorporate electron tubes of one type or another, the conduction of electricity is restricted to metallic or carbon conductors and electrolytes; however, as mentioned previously, it is possible to have electrons move through gases or vacuum. In order for electrons to move through vacuum, they must first be liberated into the vacuum from a liquid or solid. Electron emission does not occur unless the electrons within a given surface obtain sufficient energy to overcome the so-called *potential barrier* that exists at the surface. The energy per unit charge that an electron must possess in order to over-

---

* U.S. Patent No. 803,684, April, 1905.
† U.S. Patent No. 841,387, January, 1907.

come the potential barrier is a function of the type of material from which
it is to be emitted and is known as the *work function*. Commonly the work
function of a surface $E_w$ is expressed in *electron volts*. By definition, the
electron volt is the kinetic energy per unit charge acquired by an electron
in falling through a difference of potential of one volt. Accordingly, when
expressed in electron volts, the work function indicates the kinetic energy
per unit of charge (joules per coulomb) that an electron must possess in
order to break through the potential barrier of the material and move out
into the space surrounding it.

Each material has a certain definite work function. Tungsten, for example, has a work function of 4.52 electron volts; thus for an electron to be
emitted from a pure tungsten surface it must possess kinetic energy to the
extent of $4.52e$ joules. By equating the minimum kinetic energy the electron must possess in order to break through the surface, to the expression for
the kinetic energy of any moving particle, the minimum velocity that the
electron must attain in order to be emitted from the surface can be determined.

The minimum kinetic energy required for emission is

$$KE = eE_w \tag{1-1}$$

where     $e$ = charge of electron in coulombs

      $E_w$ = work function of material in electron volts

      $KE$ = minimum kinetic energy in joules the electron must possess
            in order to break through the potential barrier

The relationship between kinetic energy and velocity of a particle of mass
$m$ is

$$KE = \tfrac{1}{2}mv^2 \tag{1-2}$$

where $m$ = mass of particle in kilograms

      $v$ = velocity * of particle in meters/second

Equating the right hand members of (1–1) and (1–2) yields

$$\tfrac{1}{2}mv^2 = eE_w$$

whence

$$v = \sqrt{\frac{2eE_w}{m}} \tag{1-3}$$

EXAMPLE. Determine the minimum velocity an electron must attain in order
to be emitted from a pure tungsten surface.

*Solution:* Substituting the values † of $e$, $m$ and $E_w = 4.52$ in Eq. (1–3) gives

$$v = \sqrt{\frac{(2)(1.602 \times 10^{-19})(4.52)}{9.106 \times 10^{-31}}}$$
$$= 12.62 \times 10^5 \, \text{m/sec}$$

---

* Unless specifically indicated to the contrary, "velocity," "force," "field intensity,"
etc., refer merely to the scalar value of the vector quantity or component of it under
discussion.

† The values of $e$ and $m$ used in calculations are rounded off to three decimal places.

Thus an electron must attain a very high velocity in order to break through the potential barrier at a tungsten surface; such is true of metallic surfaces in general.

## Types of Electron Emission

At present there are five known types of emission:

1. Thermionic emission
2. Photoelectric emission
3. High-field emission
4. Secondary emission
5. Radioactive disintegration

**1–3. Thermionic Emission.**  Thermionic emission is, in so far as electron tubes are concerned, the most important type of emission.  As the temperature of a given body is increased, the average kinetic energy of the electrons is increased.  If the temperature is raised sufficiently, some of the electrons near the surface attain enough energy to overcome the potential barrier at the surface and move out into the space surrounding the hot body.  Thus the emission of electrons from a hot body is somewhat analogous to the evaporation of water due to boiling.

Unless a positive potential gradient exists in the region of the emitter, (commonly referred to as the cathode, in electron tubes) the electrons that are emitted will move only a very short distance from the emitter.  The exit of electrons from the cathode leaves a deficiency of electrons at the cathode; and, in turn, this deficiency results in a negative potential gradient tending to cause the electrons to return to the cathode.  In consequence, unless a counter positive potential gradient produces a greater force on the electrons that have been emitted than does the negative gradient due to electron deficiency in the cathode, all electrons will return to the cathode.

As mentioned previously, the work function is a measure of the amount of energy per unit charge an electron must possess in order to be emitted from a given surface; thus, the higher the work function of a surface the greater is the energy per unit charge required for emission.  This, in turn, necessitates a greater temperature for a given amount of emission.  Again, the higher the temperature of an emitter of given work function the greater will be the number of electrons emitted.  However, the temperature cannot be increased indefinitely; for eventually a temperature would be reached at which the atoms themselves would evaporate, resulting in disintegration of the emitter.

Structurally there are two general types of thermionic cathodes or emitters.  In one type the emitter consists of wire of high resistance (usually tungsten or some alloy) which is coated with a material of relatively low work function.  The emitter is brought to the correct temperature by the heat resulting from the $I^2R$ loss in the wire when a potential difference is applied to its terminals. Such an arrangement is illustrated by Fig. 1–5. This type of emitter is referred to as a filamentary or directly heated type of cathode. The other type of emitter is comprised of a heater wire, to which a potential difference is applied, enclosed by, and insulated from, a close fitting metallic sleeve. This sleeve is coated with a suitable emitting material. A cathode of this structure is termed an indirectly heated or heater-type cathode.

Modern thermionic electron tubes employ one of the following types of emitting surfaces:

1. Pure tungsten
2. Thoriated-tungsten
3. Oxides of barium and strontium

Fig. 1–5. Filamentary or directly heated type thermionic emitter.

The pure tungsten cathode was the earliest type of thermionic emitter employed in electron tubes. It is still used in the larger types of transmitting tubes. Commonly, a pure tungsten cathode, having a work function of 4.52 electron volts, is operated at a temperature of around 2,400° Kelvin.

The thoriated-tungsten filament was developed by I. Langmuir.* This type filament exhibits a much lower work function than tungsten, hence is normally operated at a much lower temperature. 1,900° Kelvin is a typical operating temperature. Although the work function of thoriated-tungsten surfaces differs, $E_w = 2.65$ is probably representative. The thoriated-tungsten filament is formed by impregnating a pure strip of tungsten with an extremely small amount of carbon and thorium oxide. The tungsten filament is then coated, placed in the tube, the tube evacuated, and the filament baked at a temperature of about 2,800° Kelvin for approximately one minute. This baking process reduces some of the thorium oxide to pure thorium and the thorium thus formed slowly works its way to the surface, forming a layer of atomic thickness. The emission is from the layer of thorium atoms.

The most widely used cathode is one which was developed by A. Wehnelt in 1903. He coated a nickel ribbon with a mixture of barium and strontium carbonates and obtained a resulting surface exhibiting a work function appreciably lower than that of thoriated-tungsten. The oxide-coated cathode is the most efficient type of emitter known. The normal operating temperature is around 1,000° Kelvin and the work function is in the vicinity of one electron volt. An oxide-coated cathode is made by coating a mixture of barium and strontium carbonates, which are suspended in an organic

---

* I. Langmuir, Electron Emission from Thoriated Tungsten Filaments, *Phys. Rev.*, 1923, **22**, 357.

binder on a cylindrical nickel or konel metal (alloy of cobalt, iron, nickel and titanium) sleeve, within which is placed a heater element of the necessary thermal capacity. The cathode, along with the other electrodes, is mounted in the tube which is then evacuated and baked at a temperature of about 1,300° Kelvin for the time necessary to drive out the binder and reduce the carbonates to oxides. The temperature is then reduced to 1,200° Kelvin and the potential difference between anode and cathode is increased until the emission current reaches a constant value. The graph of Fig. 1–6 gives a comparison of the relative emitting properties of oxide-coated, thoriated-tungsten, and tungsten cathodes.

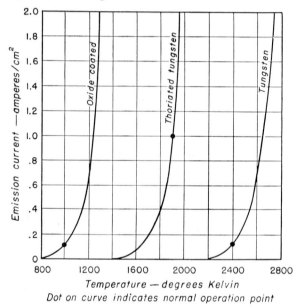

Fig. 1–6. Emission from thermionic emitters. (Adapted by permission from *Applied Electronics* by Electrical Engineering Staff of M.I.T., published by John Wiley & Sons, Inc. and The Technology Press.)

In the design of thermionic emitters for high-vacuum tubes, one important consideration is the *emitting efficiency* of the cathode. The emitting efficiency is defined as the ratio of the emission current per unit area to the heating power per unit area. The emission current is usually expressed in milliamperes and the heating power in watts. The emitting efficiency is a function of the physical and chemical make-up of the emitting surface and depends to a large extent on the work function of the material. For a given physical structure, the lower the work function the higher the emitting efficiency. The oxide-coated cathode gives the highest emitting efficiency of any known emitter and is used in practically all modern receiving tubes and most transmitting tubes which operate at a cathode-anode voltage of less than 1,000 volts. Oxide-coated cathodes will not stand up well under very high potential gradients. In consequence, thoriated-tungsten filaments are generally employed if the plate voltage is from 1,000 to around 2,500 volts and pure tungsten filaments are generally used when potential differences in excess of 2,500 to 3,000 volts are employed.

**1–4. Photoelectric Emission.** In 1887 H. R. Hertz, while experimenting with electric arcs, discovered that the discharge across a given arc was greater when illuminated by radiation from a second arc. Later, Elster and Geitel established the fact that the increase in the intensity of the arc was due to the emission of electrons from the negative electrode, caused by ultraviolet radiation falling on the negative electrode. Further investigation showed that emission could be readily obtained from alkali metals when radiations of certain wave lengths were allowed to fall on them.

In order to obtain an understanding of photoelectric emission, radiant energy is considered as comprised of photons, i.e., concentrated packets of energy possessing momentum and mass but no charge. The energy of the photon is equal to the product of the frequency of the radiation and Planck's constant.* Many experimental determinations of Planck's constant have been made and resulting numerical values determined from test data differ somewhat. The value accepted at present is that of $6.6234 \times 10^{-34}$ joule-seconds, listed in Table 1–1. If an electron is in the path of an impinging photon and absorbs the photon, it may or may not receive enough energy to be emitted. Whether or not the electron will be emitted will depend upon the frequency of the radiation, the work function of the surface, and the initial energy of the electron. If the temperature of a surface is above absolute zero, the electrons within the surface will possess some energy. However, the temperature of a photoelectric emitter generally is not sufficiently great to contribute appreciably to the total energy necessary for electrons to escape from the surface. If it is assumed that the initial energy of an electron within the surface is zero, then the energy that the electron must obtain from a photon in order to be emitted with just zero velocity is expressed by Eq. (1–4).

$$hf = eE_w \tag{1–4}$$

where  $h$ = Planck's constant in joule-seconds
$\quad\quad\quad f$ = frequency of the impinging radiation in cycles/second
$\quad\quad\quad e$ = charge on the electron in coulombs
$\quad\quad\quad E_w$ = work function of the surface in electron volts

Solving Eq. (1–4) for $f$ gives the minimum frequency at which photoelectric emission can take place.

$$f = \frac{E_w e}{h} \tag{1–5}$$

---

* For a discussion of the quantum theory, see F. K. Richtmyer and E. H. Kennard, *Introduction to Modern Physics* (4th ed.; New York: McGraw-Hill Book Co., Inc., 1947), p. 91.

Substituting $c/\lambda$ for $f$ gives the maximum wave length at which photo-electric emission can take place.

$$\lambda = \frac{ch}{eE_w} \tag{1-6}$$

where $\lambda$ = wave length of radiation in meters
$\quad\quad c$ = velocity of radiation in meters/second

Substituting numerical values for $c$, $h$ and $e$ and converting wave length to Angstrom units,*

$$\lambda = \frac{(2.998 \times 10^8)(6.623 \times 10^{-34})}{(1.602 \times 10^{-19})E_w} \times 10^{10}$$

$$= \frac{12,400}{E_w} \tag{1-7}$$

For a given homogeneous surface the work function $E_w$ will be of fixed value. Accordingly, substituting the value of $E_w$ for the surface in question and solving for $f$ in Eq. (1–5) will give the lowest value of frequency of the impinging radiation at which photoelectric emission can occur, regardless of the intensity of the radiation or the length of time for which it is applied. This value of frequency is known as the *threshold frequency*. The corresponding value of wavelength $\lambda$ as defined by Eqs. (1–6) and (1–7) is known as the *threshold wavelength*. Photoelectric emission cannot be obtained unless the wavelength is equal to or shorter than the value as defined by Eq. (1–7).

In industrial practice monochromatic radiation is seldom, if ever, employed as a source of excitation of photosensitive surfaces. Consequently, any source of visible radiation capable of causing photoelectric emission will contain wavelengths much shorter than the threshold value and correspondingly higher frequency components than the threshold frequency. In most instances, then, electrons will be emitted with some initial velocity. The initial velocity can be determined from the following equation:

$$\tfrac{1}{2}mv^2 = (hf - eE_w) \tag{1-8}$$

or

$$v = \sqrt{\frac{2(hf - eE_w)}{m}} \tag{1-9}$$

where $m$ = mass of the electron in kilograms
$\quad\quad v$ = velocity of electron in meters/second
$\quad\quad$ and the other symbols are as previously defined

A typical photoelectric emitter consists of a relatively large metallic strip (much larger surface area than in the case of the high-vacuum thermionic diode) of copper or other suitable metal, coated with a photosensitive

---

* The Angstrom unit, commonly abbreviated Å, is generally used as a measure of the wave length of radiation. (1 meter = $10^{10}$ Å)

material on the side to be exposed to light.  The strip is usually pressed in the form of a cylinder of semicircular cross section.  Therefore the distance from the cathode to the small cylindrical anode in the center is approximately the same at any point on the surface of the cathode.  This type of cathode structure also results in maximum surface area for a given size tube envelope.

Several common photosensitive materials together with their respective work functions and threshold wavelengths are listed in Table 1–2.

TABLE  1–2

| Metal | Work Function * (electron volts) | Threshold Wavelength (Angstrom units) |
| --- | --- | --- |
| Lithium.................. | 2.36 | 5,250 |
| Potassium............... | 1.55 | 8,000 |
| Rubidium................ | 1.45 | 8,560 |
| Caesium................. | 1.36 | 9,120 |

* The values for work function are from V. K. Zworykin and H. D. Wilson, *Photocells and Their Applications* (New York: John Wiley & Sons, 1934), p. 34.  The values for wavelength are calculated from Eq. (1–7).

The curves of Fig. 1–7 show the relative wavelength response of several photosensitive materials.  At present one commonly used photosensitive

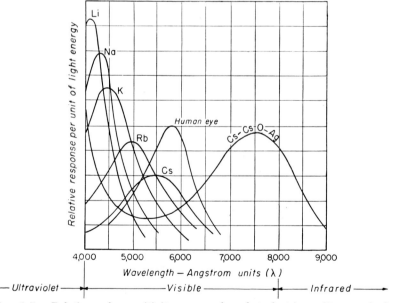

Fig. 1–7.   Relative color-sensitivity curves for photoelectric emitters and the human eye.  (Adapted by permission from *Applied Electronics* by the Electrical Engineering Staff of M.I.T., published by John Wiley & Sons, Inc. and The Technology Press.)

surface is Cs-CsO-Ag. This type of emitter is more sensitive to the radiation from an incandescent lamp than any other type.

Photoelectric emission is important in many types of industrial control such as counting circuits, inspection circuits, etc. Modern sound movies would not be possible without the photoelectric tube.

**1-5. High-Field Emission.** It is possible, by means of an externally applied electric field, to exert sufficient force on the electrons within a metal to enable them to overcome the potential barrier at the surface and move out through the surface. If electrons are extracted in this manner, the phenomenon is known as high-field emission. Potential gradients necessary to give rise to high-field emission are in the order of billions of volts per meter. It has been determined that a potential gradient of around $10^{10}$ volts per meter is necessary to produce high-field emission from a pure tungsten surface. It is thought that high-field emission plays a major part in the availability of current in pool-type mercury-arc rectifiers. In the case of mercury-arc rectifiers, the potential between the mercury pool and anode is extremely small, usually about 10 to 20 volts. However, since most of the drop exists across a very thin space adjoining the mercury pool, the electric field intensity at the surface of the pool is sufficiently great to result in high-field emission.

**1-6. Secondary Emission.** J. Bragg, in 1908, found that if electrons are made to bombard a metallic surface with sufficient velocity, other electrons will be emitted from the surface. The emission is due to the fact that electrons within the metal are receiving sufficient energy from the primary electrons striking the surface to overcome the potential barrier at the surface. This phenomenon is known as secondary emission.

It is also possible by bombardment with ions to impart enough energy to electrons at the surface of a metal to produce secondary emission. However, due to the very low velocity of ions within an electron tube, this type of bombardment gives rise to very little emission.

Some secondary emission may occur in tubes when the energy of the impinging electrons is as low as 10 electron volts; however, a much higher potential is necessary to obtain any appreciable emission. One primary electron can give rise to several secondary electrons; the ratio of secondary to primary electrons can often be as high as ten to one. This ratio is called the *secondary emission coefficient* and is a function of the velocity of the primary electrons and the type of surface which they strike. The number of secondary electrons per primary electron does not increase indefinitely with the energy of the primary electrons. The emission coefficient reaches a maximum value at primary electron energies of around 500 electron volts; further increase in energy results in a gradual decrease in the number of secondary electrons. The decrease in secondary emission with an increase in primary electron energy is thought to be due to the fact that higher velocity primary electrons energize would-be secondary electrons which are deeper in the metal and are likely to be absorbed by atoms before they reach the surface.

Most secondary electrons leave the surface with very little initial velocity; however, some secondary electrons have been observed with velocities corresponding to energies of around 30 electron volts.

The phenomenon of secondary emission occurs in all types of electron tubes but is not usually undesirable except in cases where there is within the tube, in addition to the anode (or plate),* another positive electrode which will collect secondary electrons. In the case of tubes where there is a possibility of secondary electrons being collected by another electrode, a suppressor-electrode which suppresses the effects of secondary emission is incorporated within the tube. There are some tubes, however, that make use of secondary emission. One such tube is the electron-multiplier tube which gives an amplification of several million.

**1–7. Radioactive Disintegration.** The first evidence of radioactive disintegration was reported by H. Becquerel in 1896. Becquerel discovered that an invisible radiation was emitted from uranium salts. Among the several properties which he reported concerning this radiation was that the region near the salts was electrically conducting. F. O. Giesel, in 1899, found that it was possible to deflect part of the radiation from a radioactive material by a strong magnetic field. The direction of the deflection was the same as that of a beam of electrons moving in the same direction through a magnetic field oriented in the same way. This gave evidence that the radiation might be electrons moving out from the surface.

Several years later (1903), E. Rutherford was able to detect deflection of a smaller part of the radiation in the same direction that positively charged particles would be deflected by a magnetic field. During the same year, R. J. Strutt discovered a third component of radiation which was not influenced by a magnetic field and was similar in nature to x-rays. From these experiments it was concluded that three types of rays were emitted from radioactive substances. These rays are now known as $\beta$-rays, $\alpha$-rays and $\gamma$-rays, respectively. Radioactive substances can be classified as to natural radioactive materials and artificial radioactive materials. Several elements are radioactive as they exist in their natural state. However, in recent years scientists have been able to produce radioactivity by bombarding certain elements with very high energy particles.

Radioactive substances, such as radium, have been important in the medical field for many years. The real significance of artificially produced radioactivity has yet to be determined. Today radioactive disintegration is of utmost concern to the leading scientists and statesmen of the world.

---

* *Anode* and *plate* are used interchangeably throughout the text.

## Movement of Electrons Within a Vacuum

In order for electrons to be "put to work" so that they can be made to play their role in the operation of the many types of intricate and complicated electronic devices that are now in existence, they must first be emitted and then they must be set in motion within an electron tube. The motion of an electron or a beam of electrons can be controlled by either an electric or a magnetic field. In some applications the path of the electrons is determined by concurrent electric and magnetic fields. In the majority of applications, however, the path of the electrons is determined by electrostatic rather than magnetic fields.

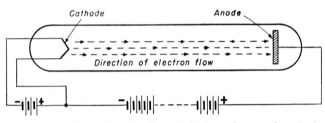

Fig. 1–8. Diagram illustrating the flow of electrons from a thermionic emitter to a positive anode.

**1–8. Effects of an Electrostatic Field on the Motion of Electrons Within a Vacuum.** Consider the two-electrode tube in Fig. 1–8. In order for thermionic emission to be accomplished, the tube must be evacuated. If the tube is not evacuated the cathode will oxidize before reaching the temperature necessary for emission.

Let it be assumed that electrons are thermionically emitted from the cathode. If the difference of potential between the cathode and anode is zero, the emitted electrons will not be attracted to the anode but will accumulate in the space directly in front of the cathode, forming what is termed negative space charge. These electrons will continue to accumulate until the negative space charge resulting from their presence becomes just great enough to counteract emission; thus equilibrium will exist. If, however, the anode is made positive with respect to the cathode, it will attract electrons which are emitted from the cathode. The magnitude of the attracting force, as stated by Preece in 1885, is proportional to the difference of potential between the cathode and anode and inversely proportional to the distance between the cathode and anode.

Before considering a quantitative analysis of the above-mentioned phenomenon, several properties of the electron will be reviewed. All electrons are identical regardless of the substance of which they are a part. Each has an approximate radius of $1 \times 10^{-15}$ meter, possesses a mass of $9.106 \times 10^{-31}$ kilogram and carries a negative charge of $1.602 \times 10^{-19}$ coulomb. The mass as given is the mass at rest. The mass of an electron actually is not constant but increases with the velocity of the electron. Eq. (1–10), which has been verified experimentally, expresses the mass of an electron as a function of its velocity.

$$m_v = \frac{m_r}{\sqrt{1 - \left(\dfrac{v}{c}\right)^2}} \qquad (1\text{–}10)$$

where $m_v$ = mass of electron at velocity in question
$\quad m_r$ = mass of electron at rest
$\quad\ \ v$ = velocity of electron in meters/second
$\quad\ \ c$ = velocity of light in meters/second

It is interesting to note the change in mass of an electron when accelerated by a potential of 3,000 volts. An electron on dropping through a potential of 3,000 volts attains a velocity of approximately one tenth the speed of light. Hence, applying Eq. (1–10)

$$m_v = \frac{m_r}{\sqrt{1 - (0.1)^2}}$$

$$= 1.005 m_r$$

Thus, it is seen that the change in mass is very slight for the relatively low voltage employed in most electron tubes. In all discussion which follows, the variation of mass with velocity is neglected.

Consider the forces acting on a charged particle in an electrostatic field. By definition, the component $\mathcal{E}_x$ of the field intensity $\mathcal{E}$ at any point is the negative of the rate of increase of potential $\phi$ with respect to $x$ at the point in question. If a potential difference of $E_a$ volts is impressed between two parallel plates which are perpendicular to the $x$ axis (Fig. 1–9), the field intensity $\mathcal{E}_x$ at any point between the plates is

$$\mathcal{E}_x = -\frac{d\phi}{dx}$$

It can be shown that the potential distribution curve in the case under consideration is a linear function of $x$, as indicated in Fig. 1–9. Accordingly, the field intensity of $\mathcal{E}_x$ is expressed by

$$\mathcal{E}_x = -\frac{E_a}{d} \qquad (1\text{–}11)$$

where $\mathcal{E}_x$ = $x$-component of field strength in volts/meter
$\quad E_a$ = accelerating difference of potential in volts
$\quad\ \ d$ = spacing between plates in meters

The force on a charged particle in an electrostatic field is equal to the product of the signed charge and the field intensity. Thus, recalling that the signed charge of the electron is $-e$,

$$F_x = -e\mathcal{E}_x \qquad (1\text{–}12a)$$

Whence from Eq. (1–11)

$$F_x = e\,\frac{E_a}{d} \qquad (1\text{–}12b)$$

where $F_x$ = force on electron in newtons
$\quad\ \ e$ = charge on electron in coulombs

$F_x$ in Eq. (1–12b) is of positive value indicating that the force on the electron is directed from the cathode ($x = 0$) to the anode ($x = d$). The component $a_x$ of the acceleration $a$ of any moving particle is described by the following equation:

$$F_x = m a_x \qquad (1\text{–}13a)$$

or

$$a_x = \frac{F_x}{m} \qquad (1\text{–}13b)$$

where $a_x$ = $\dot{x}$ component of acceleration in meters/second²
$\quad\ \ F_x$ = $x$ component of force in newtons
$\quad\ \ m$ = mass in kilograms

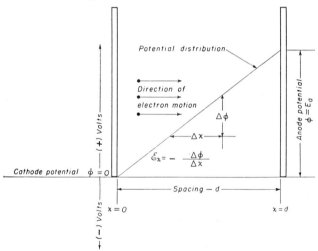

Fig. 1–9.  Potential distribution between two parallel plates when a potential difference of $E_a$ volts is applied.

Substituting the value of $F_x$ from Eq. (1–12a) in Eq. (1–13b) gives

$$a_x = -\,\frac{e\mathcal{E}_x}{m} \qquad (1\text{–}14a)$$

and using Eq. (1–11)

$$a_x = \left(\frac{e}{m}\right)\!\left(\frac{E_a}{d}\right) \qquad (1\text{–}14b)$$

Substituting numerical values for $e$ and $m$

$$a_x = 1.759\left(\frac{E_a}{d}\right) \times 10^{11} \qquad (1\text{–}15)$$

From Eq. (1–15) it follows that if the electrostatic field through which the electron is moving is uniform, the acceleration is constant.

EXAMPLE. An electron emitted from the cathode in Fig. 1–9 is accelerated by a difference of potential of 1,000 v. If the distance between cathode and anode is $1 \times 10^{-2}$ m and the field strength is uniform, determine the acceleration of the electron.

*Solution:*

$$a_x = 1.759 \left(\frac{E_a}{x}\right) \times 10^{11}$$

$$= \frac{1.759 \ (1 \times 10^3)}{1 \times 10^{-2}} \times 10^{11}$$

$$= 1.759 \times 10^{16} \ \text{m/sec}^2$$

The $x$ component of acceleration of any moving particle can be expressed in terms of the $x$ component of velocity by

$$a_x = \frac{dv_x}{dt}$$

whence

$$dv_x = a_x \, dt$$

If $v_x = 0$ when $t = 0$, then

$$v_x = \int_0^t a_x \, dt \qquad (1\text{–}16)$$

If $a_x$ is constant—as, for example, in the case of a charged particle acted on by a uniform electrostatic field,

$$v_x = a_x t \qquad (1\text{–}17)$$

Now

$$v_x = \frac{dx}{dt}$$

Therefore

$$dx = v_x \, dt$$

whence

$$dx = a_x t \, dt$$

Thus

$$x = a_x \int_0^t t \, dt$$

whence

$$x = \tfrac{1}{2} a_x t^2 \qquad (1\text{–}18)$$

where  $x = $ distance traveled in meters from point at which $x = 0$ and $t = 0$
$\qquad a_x = x$ component of acceleration in meters/second$^2$
$\qquad t = $ time in seconds

Solving Eq. (1–18) for $t$

$$t = \sqrt{\frac{2x}{a_x}} \qquad (1\text{–}19)$$

EXAMPLE. Find the time it takes the electron of previous example to travel from cathode to anode.

*Solution:*

$$t = \sqrt{\frac{2x}{a_x}}$$

$$= \sqrt{\frac{(2)(1) \times 10^{-2}}{1.759 \times 10^{16}}}$$

$$= 1.0673 \times 10^{-9} \text{ sec}$$

From the above example it can be seen that the time required for an electron to travel from the cathode to the anode of a vacuum tube, where the field is approximated by the conditions of Fig. 1–9, is extremely small. This time is usually referred to as the transit time of the tube.

Consider the kinetic energy attained by an electron when accelerated by a given difference of potential from an initial velocity of zero. Returning to Eq. (1–13)

$$F_x = ma_x$$

Multiplying both sides of the equation by $dx$

$$F_x \, dx = ma_x \, dx \tag{1–20}$$

Substituting $a_x = dv_x/dt$ and $dx = v_x \, dt$ in Eq. (1–20) yields

$$F_x \, dx = m\left(\frac{dv_x}{dt}\right)v_x \, dt$$

If $F_x$ is constant as in the case of the force acting on a particle in a uniform electric field

$$F_x \int_0^x dx = m \int_0^{v_x} v_x \, dv_x$$

$$F_x x = \tfrac{1}{2}mv_x^2$$

Thus

$$KE = \tfrac{1}{2}mv_x^2 \tag{1–21}$$

where $KE$ = kinetic energy of particle in joules
   $m$ = mass of particle in kilograms
   $v_x$ = x-component of velocity in meters/second

The kinetic energy acquired by an electron in dropping through a given difference in potential is

$$KE = Ee \text{ joules} \tag{1–22}$$

where $E$ = potential difference in volts through which electron has dropped
   $e$ = charge on the electron in coulombs

Equating Eqs. (1–21) and (1–22) yields

$$\tfrac{1}{2}mv_x^2 = Ee \tag{1–23}$$

whence

$$v_x^2 = \frac{2Ee}{m}$$

and thus

$$v_x = \sqrt{\frac{2Ee}{m}} \qquad (1\text{-}24)$$

Substituting numerical values for $e$ and $m$ gives

$$v_x = \sqrt{\frac{(2)(1.602 \times 10^{-19})E}{9.106 \times 10^{-31}}}$$

$$= 5.93 \times 10^5 \sqrt{E} \qquad (1\text{-}25)$$

EXAMPLE. Assume that the spacing between the cathode and anode of a certain high vacuum tube is $1 \times 10^{-2}$ m and the difference of potential between cathode and anode is 400 v. Assuming that the initial velocity of the electrons is zero, determine the velocity with which electrons will strike the anode.

*Solution:*

$$v_x = 5.93 \times 10^5 \sqrt{E}$$

$$= 5.93 \times 10^5 \sqrt{400}$$

$$= 1.186 \times 10^7 \text{ m/sec}$$

It is interesting to compare the velocity of the electrons within this tube to that of the fastest moving airplane. The velocity with which electrons strike the anode of the tube under consideration is $1.186 \times 10^7$ meters per second or almost 27 million miles per hour. This means that the velocity of the fastest airplane is practically negligible compared to the velocity of electrons within vacuum tubes, even though they are accelerated by a relatively small difference of potential.

**1–9. Effects of a Magnetic Field on the Motion of Electrons in a Vacuum.** The path of a beam of electrons can be controlled by magnetic as well as electrostatic forces.

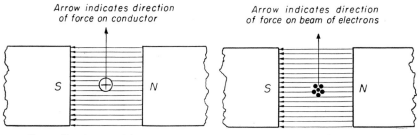

FIG. 1–10. Force on a current-carrying conductor in a magnetic field.          FIG. 1–11. Force on a beam of electrons in a magnetic field.

Consider Figs. 1–10 and 1–11. Fig. 1–10 illustrates the well-known motor principle. If the current is into the paper (away from the observer) as indicated, the force on the conductor will be upward. The electrons

within the conductor are moving in the opposite direction from that of the
assumed conventional current flow.  The net force acting on a current
carrying conductor is actually equal to the summation of the forces on the
individual electrons moving through the conductor, but due to the fact
that the electrons are a part of the conductor, it is impossible to change
the path of the electrons without moving the conductor through which they
are flowing (assuming, of course, that the electrons are not emitted from

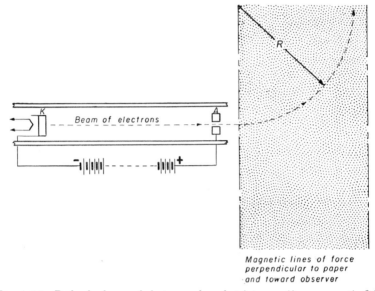

Magnetic lines of force
perpendicular to paper
and toward observer

Fig. 1–12.  Path of a beam of electrons when shot into a uniform magnetic field.

the surface of the conductor).  If the electrons are not confined within the
surface of a conductor but are shot in the form of a beam through a magnetic field as shown in Fig. 1–11, they will tend to be deflected in the same
direction as the electrons flowing through the conductor of Fig. 1–10.  This
assumes, of course, that the electrons in both cases are flowing in the same
direction.  Fig. 1–12 illustrates the path a beam of electrons will follow
when shot into a uniform magnetic field.  In the case under consideration
the magnetic lines of force are perpendicular to the motion of the beam of
electrons, out of the paper and toward the observer.  When an electron leaves
the cathode of Fig. 1–12 it will be accelerated toward the anode and will
attain its maximum velocity as it passes through the hole in the anode.  If
the electron, after attaining a constant velocity, enters a uniform magnetic
field, the force at any instant is perpendicular to the motion and does no
work on the electron; therefore, its speed is not altered.

Since the magnetic field and the velocity of the electron are both constant, the force acting on the electron is at all times constant.  A force of
this sort, always acting at right angles to the direction of motion of a par-

ticle which possesses a constant linear velocity, results in the particle moving in a circular path with constant speed. Such a motion is analogous to the motion of a ball when tied to the end of a string and twirled at constant velocity.

Any mass moving in a circular path with constant velocity of magnitude $v$ has an acceleration toward the center, the magnitude of which is

$$a = \frac{v^2}{R} \tag{1-26}$$

where $R$ = radius of the path

Since

$$F = ma$$

then

$$F = \frac{mv^2}{R} \tag{1-27}$$

The force on an electron when moving through a magnetic field is expressed by

$$F = Bev \tag{1-28}$$

where $B$ = flux density in webers/square meter
  $e$ = charge on an electron in coulombs
  $v$ = velocity of electron in meters/second
  $F$ = force in newtons

If the terms in Eq. (1–27) are expressed in the mks system, $F$ is in newtons and Eq. (1–27) can be equated to Eq. (1–28) yielding

$$Bev = \frac{mv^2}{R}$$

whence

$$R = \frac{mv}{Be} \tag{1-29}$$

where $R$ = radius of path in meters

Substituting for $v$ the values given by Eq. (1–25) and numerical values for $e$ and $m$, Eq. (1–29) reduces to the following:

$$R = \frac{9.106 \times 10^{-31} \times 5.93 \times 10^5 \sqrt{E}}{1.602 \times 10^{-19} B}$$

$$= \frac{3.37 \times 10^{-6} \sqrt{E}}{B} \tag{1-30}$$

Here $R$ is the radius of the circular path taken by an electron when shot into a uniform magnetic field of flux density $B$ webers per square meter. The angular velocity of the electron can be determined as follows:

$$\omega = \frac{v}{R} \tag{1-31}$$

Substituting the value of $R$ as given by Eq. (1–29) yields

$$\omega = \left(\frac{e}{m}\right) B$$

Substituting numerical values for $e$ and $m$

$$\omega = 1.759 \times 10^{11} B \qquad (1\text{–}32)$$

where $\omega$ = angular velocity in radians/second

The time $T$ for one complete revolution can be determined as follows:

$$T = \frac{2\pi}{\omega} \qquad (1\text{–}33)$$

$$= \frac{2\pi}{1.759 \times 10^{11} B}$$

$$= \frac{3.57 \times 10^{-11}}{B} \qquad (1\text{–}34)$$

In this presentation, the field of electron ballistics has only been touched upon. However, it is thought that the general principles of behavior of electrons in magnetic and electric fields as presented here are sufficient to give the student insight into the effects of electric and magnetic fields on the motion of a charged particle. Electron ballistics is of primary importance in the design of cathode-ray tubes, television tubes, electron microscopes, magnetrons, linear accelerators, cyclotrons, betatrons, mass spectrographs, etc.

## PROBLEMS

**1–1.** Determine the amount of energy necessary to release an electron from a barium-strontium oxide surface which has a work function 1.25 ev. Repeat for a thoriated-tungsten surface having a work function of 2.65 ev.

**1–2.** Find the minimum frequency of radiation that can cause photoelectric emission from a potassium surface having a work function of 1.55 ev. Repeat for a tungsten surface which has a work function of 4.52 ev.

**1–3.** Radiation of wavelength 5,895 Å falls on a sodium surface, the work function of which is 1.82 ev. Calculate the maximum velocity with which electrons will be emitted. Repeat for a lithium surface which has a work function of 2.36 ev.

**1–4.** If the secondary-emission coefficient of a given surface is 8, determine the number of electrons leaving the surface per second when the primary current is 1 ma.

**1–5.** What would be the mass of an electron if it were moving at a velocity of $1 \times 10^8$ m/sec? What velocity must it attain before its mass will be twice as great as its mass at rest?

**1–6.** An electron with zero initial velocity starts at the center of a large capacitor plate and moves to a parallel plate $5 \times 10^{-2}$ m away. If the second plate is 1,000 v positive with respect to the first, determine:

*a*) The acceleration of the electron during flight.

*b*) The maximum velocity attained by the electron during flight.

*c*) The position at which maximum velocity is attained.

*d*) The average velocity during flight.

*e*) The time the electron is in flight between the two plates.

*f*) The kinetic energy of the electron when it reaches the plate.

**1–7.** An electron starts with zero initial velocity at the negative plate of a parallel plane capacitor across which exists a difference of potential of 1,132 v. If the spacing between the plates is $2 \times 10^{-2}$ m, determine:

*a*) The time the electron has been in flight before acquiring a velocity of $1 \times 10^7$ m/sec.

*b*) The distance traveled before acquiring this velocity.

*c*) The potential difference through which the electron has dropped on acquiring the velocity of $1 \times 10^7$ m/sec.

*d*) The velocity with which the electron strikes the plate.

*e*) The kinetic energy imparted to the plate.

**1–8.** An electron, after having fallen through a potential difference of 1,600 v, enters a parallel plate capacitor through a small hole in the lower plate with which it makes a 30° angle. Determine the voltage that must be applied between the upper and lower plate in order for the electron to strike the upper plate which is $3 \times 10^{-2}$ m away, at a point $2 \times 10^{-2}$ m to the right of the point at which the electron entered the field.

**1–9.** An electron, after having been accelerated through a potential difference of 1,000 v, enters a uniform magnetic field of flux density $1 \times 10^{-4}$ w/m². Assuming that the motion of the electron is normal to the magnetic flux at all times, determine:

*a*) The radius of the circular path taken by the electron while in the magnetic field.

*b*) The angular velocity of the electron while in the magnetic field.

*c*) The time required for the electron to make a complete orbit.

**1–10.** An electron enters a magnetic field of flux density $5 \times 10^{-4}$ w/m² with a component of velocity $V_x$ of $1 \times 10^7$ m/sec parallel to the flux lines. If the electron also possesses a component of velocity $V_y$ of $1 \times 10^6$ m/sec normal to the magnetic field, sketch the path taken by the electron.

## BIBLIOGRAPHY

ALBERT, A. L. *Fundamental Electronics and Vacuum Tubes.* New York: The Macmillan Co., 1947, pp. 3–16, 38–50.

*American Standard Definitions of Electrical Terms.* New York: American Institute of Electrical Engineers, 1941, p. 231.

BENDZ, W. I. *Electronics for Industry.* New York: John Wiley & Sons, Inc., 1947, pp. 1–19.

BETHE, H. A. *Elementary Nuclear Theory.* New York: John Wiley & Sons, Inc., 1947, pp. 23–8.

CHAFFEE, E. L. *Theory of Thermionic Vacuum Tubes.* New York: McGraw-Hill Book Co., Inc., 1933, pp. 5–10, 24–34, 55–93.

COBINE, J. D. *Gaseous Conductors.* New York: McGraw-Hill Book Co., Inc., 1941, pp. 106–22.

CORK, J. M. *Radioactivity and Nuclear Physics.* New York: D. Van Nostrand Co., Inc., 1947, pp. 1–32.

CRUFT LABORATORY STAFF. *Electronic Circuits and Tubes*. New York: McGraw-Hill Book Co., Inc., 1947, pp. 260–65.

DOW, W. G. *Fundamentals of Engineering Electronics*. New York: John Wiley & Sons, Inc., 1937, pp. 56–80.

DUMOND, J. W. M., and COHEN, E. R. Our Knowledge of the Atomic Constants $F$, $N$, $m$ and $h$ in 1947 and of Other Constants Derivable Therefrom. *Rev. Mod. Phys.*, 1948, **20**, 85.

EASTMAN, A. V. *Fundamentals of Vacuum Tubes*. 2nd ed. New York: McGraw-Hill Book Co., Inc., 1941, pp. 5–21.

FINK, D. G. *Engineering Electronics*. New York: McGraw-Hill Book Co., Inc., 1938, pp. 17–32.

HOUSTON, E. J. Notes on Phenomena in Incandescent Lamps, *A.I.E.E. Trans.*, 1884, **1**, 1.

KENNELLY, A. E. Biographical Memoir of Thomas Alva Edison. *Proc. nat. Acad. Sci. Wash.*, 1933, **15**.

MCARTHUR, E. D. *Electronics and Electron Tubes*. New York: John Wiley & Sons, Inc., 1936, pp. 1–7.

M.I.T. STAFF. *Applied Electronics*. New York: John Wiley & Sons, Inc., 1943, pp. 1–18, 36–50, 70–110.

MILLMAN, J., and SEELY, S. *Electronics*. New York: McGraw-Hill Book Co., Inc., 1941, pp. 15–56.

MORECROFT, J. H. *Electron Tubes and Their Applications*. New York: John Wiley & Sons, Inc., 1933, pp. 10–42.

REICH, H. J. *Theory and Applications of Electron Tubes*. 2nd ed. New York: McGraw-Hill Book Co., Inc., 1944, pp. 1–18.

RICHTMYER, F. K., and KENNARD, E. H. *Introduction to Modern Physics*. 4th ed. New York: McGraw-Hill Book Co., Inc., 1948, p. 99.

RYDER, J. D. *Electronic Engineering Principles*. New York: Prentice-Hall, Inc., 1947, pp. 1–34, 55–75.

SPANGENBERG, K. R. *Vacuum Tubes*. New York: McGraw-Hill Book Co., Inc., 1948, pp. 19–57, 97–124.

STRANATHAN, J. D. *The "Particles" of Modern Physics*. Philadelphia: The Blakiston Co., 1942, pp. 101–212.

TERMAN, F. E. *Radio Engineers' Handbook*. New York: McGraw-Hill Book Co., Inc., 1943, pp. 274–86.

THOMSON, J. J. Cathode Rays, *Annual Report of The Smithsonian Inst.*, 1897, 157.

———. *Electricity and Matter*. New Haven, Conn.: Yale University Press, 1903, pp. 70–89.

ZWORYKIN, V. K., and MORTON, G. A. *Television*. New York: John Wiley & Sons, Inc., 1940, pp. 3–41.

ZWORYKIN, V. K., and WILSON, H. D. *Photocells and Their Applications*. New York: John Wiley & Sons, Inc., 1934, p. 34.

## CHAPTER 2

## THERMIONIC HIGH–VACUUM TUBES

A thermionic high-vacuum tube is, as the name indicates, a tube which contains no gas, is evacuated to a pressure of around $1 \times 10^{-6}$ percent of an atmosphere, and depends upon heat energy as a means of producing electron emission. Such tubes, in general, contain from two to eight electrodes (multiple unit tubes often have more electrodes), enclosed by either a metal or a glass envelope. They range in size from a fraction of an inch in height, in the case of specialized applications such as hearing aids and

FIG. 2–1. Acorn pentode and triode compared to a golf ball. (Courtesy Radio Corp. of America.)

radio proximity fuses, to six feet in height for large transmitting tubes, such as those employed in the larger broadcasting stations and in radio-frequency heating apparatus. Examples of small high-vacuum tubes are shown in Fig. 2–1. Fig. 2–2 shows a large water-cooled high-vacuum tube. This tube, which has an over-all length of $60\frac{3}{8}$ inches, is a transmitting triode (three-electrode tube). Thermionic high-vacuum tubes comprise the oldest and most widely used group of tubes. Both wire and wireless transmission, as well as the controls of numerous industrial processes, are dependent on thermionic high-vacuum tubes of one type or another.

### Diodes

**2–1. Structure.** The thermionic high-vacuum tube in its simplest form is a two-electrode tube comprised of an emitter, termed the cathode, sur-

rounded by a metallic or carbon cylinder which serves as the anode.  The
cathode acts as a source of electrons, the anode as a collector of electrons.
Electrons released from the surface of the cathode are accelerated toward
the anode, which is at a positive potential with respect to the cathode.

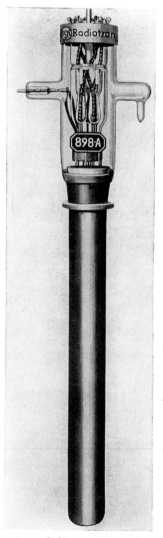

FIG. 2–2.  100-kw water-cooled transmitting tube.  Height: 60⅜ inches.
(Courtesy Radio Corp. of America.)

These electrons, striking the anode at high velocities, release their energy
of motion in the form of heat.  For this reason it is necessary that anodes
be large in size compared to cathodes and capable of dissipating appreciable
heat.  Structurally there are two general types of cathodes: the directly

heated cathode, commonly known as the filamentary cathode; and the indirectly heated cathode, often referred to as the heater-type cathode.

The filamentary cathode in its simplest form consists of a wire of circular cross section coated with a thin layer of a suitable emitting material. The structure usually takes the form of a straight wire, a *V* or a *W*. Typical structures are shown in Fig. 2–3.

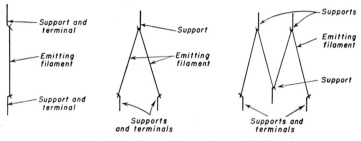

FIG. 2–3.   Typical filamentary cathodes.

The heater-type cathode, which is employed in practically all modern ac-operated radio tubes, was developed primarily to minimize the hum arising from the effects of ac heater operation. This type of cathode consists of a heater wire, enclosed by and insulated from a close fitting metallic sleeve which, in turn, is coated with a suitable emitting material. The insulating material employed must insulate the heater wire and also be a fair conductor of heat in order for maximum emitting efficiency to be realized. Oxides of beryllium and aluminum are ceramic materials that are commonly used for this purpose. The heater wire is usually made of an alloy of tungsten; the metallic sleeve of nickel or konel metal, coated with oxides of barium and strontium. Typical structures of heater-type cathodes are shown in Fig. 2–4.

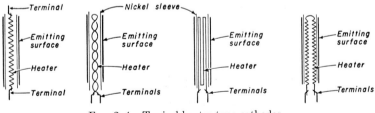

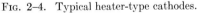

FIG. 2–4.   Typical heater-type cathodes.

Anodes or plates of small high-vacuum diodes are made of nickel or iron, or alloys of these two metals. They are pressed from sheet material and are usually crimped and flanged in order to give increased mechanical strength and increased radiation. Large anodes, such as those employed in the larger air-cooled transmitting tubes, are often made of graphite. Most metallic substances will not stand up under the extremely high anode temperatures that exist in large air-cooled transmitting tubes. Large transmitting tubes, i.e., those with ratings of around 2.5 kw and above, employ metallic plates which also serve as part of the tube envelope. Such tubes are water-cooled or forced-air-cooled. If water-cooled, a water jacket

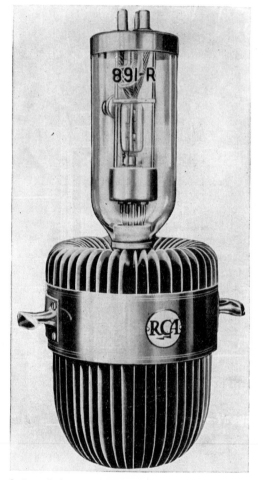

FIG. 2–5.  Forced-air-cooled transmitting tube.  (Courtesy Radio Corp. of America.)

is placed around the anode; thus the temperature of the anode is kept within the required range by circulation of water at the proper rate. A 100-kw transmitting tube is shown in Fig. 2–2. Water-cooled tubes are made in power ratings from 1 to 250 kw. In recent years, forced-air-cooled transmitting tubes of fairly high power capacity * have been dezveloped. Such tubes are quite similar in structure to water-cooled tubes.

---

* Although most forced-air-cooled transmitting tubes have an output rating of less than 10 kw, such tubes are made with power ratings up to 50 kw.

However, the water jacket is replaced by a radiator, from which heat is carried away by forced-air ventilation. A typical forced-air-cooled transmitting tube is shown in Fig. 2–5. When the power demands are such that tubes can be cooled satisfactorily by forced-air ventilation, this method, because of its simplicity and economy, is usually preferred to water cooling.

The diode is used chiefly as a rectifier. At present, almost all direct current energy being used is obtained by converting alternating current energy to direct current energy. The amount of energy supplied by storage batteries is negligible compared to the amount supplied by conversion units. All radio receivers, radio transmitters, amplifiers, oscillators, etc., require dc for operation and in the majority of cases this dc is obtained by means of electronic rectifiers. In the past, the large blocks of dc power, i.e., amounts measured in hundreds and thousands of kilowatts, required for subway and trolley car operation and for electrolytic processes in aluminum and copper plants, etc., were supplied exclusively by direct current generators or rotary converters. Now, however, large polyphase mercury-arc rectifiers are replacing rotating machinery as a means of obtaining dc power for the operation of dc transportation systems and for use in aluminum plants, etc. The nature of this type of conversion, including its advantages and disadvantages compared to rotating machinery, is discussed in Chapter 7.

**2–2. Characteristics.** The characteristics of a diode can be determined by a few very simple tests. Consider the circuit diagram of Fig. 2–6. The battery labeled $A$ supplies current for the indirectly heated filament.

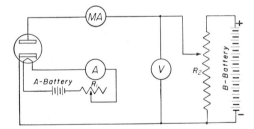

Fig. 2–6. Circuit for determining the characteristics of a diode.

The current through the heater, of which the temperature is a function, is controlled by the variable resistor $R_1$. The magnitude of the heater current can be determined from the ammeter in the heater circuit. The $B$ battery supplies the plate potential * which can be varied from zero to the maximum value obtainable from the battery by proper adjustment of the potentiometer rheostat $R_2$. The magnitude of the difference of potential between cathode and plate is measured by the voltmeter $V$ and the magnitude of the plate current is determined by the milliammeter labeled $MA$.

---

* The term plate (or anode) potential is used to indicate the increase in potential above that of the cathode, the latter being taken arbitrarily as zero value.

There are two families of static characteristics that define the merits of a diode. The first family is obtained by holding the filament current constant and determining the variation of plate current with plate potential.

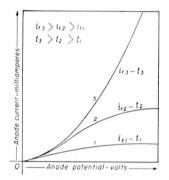

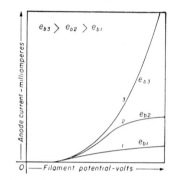

FIG. 2–7.   Static characteristics of a diode. $i_b$ vs. $e_b$ for fixed values of filament temperature $t$.

FIG. 2–8.   Static characteristics of a diode. $i_b$ vs. $e_f$ for fixed values of plate potential $e_b$.

Several suitable values of filament current should be used in order for a typical family of curves to be obtained. The second family of characteristics is obtained by holding the plate potential constant and determining the variation of plate current with filament current. It is usually desirable to obtain curves for several different values of plate potential. Typical curves are shown in Figs. 2–7 and 2–8, respectively.

In order to understand the characteristics of a diode, it is necessary to study the reasons for the various shapes of the characteristic curves. Let

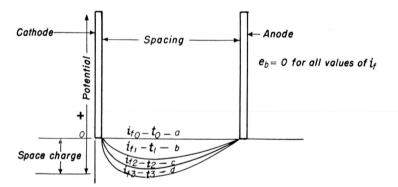

FIG. 2–9.   Potential distribution curves for parallel-plane diode when plate potential $e_b$ is held at zero.   (Magnitude of space charge greatly exaggerated.)

the cathode and anode of a diode be considered as two infinite parallel planes (Fig. 2–9). If the difference of potential between the cathode and anode is zero, and the cathode is not heated sufficiently to emit electrons, the potential distribution between the cathode and anode will be represented by the straight line $a$. If the temperature is increased to a temperature $t_1$ which is great enough to give a small amount of emission, the emitted electrons will accumulate in the space in front of the cathode, forming a cloud of negative charge which is commonly termed *space charge*.* The space charge under equilibrium conditions will always be just great enough to counteract emission. The potential distribution curve in this case will be represented by the curve $b$. Now if the temperature is increased still further to a new temperature $t_2$, the emission will be increased and thus the magnitude of the space charge will increase until equilibrium between space charge and emission exists. In most cases the flow of current to the plate, for the conditions just described, will be zero; but in cases where the spacing between the cathode and anode is extremely small, a few electrons may possess enough initial energy to find their way to the plate giving rise to a small amount of plate current with zero plate voltage. A further increase in the temperature will result in a greater dip in the potential distribution, as illustrated by curve $d$ of Fig. 2–9.

Now assume that the temperature of the cathode is held at a value below that necessary for emission and the plate potential is varied (Fig. 2–10). If the difference of potential between the cathode and anode

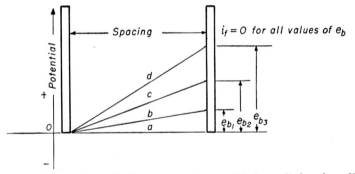

Fig. 2–10. Potential distribution curves for parallel-plane diode when filament temperature $t$ is below the value necessary for emission.

is zero, the potential distribution curve will be a straight line as illustrated by line $a$. A potential $e_{b1}$ will give a potential distribution curve as illustrated by line $b$, a higher plate potential $e_{b2}$ will result in line $c$, and a still higher plate potential $e_{b3}$ will give a distribution curve represented by line $d$.

By superimposing the conditions of Fig. 2–10 on those of Fig. 2–9, the action of a diode may be understood. Consider the condition represented by curve $b$ of Fig. 2–9 which is reproduced in Fig. 2–11. There are many

---

* The space charge, as illustrated by Figs. 2–9, 2–11, 2–13 and subsequent figures in this chapter, is plotted to a much larger scale than plate potential. If both were plotted to the same scale, the dip due to space charge would be very small and difficult to illustrate.

electrons in the space near the cathode; but because the anode is not positive with respect to the cathode, none of these electrons will be attracted to the anode. If the anode is made positive with respect to the cathode by the amount $e_{b1}$, the anode will exert a force on the electrons in the

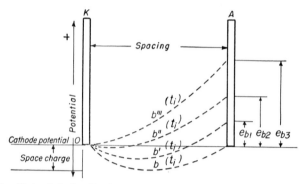

FIG. 2–11. Potential distribution curves for several values of $e_b$. (Space charge exaggerated.)

region near the cathode and a large number of the electrons will be attracted to the anode. The electrons that find their way to the anode will be those with greatest initial velocities. The potential distribution curve will now be as illustrated by line $b'$. Removing electrons from the space in front of the cathode is usually referred to as neutralization of the space charge. The space charge is not completely neutralized unless all electrons emitted are collected by the anode. An increase in the plate potential to a value $e_{b2}$ will neutralize still more of the space charge by attracting a greater number of electrons; thus, the plate current will increase. A still further increase in $e_b$ to the value of $e_{b3}$ will continue to increase the plate current. The potential distribution curve $b'''$ corresponds to plate potential $e_{b3}$. This curve has a positive slope at all points, indicating that all emitted electrons are being attracted to the anode. The plate current is now the theoretical maximum obtainable for the temperature $t_1$ and is termed the *saturation current*. If the plate potential is increased above $e_{b3}$, the velocity with which the electrons strike the plate will be increased; but since the value of plate potential $e_{b3}$ is sufficiently great to bring all the emitted electrons across to the plate, the number of electrons arriving at the plate per unit time cannot be increased by a further increase in plate potential. Therefore, the plate current is a maximum for the temperature $t_1$ and is said to be *temperature limited*. This condition is illustrated by curve 1 of Fig. 2–12. If the temperature is raised to a higher value $t_2$, more emitted electrons will be available and the plate potential can be raised to a higher value before maximum plate current is realized. This condition is illustrated by curve 2 of Fig. 2–12. If the filament current is increased to the rated value, as specified by the manufacturer, the corresponding temperature $t_3$ will be sufficiently great to prevent the current from becoming temperature limited for all practical values of plate voltage and some space charge will always exist in the region near the cathode. When the plate current is limited in this way, it is said to be *space-charge limited*.

It will be noticed that the theoretical curves of Fig. 2–12 have the same general contour as the corresponding experimental curves in Fig. 2–7. The main difference is in the knees of the saturation curves. The theoretical curves indicate a definite point of saturation while the experimental curves have a much more gradual change in slope. This difference is due primarily to the fact that the spacing between the cathode and plate is not the same at all points and the temperature of the cathode is not uniform;

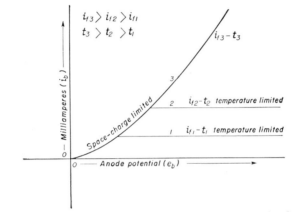

FIG. 2–12. Theoretical static characteristics of a diode. $i_b$ vs. $e_b$ for fixed values of $t$.

thus, not all points on the surface of the cathode become temperature limited at the same value of plate potential. This condition gives rise to a gradual bend instead of the abrupt bend that would be expected from theoretical considerations where the anode and the cathode are treated as perfect parallel planes and the temperature of the cathode is assumed to be uniform over its entire surface.

Consider the case where the plate potential is held at a fixed value and the temperature of the filament is varied by changing the filament current (Fig. 2–13). If the cathode is cold and the plate potential is zero, the potential distribution will be as illustrated by straight line $a$ of Fig. 2–13. If the plate potential is increased to the value $e_{b1}$ with the cathode still cold, the potential distribution will be represented by curve $b$. There now exists a positive potential gradient; but since there are no emitted electrons, there will be no current flow. Now if the temperature is increased to a value sufficient in magnitude to give rise to emission, the emitted electrons will be attracted by the anode. The potential distribution is now represented by curve $b'$. The plate current will continue to increase with an increase in the temperature of the cathode until the space charge, due to the cloud of electrons in the immediate vicinity of the cathode, becomes so great that it cannot be completely neutralized by the plate potential. This condition is illustrated by curve $b''$ of Fig. 2–13. A further increase in filament current will not result in an increase in plate current; however,

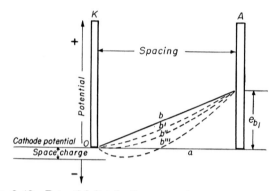

Fig. 2–13. Potential distribution curves for several values of $t$.

it will result in greater space charge and a potential distribution as illustrated by curve $b'''$. The current is now space-charge limited. From this line of reasoning the curves of Fig. 2–14 follow.

Referring to the curves of Fig. 2–14, it will be noticed that plate current does not begin to flow until the filament current has reached an appreciable

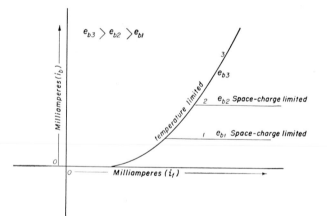

Fig. 2–14. Theoretical static characteristics of a diode. $i_b$ vs. $i_f$ for fixed values of $e_b$.

value. This is due to the fact that the cathode must reach a fairly high temperature before any electrons are emitted. For a low value of plate voltage such as $e_{b1}$, it takes only a very small filament current to cause more space charge to form than can be neutralized by the plate potential.

If the plate potential is increased to the value of $e_{b2}$, the filament current can be raised to a higher value before the current becomes space-charge limited. Curve 3 of Fig. 2–14 illustrates a condition where the plate potential is extremely high and for reasonable values of filament current the plate current will not become space-charge limited. These curves differ from the experimental curves of Fig. 2–8 in the same way that the theoretical curves of Fig. 2–12 differ from the experimental curves of Fig. 2–7. The main reason for the difference in the theoretical and experimental curves is that the theoretical curves are based on the assumptions that the temperature over the entire surface of the cathode is uniform and the cathode and anode are both perfect parallel planes, and in the practical case the spacing between the cathode and anode is not constant at all points and the temperature of the cathode surface is not uniform.

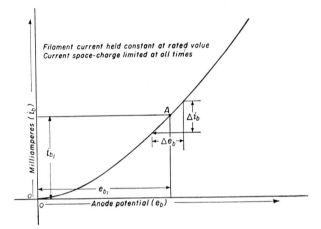

Fɪɢ. 2–15. Construction illustrating how both static and dynamic plate resistance can be determined from the static characteristics of a diode.

**2–3. Plate Resistance.** The diode is a nonlinear circuit element, i.e., the plate current is not directly proportional to the plate potential. The ratio of the plate potential to the plate current is called the *static* or *dc plate resistance*. The ratio of an increment in plate voltage $\Delta e_b$ to the corresponding increment in plate current $\Delta i_b$, as $\Delta i_b$ approaches zero as a limit, is termed the *ac* or *dynamic plate resistance*. The dynamic plate resistance is a very important tube coefficient; however, the static or dc plate resistance has very little significance. These two terms are defined mathematically by Eqs. (2–1) and (2–2), respectively. The static cr dc plate resistance at point $A$ (Fig. 2–15) is defined as follows:

$$r_{\text{dc}} = \frac{e_{b1}}{i_{b1}} \qquad (2\text{–}1)$$

where $e_{b1}$ is expressed in volts
$\quad\quad i_{b1}$ is expressed in amperes

The dynamic or ac plate resistance at point $A$ (Fig. 2–15) is defined as follows:

$$r_p = \lim_{\Delta i_b \to 0} \left[\frac{\Delta e_b}{\Delta i_b}\right] \tag{2-2a}$$

where $\Delta e_b$ is expressed in volts

$\Delta i_b$ is expressed in amperes

or

$$r_p = \frac{de_b}{di_b} \tag{2-2b}$$

An analysis of the curve of $i_b$ vs. $e_b$ (Fig. 2–15) will show that neither the static nor the dynamic plate resistance is constant; rather, both vary with the magnitude of the plate current. The variation of dynamic and static plate resistance with respect to plate current is illustrated in Fig. 2–16.

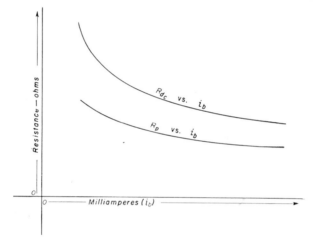

FIG. 2–16. Static and dynamic plate resistance vs. plate current.

**2–4. Current, Voltage, and Temperature Relationships.** The equation of the curve of Fig. 2–15 is of the family, $i_b = Ke_b{}^\alpha$. Both of the constants in this equation can be determined experimentally for any given tube. Consider the equation

$$i_b = Ke_b{}^\alpha \tag{2-3}$$

Taking the logarithm of both sides of the equation

$$\log i_b = \alpha \log e_b + \log K \tag{2-4}$$

Eq. (2–4) is that of a straight line

$$y = mx + b$$

where $y$ corresponds to $\log i_b$

$x$ corresponds to $\log e_b$

$m$ corresponds to $\alpha$

$b$ corresponds to $\log K$

Therefore, by plotting the plate current against plate voltage on logarithmic paper, $\alpha$, the slope of the straight line, and $\log K$, the $y$-intercept, can be determined. Although $\log K$ is the $y$-intercept, the paper is so marked that the value of $K$ can be read directly from the paper.

O. W. Richardson in 1914 developed a theoretical equation (Eq. 2–5) which expresses the emission current density in terms of emission constants and temperature.

$$J = A T^{1/2} \epsilon^{-b/2T} \tag{2–5}$$

The terms in Eq. (2–5) are defined following Eq. (2–6).

The emission current as predicted by this equation does not agree very closely with experimental values. In the case of most diodes the emission current is much greater than the value given by this equation.

Later S. Dushman (1923) developed a modified form of Richardson's equation (Eq. 2–6) which more nearly predicts the actual emission current. This equation, which is referred to in the literature both as Dushman's and as Richardson's equation, is

$$J = A T^2 \epsilon^{-b/T} \tag{2–6}$$

where  $J$ = emission current density in amperes/square meter of emitting surface

$A$ = constant for the emitting surface under consideration (Table 2–1)

$T$ = temperature of emitting surface in degrees Kelvin

$b$ = constant for the emitter material under consideration (Table 2–1)

$\epsilon$ = 2.71828

Representative values of constants for commonly used emitting surfaces are listed in Table 2–1.

TABLE 2–1

| Emitting Surface | $b$ (degrees Kelvin) | $A$ (amp/m²/deg K²) |
|---|---|---|
| Barium-Strontium Oxides (BaO-SrO)... | 12,000 | $1 \times 10^2$ |
| Thoriated Tungsten (Th-W).......... | 31,500 | $3 \times 10^4$ |
| Tungsten (W)...................... | 52,400 | $60.2 \times 10^4$ |

In 1911 C. D. Child developed an equation for plate current in a diode when space-charge limited, i.e., when the current is limited by the difference of potential between the cathode and plate and there is always ample emission regardless of the value of the applied plate potential. Child's equation is as follows:

$$J = 2.33 \times 10^{-6} \left( \frac{e_b^{3/2}}{d^2} \right) \tag{2–7}$$

where $J$ = plate current density in amperes/square meter

$e_b$ = difference in potential between cathode and anode in volts

$d$ = spacing between cathode and anode in meters

This equation applies only for large parallel plane electrodes. An equation which gives the relationship between space-charge limited current, plate potential and tube geometry for concentric cylindrical electrodes has been developed; however, a discussion of this equation is beyond the scope of this text.*

**2–5. Power Considerations.** As pointed out previously, the plate of a diode must be large in order to be able to dissipate appreciable heat. It was also pointed out that each electron as it strikes the plate gives up its kinetic energy to the plate and that this energy in turn is dissipated as heat. Consider the power that a given anode must be capable of dissipating.

$$\text{kinetic energy of electron} = E_b e \text{ joules} \tag{2-8}$$

where $e$ = charge on the electron in coulombs

$E_b$ = difference of potential between cathode and anode

If $a$ = rate at which electrons arrive at the anode in electrons/second, then

$$P = E_b e a \text{ joules/second} \tag{2-9}$$

which is the power that the plate must be capable of dissipating. By substituting $I_b$ for $ea$, the expression of Eq. (2–9) takes on a more practical form.

$$P = E_b I_b \tag{2-10}$$

where $P$ = power in watts

$E_b$ = difference of potential between cathode and anode

$I_b$ = anode current in amperes

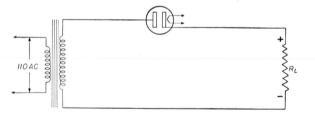

FIG. 2–17.  Half-wave rectifier employing a heater-type cathode.

**2–6. Rectifier Action.** Consider the rectifier action of the diode. The simplest type of rectifier circuit is illustrated by Fig. 2–17. This circuit consists of a diode connected in series with an alternating voltage and a load resistance $R_L$. During the half cycle when the anode of the tube is

---

* For a discussion of the expression for space-charge limited current in a diode employing concentric cylindrical electrodes see M.I.T. Staff, *Applied Electronics* (New York: John Wiley & Sons, Inc., 1943), p. 123.

positive with respect to the cathode, electrons will flow through the tube and resistor $R_L$. During the half cycle when the anode is negative with respect to the cathode, no electrons will flow from cathode to anode and through the external circuit; thus the current will be zero (Fig. 2–18).

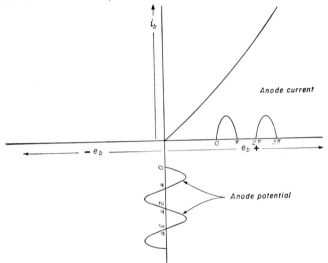

FIG. 2–18. Diagram illustrating the rectifier action of a diode when placed in series with an alternating voltage.

Referring to the illustration of Fig. 2–18, it is shown that the current through the circuit of Fig. 2–17 occurs in pulses of 180 degrees duration when a sine wave voltage is applied to the input terminals. Such an arrangement is known as a half-wave rectifier circuit. The current flowing through the load is pulsating dc, which, in most applications, cannot be

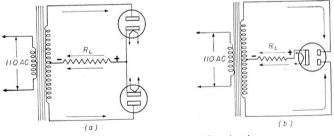

FIG. 2–19. Full-wave rectifier circuits.

tolerated unless it is smoothed out considerably by a suitable filter circuit. (Filter circuits are discussed in Chapter 7.) The most frequently used type of rectifier circuit is a full-wave rectifier. A full-wave rectifier circuit employs two single-unit diodes (often referred to as half-wave rectifier tubes) or one tube with two units (generally referred to as a full-wave rectifier tube). Fig. 2–19a illustrates a full-wave rectifier circuit utilizing two single diodes, and Fig. 2–19$b$ illustrates a full-wave rectifier circuit which utilizes a full-wave rectifier tube.

The circuit of Fig. 2–19$a$ is arranged so that the plate of one or the other of the tubes will be positive at all times; thus there will be a flow of current through the load resistance $R_L$ at all times.

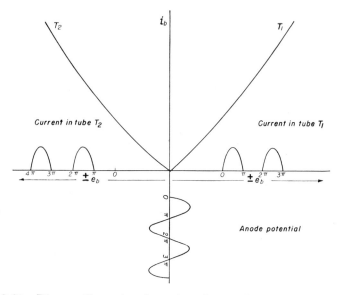

Fig. 2–20.   Diagram illustrating the action of two tubes in a full-wave rectifier circuit.

Consider Fig. 2–20. When the plate of tube 1 is positive with respect to its cathode, current will flow through $R_L$ as indicated by the arrow. During this period the anode of tube 2 will be negative with respect to its cathode; hence, it will not conduct. On the next half cycle, however, the cathode of tube 1 will be negative with respect to its anode and will be non-conducting, but at the same time the anode of tube 2 will be positive with respect to its cathode and current will flow through $R_L$ in the same direction as when tube 1 was conducting. This process repeats itself as long as ac is applied to the input circuit. The wave form of the current through the resistor is sketched in Fig. 2–21. Rectifier circuits are discussed in more detail in Chapter 7.

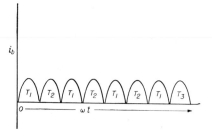

Fig. 2–21.   Wave-form of the load current for a full-wave rectifier circuit.

## Triodes

Introduction of the grid between the cathode and anode of a diode was, perhaps, the greatest single advance in the history of the vacuum tube. The resulting three-electrode tube,* which is commonly known as a triode, makes amplification possible. If it were not for amplification, very few modern electronic devices would be in existence. Amplification makes possible the long distance telephone, sound pictures, radio, television, radar, electronic control circuits and many other devices too numerous to mention.

**2–7. Grid Structure.** The grid is a screen-like electrode with an open mesh structure. The openings in the grid structure are sufficiently large to offer negligible mechanical retardation to the electrons traveling from cathode to anode. Molybdenum, nichrome, iron and iron-nickel and manganese-nickel alloys are typical grid materials. Typical filamentary and heater-type triode structures are illustrated in Fig. 2–22.

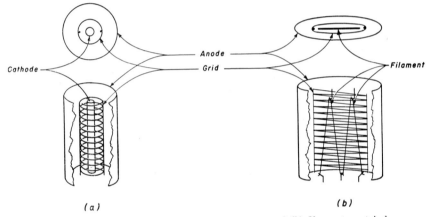

Fig. 2–22. Structure of typical (a) heater-type and (b) filamentary triodes.

Because of its proximity to the cathode, the grid electrode has much more influence on the pattern of the electrostatic field near the cathode than does the anode. Therefore a small change of grid potential will cause a greater change in plate current than will result if the plate potential is changed by the same increment of voltage. By virtue of this fact, the triode can be made to function as an amplifier.

The grid is normally operated at a negative potential with respect to the cathode. Because of this, it does not attract electrons, hence the grid current is essentially zero. If the grid is operated at a positive potential with respect to the cathode, it will collect electrons resulting in grid current. In most applications grid current is undesirable.

---

\* The three-electrode tube was patented by Lee DeForest in 1907.

**2–8. Characteristics.** The static characteristics of a triode can be determined by employing the circuit of Fig. 2–23.

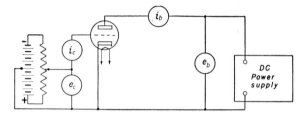

FIG. 2–23.  Circuit for determining the characteristics of a triode.

There are three very important families of static characteristics from which the merits of a triode can be determined. The first family of characteristics is obtained by holding the grid potential constant and determining the variation of plate current with plate potential. The second family is obtained by employing fixed values of plate potential and determining the

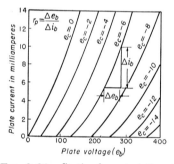

FIG. 2–24.  Static characteristics of a triode.  $i_b$ vs. $e_b$ for fixed values of $e_c$.

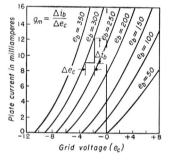

FIG. 2–25.  Static characteristics of a triode.  $i_b$ vs. $e_c$ for fixed values of $e_b$.

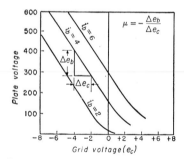
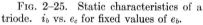

FIG. 2–26.  Static characteristics of a triode.  $e_b$ vs. $e_c$ for fixed values of $i_b$.

variation of plate current with grid voltage. The third family represents plate voltage versus grid voltage for fixed values of plate current. The filament current is held at rated value while obtaining data for each family of curves. Typical triode characteristics illustrating each family of curves are sketched in Figs. 2–24, 2–25 and 2–26, respectively.

The characteristics of a triode may be understood by considering the cathode, grid and plate as infinite parallel planes and studying the potential distribution between electrodes for changing values of both grid and plate potential.

In the analyses which follow it will be assumed that rated heater voltage is applied; therefore the plate current, except when otherwise specified, will be space-charge limited at all times.

If the grid is allowed to "swing-free" (i.e., if there is no connection between it and either of the other two electrodes within the tube) and the plate potential is zero, the potential distribution curve will be represented by curve $a$ of Fig. 2–27. (The scale for space charge is greatly exaggerated.)

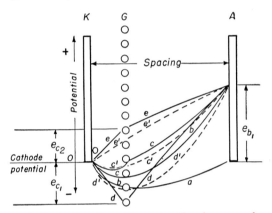

Fig. 2–27. Sketch illustrating the effects of grid voltage on the potential distribution in a triode.

Under these conditions the grid will collect electrons until it acquires a negative potential equal in magnitude to the space charge in the region in which it is located. With the grid still disconnected, assume that the plate potential is increased to a value $e_{b1}$. Now the potential distribution will be as illustrated by a curve $b$ and a milliammeter connected between cathode and plate will indicate current. If the grid is now connected directly to the cathode, the individual grid wires will be at the same potential as the cathode, but this does not mean that the average potential over the plane in which the grid wires are located is at the same potential as the cathode. The average potential over the plane of the grid will be affected by the plate potential as well as the grid potential. Under these conditions the potential distribution from the cathode to an individual grid wire and from grid wire to plate will be as illustrated by curve $c$, while the potential distribution curve $c'$ (dotted line) illustrates the average distribution. From study of either curve $c$ or $c'$ it can be seen that electrons now leaving the cathode encounter a lower negative potential gradient in the vicinity of the cathode than they do in the case where the grid is allowed to "swing-free."

Thus electrons with smaller initial velocities will be able to overcome the space charge and move to the anode.

If, under normal operating conditions for the tube under consideration, the grid-cathode spacing is such that negative space charge exists in the region of the grid, connecting the grid to the cathode will neutralize to a certain extent the existing space charge and plate current will be increased slightly. If there is no space charge existing in the plane of the grid under normal operating conditions and the potential in the plane is positive, then connecting the grid to the cathode will cause the potential in the region of the grid to become more negative, and there will be a tendency for plate current to decrease.

Consider the case where a negative potential is applied to the grid. Let the negative grid potential be of magnitude $e_{c1}$. This value of grid potential will give rise to a cathode to grid wire, grid wire to plate distribution curve as illustrated by curve $d$, and an average distribution curve $d'$ (dotted line) which will result in a net decrease in the flow of electrons to the plate. A further decrease in grid potential (more negative value) will result in a further decrease in plate current. At some negative value of grid potential the negative potential gradient in the vicinity of the cathode will be so great that no electrons will be able to get through to the plate. The value of grid potential necessary to give rise to this condition is known as the *cut-off* value. The value of negative grid potential necessary to give cut-off is different for each value of plate potential. A positive value of grid potential $e_{c2}$ will give distribution curves as illustrated by lines $e$ and $e'$. From an analysis of these curves it will be seen that the potential gradient near the cathode is more positive; thus more electrons will be able to get to the plate, giving rise to greater current flow. It is possible, even with a very low plate potential, to cause saturation current to flow if the grid is made sufficiently positive. A positive grid will attract electrons; thus some of the emitted electrons will flow through the grid circuit. Because of the small surface area of the grid wires the ratio of the grid current to the plate current will be very small, and the decrease in plate current as a result of electrons striking the grid will be almost negligible. Grid current is extremely undesirable in that it tends to change the input impedance of a tube; therefore, in most applications the grid is operated at a negative potential with respect to the cathode.

In the preceding discussion the variation of plate current with grid potential for fixed values of plate potential has been considered. The variation of plate current with plate voltage for fixed values of grid potential will now be discussed.

Consider Figs. 2–28a and 2–28b. Curve $oab$ of Fig. 2–28a represents the potential distribution from cathode to individual grid wires and from grid wires to anode when a negative potential $e_{c1}$ is applied to the grid, and a positive potential $e_{b1}$ is applied to the plate. Now let it be assumed that the grid potential is held constant at the value of $e_{c1}$ and the plate potential is increased to a greater value $e_{b2}$. The potential distribution between grid wires and plates will change as illustrated by curve $oac$, but the gradient between cathode and grid wires will not change. A still further increase in the plate potential to a value of $e_{b3}$ will give a greater positive gradient between grid-wires and anode (illustrated by curve $oad$) but the distribution between the cathode and grid wires will remain unchanged. From this line of reasoning it would seem that an increase in plate potential would not reduce the negative gradient near the cathode, and plate

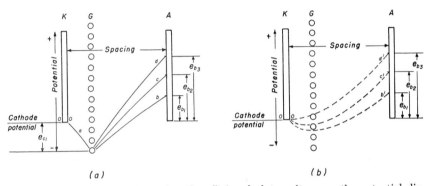

Fig. 2–28. Sketches illustrating the effects of plate voltage on the potential distribution in a triode.

current could not be increased by increasing the plate potential. This is not the complete picture, however, for if the average potential distribution curves are considered, it will be seen that an increase in plate potential will result in an increase in plate current. The average distribution curve when the grid potential is held at $e_{c1}$ ($e_{c1}$ is the grid potential as measured by a voltmeter and not the average potential in the plane of the grid) and the plate potential is $e_{b1}$ is illustrated by curve $ob'$ in Fig. 2–28b. An increase in plate potential to the value of $e_{b2}$ will change the average potential distribution in the region of the grid as illustrated by curve $oc'$. This results in a less negative field in the vicinity of the grid. If $e_b$ is made sufficiently positive, the average potential in the region of the grid can actually become positive as illustrated by curve $od'$, although a voltmeter connected between the cathode and grid will indicate that the grid wires are several volts negative with respect to the cathode.

From a study of the change in the average distribution curves as a result of increasing plate potential, it can be seen that the potential gradient near the cathode becomes less negative with increasing plate potential. For this reason the plate current will increase with an increase in plate potential. These curves also show that the magnitude of the change in plate voltage necessary to change the average potential distribution between cathode and grid by a given amount must be much greater than the magnitude of the change in grid potential necessary to give the same change in the average distribution between cathode and grid; hence the grid is more effective than the plate in controlling the magnitude of the plate current.

**2–9. Factors Affecting the Effectiveness of the Grid.** The effectiveness of the grid may be increased in two ways: first, by moving the grid nearer the cathode, and second, by making the grid mesh finer, i.e., making the spacing between individual wires smaller.

Consider Figs. 2–29a, 2–29b and 2–29c. If the grid of Fig. 2–29a is in position 1, the average potential distribution curve will be illustrated by curve $oa'c$ (dotted line). Now if the grid is moved nearer the cathode to position 2, the negative gradient near the cathode for the same value of applied grid potential will be much steeper as illustrated by curve $ob'c$

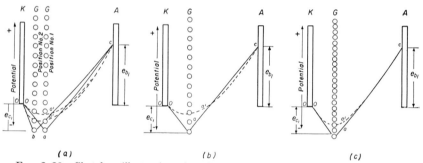

Fig. 2–29. Sketches illustrating the effects of changes in grid structure on the potential distribution in a triode.

(dotted line); thus fewer electrons will be able to move through the grid to the plate, which means that the effectiveness of the grid as a control element has been increased. Now consider what happens when the spacing between grid wires is made smaller. Assuming that the grid is negative with respect to the cathode by a potential difference of $e_{c1}$ volts and that the grid spacing is as indicated by Fig. 2–29b, the potential distribution curve between electrodes will be represented by curve $oac$ and the average potential distribution curve will be represented by curve $oa'c$ (Fig. 2–29b). Now if the grid wires are spaced much closer, i.e., if the pitch is made smaller (Fig. 2–29c) and the same plate and grid potentials as in the case of Fig. 2–29b are applied, the potential distribution curve between grid wires and anode will be as indicated by curve $oac$ of Fig. 2–29c which is identical to curve $oac$ of Fig. 2–29b. However, the average potential distribution curve $oa'c$ of Fig. 2–29c will more nearly coincide with curve $oac$ than will curve $oa'c$ of Fig. 2–29b. Thus it follows that the closer the grid-wire spacing, the more nearly the average potential in the region of the grid approaches the applied grid potential and the more effective is the grid.

**2–10. Coefficients of the Triode.** There are three very important coefficients or constants * of a triode: namely, *amplification factor* $\mu$, *dynamic plate resistance* $r_p$ and *grid-plate transconductance* $g_m$ (sometimes referred to as mutual conductance).

The *amplification factor* $\mu$ is a measure of the relative effectiveness of grid potential and plate potential in controlling plate current. $\mu$ is defined mathematically as follows:

$$\mu = \lim_{\Delta e_c \to 0} \left[ -\frac{\Delta e_b}{\Delta e_c} \right]_{i_b \text{ constant}} = -\frac{de_b}{de_c}\bigg|_{i_b \text{ constant}} = -\frac{\partial e_b}{\partial e_c} \qquad (2\text{--}11)$$

The approximate value of $\mu$ can be determined experimentally for given values of grid and plate voltages by the incremental method which consists of changing $e_b$ slightly and noting the corresponding change in $e_c$ necessary to keep the plate current constant. The amplification factor is approximately equal to the negative of the ratio of the plate voltage increment $\Delta e_b$ to the corresponding grid voltage increment $\Delta e_c$. The amplification factor can also be determined at any point by taking the negative of the slope of an $e_b$ vs. $e_c$ curve (Fig. 2–26) at the point in question.

The *dynamic plate resistance* $r_p$ of a triode is the ratio of an increment in plate potential $\Delta e_b$ to the corresponding increment in plate current $\Delta i_b$ as $\Delta i_b$ approaches zero as a limit, the grid potential remaining constant. $r_p$ is defined mathematically as follows:

$$r_p = \lim_{\Delta i_b \to 0} \left[ \frac{\Delta e_b}{\Delta i_b} \right]_{e_c \text{ constant}} = \frac{de_b}{di_b}\bigg|_{e_c \text{ constant}} = \frac{\partial e_b}{\partial i_b} \qquad (2\text{--}12)$$

The approximate value of $r_p$ can be determined experimentally for given values of grid and plate voltages by holding $e_c$ constant and changing $e_b$ slightly and noting the corresponding change in $i_b$. The dynamic plate resistance $r_p$ is approximately equal to the ratio of the change in plate potential $\Delta e_b$ to the corresponding change in plate current $\Delta i_b$. The dynamic plate resistance can also be obtained by taking the reciprocal of the slope of an $i_b$ vs. $e_b$ curve (Fig. 2–24) at the point in question.

The *grid-plate transconductance* $g_m$ is a measure of the effectiveness of the grid potential in controlling plate current. $g_m$ is defined mathematically as follows:

$$g_m = \lim_{e_c \to 0} \left[ \frac{\Delta i_b}{\Delta e_c} \right]_{e_b \text{ constant}} = \frac{di_b}{de_c}\bigg|_{e_b \text{ constant}} = \frac{\partial i_b}{\partial e_c} \qquad (2\text{--}13)$$

This limit can be determined approximately by holding the plate voltage constant and noting the change in plate current $\Delta i_b$ resulting from a slight change in grid voltage $\Delta e_c$. $g_m$ may also be determined by taking the slope of an $i_b$ vs. $e_c$ curve (Fig. 2–25) at the point in question.

---

* Although sometimes referred to as constants, $\mu$, $g_m$ and $r_p$ vary appreciably over the operating range of a given tube.

It can be shown mathematically that the three coefficients of a triode are related as follows:

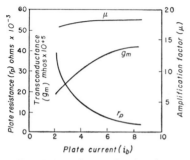

FIG. 2–30. Curves showing the variation of $\mu$, $g_m$ and $r_p$ with plate current for a typical triode.

$$\mu = r_p g_m \qquad (2\text{–}14a)$$

$$r_p = \frac{\mu}{g_m} \qquad (2\text{–}14b)$$

$$g_m = \frac{\mu}{r_p} \qquad (2\text{–}14c)$$

The coefficients of a triode can be determined graphically as illustrated in Figs. 2–24, 2–25 and 2–26. The curves of Fig. 2–30 illustrate typical variations of triode coefficients with plate current.

**2–11. Relationship Between Plate Current, Grid Voltage and Plate Voltage.** Eq. (2–15) gives an approximate relationship between the plate voltage, grid voltage and plate current of a triode for negative values of grid voltage:

$$i_b = K(e_b + \mu e_c)^\alpha \qquad (2\text{–}15)$$

Taking the logarithm of both sides of the equation

$$\log i_b = \alpha \log (e_b + \mu e_c) + \log K \qquad (2\text{–}16)$$

$K$ and $\alpha$ can be determined by plotting $i_b$ against $(e_b + \mu e_c)$ on logarithmic paper.

$$\alpha = \text{slope of curve on logarithmic paper}$$
$$\log K \,{}^* = y\text{-intercept of curve on logarithmic paper}$$

## Multielectrode Tubes

**2–12. Tetrodes.** The high-vacuum triode has been, to a large extent, superseded by the pentode (five-element tube) in conventional low power amplifier circuits. Difficulty is usually encountered if the three-electrode tube is employed in either high frequency or high gain amplifier circuits. As a voltage amplifier tube the triode is limited in both voltage gain and frequency range. The frequency limitation is due primarily to the grid-plate capacitance.†

The grid and plate form a sort of parallel cylinder capacitor (Figs. 2–31a and 2–31b). The capacitance existing between grid and plate is much less

---

* Actual value of $K$ is read directly from the log paper.

† In the case of high-power radiofrequency amplifiers such as those used in transmitters, etc., triodes are employed. However, the grid-plate capacitance is neutralized by a special type of circuit arrangement, which is not feasible in voltage amplifier circuits.

than it would be were the grid to consist of a cylinder of sheet metal, such as is indicated by Fig. 2–31a. However, as the spacing between individual grid wires becomes smaller, the capacitance between grid and plate approaches the value that would exist were the grid to consist of a sheet-metal cylinder.

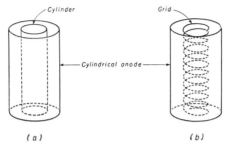

FIG. 2–31.  Sketches illustrating grid-plate capacitance in a triode.

It was shown previously (Section 2–9) that decreasing the spacing between the grid wires will increase the amplification factor of a triode; it was also pointed out that increasing the amplification factor in this manner would have the undesirable effect of causing the grid to offer more mechanical retardation to the electron stream moving from cathode to anode.  Here another undesirable result of decreasing the pitch of the grid is realized; namely, increase in the grid-plate capacitance.

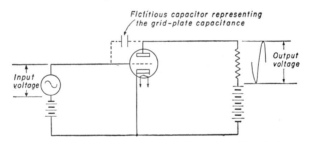

FIG. 2–32.  Circuit diagram of amplifier showing how grid and plate are connected through the grid-plate capacitance.

Because of the capacitance existing between the grid and plate there is a tendency for alternating current to flow between grid and plate circuits through the grid-plate capacitance. Although utilized in oscillator circuits,* a flow of current between grid and plate is extremely undesirable in amplifier circuits. Consider the simple voltage amplifier circuit of Fig. 2–32. If the grid of this amplifier is at all times negative with respect to the cathode, there will be no flow of direct current in the grid circuit;

_____

* Oscillator circuits are discussed in Chapter 6.

but due to the capacitance existing between the grid and plate and the difference in alternating potential existing between grid and plate, which

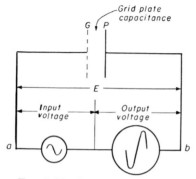

is the vector sum of the alternating input voltage and the alternating output voltage, there will be a tendency for alternating current to flow between the grid and plate. This condition is illustrated by the equivalent circuit of Fig. 2–33. This circuit may be used as a schematic circuit diagram to illustrate the tendency for alternating current to flow between grid and plate regardless of the frequency employed or the voltage gain.

Fig. 2–33. Equivalent circuit illustrating the voltage applied across the grid-plate capacitance.

The magnitude of the alternating current flowing between the grid and the plate is expressed by the following equation:

$$I = \frac{E}{X_{gp}} \qquad (2\text{-}17)$$

where $X_{gp}$ = grid-plate reactance

$X_{gp} = 1/2\pi f C_{gp}$

$f$ = frequency of applied voltage

$C_{gp}$ = grid-plate capacitance

$E$ = voltage between points $a$ and $b$ of Fig. 2–33

$I$ = alternating current flowing

Since the capacitance $C_{gp}$ depends on the geometry of the tube and does not change with frequency or gain of the circuit of which it is a part, the question as to why there will be a greater tendency for current to flow at high frequencies or high output voltages than at low frequencies or low output voltages may arise. The answer to this question may be readily answered by considering Eq. (2–17). An increase in frequency $f$ will cause a decrease in grid-plate reactance $X_{gp}$ resulting in an increase in the magnitude of the alternating current flowing between grid and plate. An increase in gain, which for the same input signal results in a larger output signal, will result in a larger value of $E$. This will give rise to an increase in the magnitude of the alternating current flowing through the grid-plate capacitance.

Although the grid-plate capacitance was early recognized as a definite limiting factor in the frequency range of amplifiers, it was not until around 1928 that a vacuum tube was developed with appreciably less grid-plate capacitance. Essentially, this new tube differed from the triode only in that an additional grid (screen-grid) was inserted between the first grid (control-grid) and the plate. All radios, transmitters, public address systems, etc., made before 1928 employed only two types of tubes, diodes and triodes.

It was found that the grid-plate capacitance of a triode could be reduced by a factor of from 500 to 1,000 by inserting an electrostatic shield between the grid and plate. Consider the sketches of Figs. 2–34a and 2–34b. Fig. 2–34a shows the electrostatic lines of force existing between the control grid and the anode when a difference of potential exists between the grid and the anode. Now if the anode is completely enclosed by a metallic shield (Fig. 2–34b), no electrostatic lines of force can terminate on the

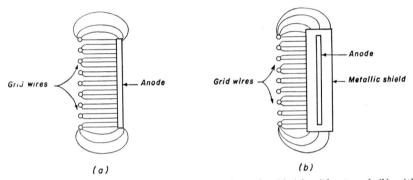

(a)                                    (b)

Fig. 2–34.  Electrostatic field between anode and grid (a) without and (b) with metallic shield surrounding anode.

anode, and there is no tendency for ac to flow between the grid and anode. It is, of course, impossible to shield the grid completely from the anode, for a complete shield would not allow any electrons to flow from the cathode to the anode. However, it is possible to obtain a great deal of electrostatic shielding and at the same time offer little mechanical retardation to the flow of electrons from the cathode to the anode. The conventional type of electrostatic shield employed in a glass tube consists of an inner part and an outer part. The inner part usually takes the form of a spiral of wire concentric about the control grid and very similar in structure to the control grid. The outer part, which is connected by means of a metallic cap or washer to the inner part, consists of a perforated metallic cylinder concentric about the plate. In the case of the metal tube the metal envelope shields the outside of the plate; thus the shield grid need not incorporate an outer part concentric about the plate. The spacing between individual grid wires of this additional grid, which is known as the shield or screen grid, is sufficiently great to prevent appreciable retardation of electrons.

The control grid-plate capacitance, usually referred to as simply grid-plate capacitance, is in the neighborhood of 0.01 to 0.005 $\mu\mu f$ for typical receiving tetrodes. The internal structure of a tetrode is illustrated in Fig. 2–35.

There is no alternating difference of potential between the screen grid $G_2$ and the cathode $K$. Because of this fact, dynamically the cathode and screen grid are at the same potential. However, it is necessary that the screen grid be statically highly positive with respect to the cathode. If the screen grid were statically at the same potential as the cathode, it would

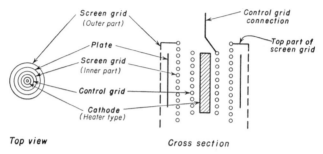

Fig. 2–35.   Internal structure of a tetrode.

cause a strong negative field to exist near the plate and repel or turn back most of the emitted electrons to the cathode; therefore, it would be impossible to obtain appreciable plate current regardless of the magnitude of the applied plate potential.

Although the screen grid was introduced as a measure to decrease grid-plate capacitance, it has a marked effect on the static characteristics of the tube of which it is a part. Since the screen grid is located between the cathode and plate, as well as between the control grid and plate, it shields the plate from the cathode as well as shielding it from the control grid; thus it decreases materially the effectiveness of the plate potential in changing the electrostatic field near the cathode. This means that plate potential becomes much less effective in controlling the plate current than it was before the introduction of the screen grid. The screen grid does not shield the control grid from the cathode and so it does not change the effectiveness of grid potential in controlling plate current. Recalling the definition of amplification factor (the amplification factor is a measure of the relative effectiveness of control grid voltage and plate voltage in controlling plate current), if the effectiveness of the plate is decreased and the effectiveness of the grid is left substantially unchanged, the amplification factor will be greatly increased. Amplification factors as high as 500 are not uncommon for tetrodes. A decrease in the effectiveness of the plate potential also results in a very high plate resistance, usually in the order of 0.5 megohm for a typical tetrode. Since the effectiveness of the grid is almost unaffected by the addition of the screen grid, the grid-plate transconductance of a tetrode does not differ greatly from values for triodes of similar geometric structure. The high amplification factor and low grid-plate transconductance of a tetrode make it superior to the triode for high frequency amplification.

The static characteristics of a tetrode can be determined by use of the circuit of Fig. 2–36. It is usually desirable to determine the variation of plate and screen-grid current with plate potential for fixed values of screen-grid and control-grid voltages. Characteristics of a typical screen-grid

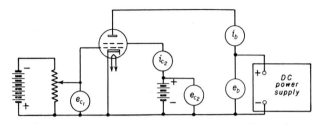

FIG. 2–36.  Circuit for determining the static characteristics of a tetrode.

tube are sketched in Fig. 2–37. These curves may best be explained by assuming the electrodes to be parallel planes and studying the change in potential distribution between the electrodes due to changing electrode potentials.

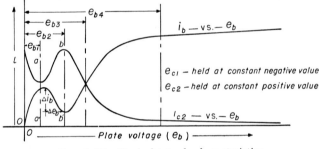

FIG. 2–37.  Typical tetrode characteristics.

Fig. 2–38a illustrates potential distribution curves between individual wires of the grids and the remaining electrodes, while Fig. 2–38b illustrates the average potential distribution curves through the grid structures. Curve *oabc* represents the potential distribution between individual grid wires when a negative potential $e_{c1}$ is applied to the control grid $G_1$, a positive potential $e_{c2}$ is applied to the screen grid $G_2$ and zero potential is applied to the plate. The average distribution curve for the same conditions is illustrated in Fig. 2–38b by curve *oa'b'c'*.

If the cathode is at operating temperature (i.e., if ample emission current is available at all times) and the screen grid is highly positive with respect to the cathode, it will attract electrons, but since the plate is at zero potential with respect to the cathode, the plate will not attract electrons; thus the plate current will be essentially zero, while the screen-grid current will be large. Now, if the plate potential is increased as indicated by the potential distribution curves of Figs. 2–38a and 2–38b, the plate will begin to attract some of the emitted electrons. This constitutes plate current. As the magnitude of the plate potential increases, the plate current will increase accordingly; thus the screen-grid current will decrease and the total number of electrons passing through the control grid will remain essentially constant. The plate current will continue to increase, as plate potential is increased, until the plate potential becomes large enough to

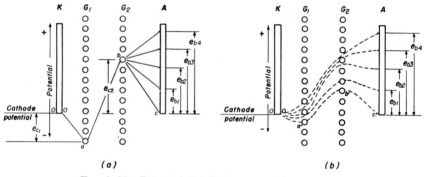

Fig. 2–38. Potential distribution curves for a tetrode.

cause the primary electrons striking the plate to arrive with sufficient velocity to dislodge secondary electrons from the surface of the plate. The secondary electrons will be attracted to the most positive electrode in the tube, which will, in the case under consideration, be the screen grid. It is assumed that voltage $e_{b1}$ of Figs. 2–37, 2–38$a$ and 2–38$b$ represents the value of plate potential necessary to give appreciable secondary emission. A further increase in $e_b$ up to a value of $e_{b2}$ will result in a decrease in plate current and an increase in the screen-grid current. This region is between $aa'$ and $bb'$ of Fig. 2–37. Consider the dynamic plate resistance of the tetrode within this region. At any point between $aa'$ and $bb'$ the slope $(de_b/di_b)$ of the $i_b$ vs. $e_b$ curve is negative. This means that the dynamic plate resistance in this region is negative. In all circuits previously considered, an increase in voltage across a circuit resulted in an increase in current, but here is a circuit element with a negative resistance, i.e., an increase in potential results in a decrease in plate current. An increase in plate potential beyond a certain value, say $e_{b2}$, will result in an increase in plate current and a decrease in screen-grid current. The plate potential is now high enough to attract an appreciable number of its own secondary electrons. When the plate potential is approximately equal to the screen-grid voltage, the screen-grid current will be approximately equal to the plate current which is the intersection of $i_b$ vs. $e_b$ and $i_{c2}$ vs. $e_b$ curves (Fig. 2–37). A further increase in plate potential will result in a continued increase in plate current, which means that the screen-grid current will continue to decrease. In operation, plate potentials greater than $e_{b4}$ are generally employed; for values of plate potential greater than this value, the plate current is substantially independent of plate potential. In the case of a tetrode the plate current is determined primarily by control-grid and screen-grid voltages. Thus, the plate acts primarily as a collector of electrons and is no longer a control element to the extent that it is in the case of a triode.

The coefficients of a tetrode are defined in a manner similar to those of a triode; however, there is an additional electrode, the screen grid, which must be considered. The screen-grid potential $e_{c2}$ is held constant as indicated by the following mathematical definitions.

$$\mu = \lim_{\Delta e_{c1} \to 0} \left[ - \frac{\Delta e_b}{\Delta e_{c1}} \right]_{\substack{i_b \text{ constant} \\ e_{c2} \text{ constant}}} = - \frac{de_b}{de_{c1}} \bigg|_{\substack{i_b \text{ constant} \\ e_{c2} \text{ constant}}} = - \frac{\partial e_b}{\partial e_{c1}} \qquad (2\text{-}18)$$

$$r_p = \lim_{\Delta i_b \to 0} \left[ \frac{\Delta e_b}{\Delta i_b} \right]_{\substack{e_{c1} \text{ constant} \\ e_{c2} \text{ constant}}} = \frac{de_b}{di_b} \bigg|_{\substack{e_{c1} \text{ constant} \\ e_{c2} \text{ constant}}} = \frac{\partial e_b}{\partial i_b} \qquad (2\text{-}19)$$

$$g_m = \lim_{\Delta e_{c1} \to 0} \left[ \frac{\Delta i_b}{\Delta e_{c1}} \right]_{\substack{e_b \text{ constant} \\ e_{c2} \text{ constant}}} = \frac{di_b}{de_{c1}} \bigg|_{\substack{e_b \text{ constant} \\ e_{c2} \text{ constant}}} = \frac{\partial i_b}{\partial e_{c1}} \qquad (2\text{-}20)$$

The symbols employed in the above relations are the same as those used in connection with the triode; however, $e_{c1}$ refers to the voltage of the control grid (grid nearest the cathode) and $e_{c2}$ refers to the screen-grid voltage. The values of $\mu$ and $r_p$ are both much larger for a tetrode than for a triode of similar design, but values of $g_m$ for typical tetrodes do not vary greatly from values expected in the case of triodes of similar geometric structure.

**2–13. Pentodes.** If the tetrode, the characteristics of which are shown in Fig. 2–37, were to be employed in an amplifier circuit, it would be necessary that the plate potential never be allowed to swing below the value represented by $e_{b4}$ (Fig. 2–37). If the plate potential were allowed to swing appreciably below the value of $e_{b4}$, the output voltage of the amplifier in which the tube is used would bear little resemblance to the input signal; thus, the distortion would be intolerable. The range of operation of a tetrode when used as an amplifier tube is limited because of the irregular curvature of the plate characteristics in the region of low plate potential. These peculiar characteristics, as pointed out previously, are due to the effects of secondary emission.

It took vacuum tube designers only a short time to solve the problem arising as a result of secondary emission. In 1930 a tube possessing the desirable features of the tetrode (i.e., low grid-plate capacitance and high amplification factor), and eliminating the undesirable characteristics arising as a result of secondary emission, was made available to commercial users. This new triple-grid tube was known as the pentode, the name indicating five electrodes. The structure of a typical pentode is shown in Fig. 2–39.

The additional grid, which is known as the suppressor grid, is concentric about the screen grid. It is very similar in structure to control and screen grids and the same materials are used in the manufacture of all three grids.

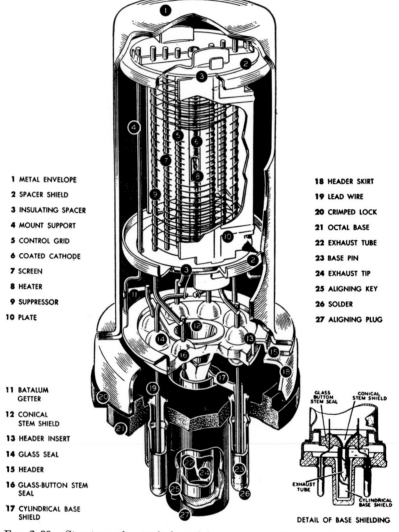

| | |
|---|---|
| **1** METAL ENVELOPE | **18** HEADER SKIRT |
| **2** SPACER SHIELD | **19** LEAD WIRE |
| **3** INSULATING SPACER | **20** CRIMPED LOCK |
| **4** MOUNT SUPPORT | **21** OCTAL BASE |
| **5** CONTROL GRID | **22** EXHAUST TUBE |
| **6** COATED CATHODE | **23** BASE PIN |
| **7** SCREEN | **24** EXHAUST TIP |
| **8** HEATER | **25** ALIGNING KEY |
| **9** SUPPRESSOR | **26** SOLDER |
| **10** PLATE | **27** ALIGNING PLUG |

**11** BATALUM GETTER

**12** CONICAL STEM SHIELD

**13** HEADER INSERT

**14** GLASS SEAL

**15** HEADER

**16** GLASS-BUTTON STEM SEAL

**17** CYLINDRICAL BASE SHIELD

DETAIL OF BASE SHIELDING

FIG. 2–39. Structure of a typical receiving pentode. (Courtesy Radio Corp. of America.)

The function of this additional grid is to eliminate the effects of secondary emission, or in plainer language, the suppressor takes the kinks out of the $i_b$ vs. $e_b$ curves.

The action of the suppressor grid can be best understood by considering the electrodes as parallel planes and studying the potential distribution between them (Figs. 2–40$a$ and 2–40$b$). Let it be assumed that the control grid $G_1$ is held at a negative potential $e_{c1}$, the screen grid $G_2$ at a positive potential $e_{c2}$, the suppressor grid $G_3$ at zero or cathode potential and the plate at a positive potential $e_{b1}$. These conditions are those existing in the

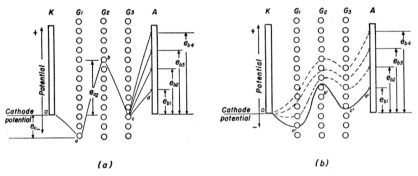

FIG. 2–40.  Potential distribution curves for a pentode.

case of most typical pentode operation. Curve $oa'b'c'd'$ of Fig. 2–40$b$ represents average potential distribution in the space within the tube under consideration. The suppressor grid sets up a negative field in the region near the anode; the strength of this negative field is affected by the magnitude of the screen-grid potential as well as the magnitude of the plate potential. The change in the average potential in the region of the suppressor grid due to variation in plate potential is illustrated by the dotted line curves of Fig. 2–40$b$. For any operating combination of screen-grid and plate potentials, the region in which the suppressor grid is located will be more negative than the anode; thus when secondary electrons leave the anode and begin their journey back toward the screen grid, they encounter a region which is highly negative and which most of them will not be able to penetrate. Since the region near the anode is much more positive than the region in which the suppressor grid is located, the secondary electrons will be returned to the plate; hence the effects of secondary emission are not evident in the case of the pentode and the kinks will be taken out of the $i_b$ vs. $e_b$ curves. There is a tendency to say that the suppressor grid eliminates secondary emission. The suppressor grid does not prevent secondary electrons from leaving the surface of the anode as a result of high velocity primary electrons impinging upon it. However, the suppressor grid does suppress the undesirable effects resulting from the collection of secondary electrons by the screen grid.

The static characteristics of a pentode can be obtained by employing the circuit of Fig. 2–41. Characteristics for a typical pentode are shown in Fig. 2–42. It will be noted that the characteristics of the pentode are similar to those exhibited by the tetrode with the exception that the irregularities in the region of low plate potential have been eliminated. The oscillograms of Figs. 2–43$a$ and 2–43$b$ represent plate current versus plate voltage with fixed screen-grid voltage for three different values of grid

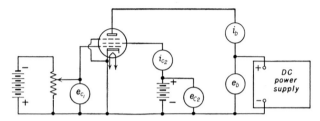

Fig. 2–41.    Circuit for determining the static characteristics of a pentode.

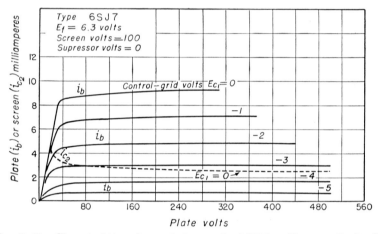

Fig. 2–42.   Characteristics of a typical pentode (6SK7).    (Courtesy Radio Corp. of America.)

voltage for a typical pentode.   In the case of Fig. 2–43$a$ the suppressor grid is connected to the screen grid causing the tube to have tetrode characteristics, and in the case of Fig. 2–43$b$ the suppressor grid is connected to the cathode giving true pentode characteristics.   The elimination of the kinks in the $i_b$ vs. $e_b$ curves gives the pentode a much greater range of operating plate potential or "plate-swing" than is possible in the case of the tetrode. Since the pentode does not exhibit any of the undesirable characteristics of the tetrode and possesses the same advantages over the triode as does the tetrode, it is superior to either as a voltage amplifier tube.   Because of its superior performance the pentode has almost completely superseded the tetrode* as a voltage amplifier tube.   The coefficients of a pentode are defined in the same manner as those of a tetrode.   (Eqs. 2–18, 2–19 and 2–20.)

---

* Low-powered (receiving) tetrodes are obsolete; however, relatively high-powered (transmitting) tetrodes are widely used.

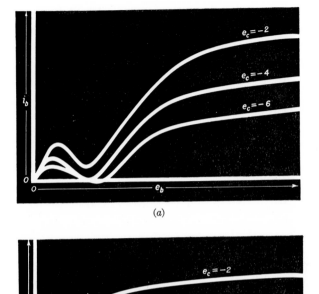

(a)

(b)

Fig. 2–43. Oscillograms of plate current vs. plate voltage for (a) a pentode with suppressor grid connected to screen grid causing the tube to exhibit tetrode characteristics and (b) suppressor grid connected to cathode so tube exhibits true pentode characteristics.

**2–14. Remote-Cut-off Pentodes.** Remote-cut-off pentodes, also known as supercontrol or variable-mu pentodes, are similar to the regular or sharp-cut-off pentodes previously described, with the exception that the control grid is wound with a variable pitch. By referring to Figs. 2–44a and 2–44b it will be noted that the control grid employed in a regular or sharp-cut-off pentode has a uniform pitch, while the control grid in the case of the remote-cut-off or supercontrol pentode is wound with fine spacing at the ends and coarse spacing in the middle. Because of this non-uniform spacing between grid wires, different sections of the grid will exert different degrees of electro-static control over the regions in which they are located. In other words, different sections of the control grid will prevent the flow of electrons for a less negative value of grid potential than other sections. In the case under consideration it would require a much greater value of negative grid potential to prevent electron flow to the plate through the middle region of the control grid than through the regions near each end.

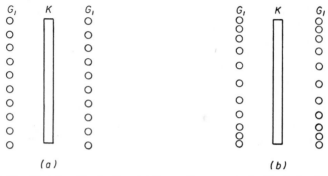

Fig. 2–44.  Sketches illustrating (a) the uniform control-grid pitch of the sharp-cut-off pentode and (b) the variable control-grid pitch of the remote-cut-off pentode.

Fig. 2–45 shows $i_b$ vs. $e_{c1}$ curves for fixed values of plate potential for both remote and sharp-cut-off pentodes.  In the case of the remote-cut-off pentode, the plate current decreases rather slowly with an increase in the magnitude of the negative grid-bias applied; thus, the plate current approaches zero much more gradually than it does in the case of a tube which

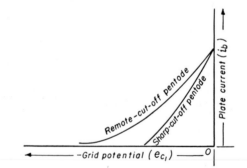

Fig. 2–45.  Sketches showing how the $i_b$ vs. $e_{c1}$ curves for remote and sharp-cut-off pentodes differ.

employs a control grid with uniform pitch.  This asymptotic approach to the ($i_b = 0$) axis is due to the fact that the sections near the end of the grid prevent electron flow through themselves at less negative values of grid potential than do the center sections.  The grid wires near the center are spaced so far apart that it is necessary to apply an extremely large negative potential to the control grid in order to obtain complete cut-off or zero plate current when the screen grid and plate have rated positive potentials applied to them.

The remote-cut-off pentode can be considered a tube made up of as many

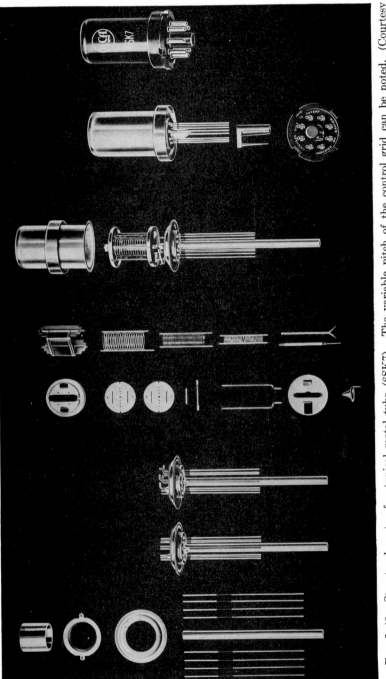

Fig. 2–46. Structural parts of a typical metal tube (6SK7). The variable pitch of the control grid can be noted. (Courtesy Radio Corp. of America.)

parallel sections as there are control-grid wires, each section having a different degree of effectiveness in controlling plate current. The effectiveness of the complete grid at any time will be the average effectiveness of all sections through which plate current is flowing. Since the number of sections through which plate current flows changes with the magnitude of the negative grid potential applied, the effectiveness of the grid will be a function of the negative potential applied to it. As the grid is made more negative both the amplification factor $\mu$ and the grid-plate transconductance $g_m$ will decrease. This variable-mu characteristic makes the remote-cut-off pentode useful in connection with automatic volume control. Fig. 2–46 shows the complete structure of a typical remote-cut-off pentode (type 6SK7) and the average characteristics of the same tube are shown in Fig. 2–47.

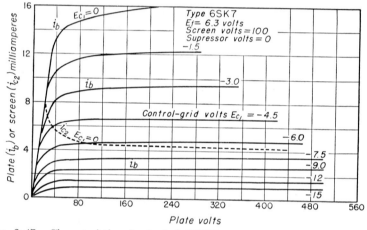

Fig. 2–47. Characteristics of a typical (6SK7) remote-cut-off pentode. (Courtesy Radio Corp. of America.)

**2–15. Beam-Power Tubes.** The beam-power tube was the outgrowth of an attempt to increase the operating range of the pentode. Referring to the characteristics of a typical pentode as shown in Fig. 2–42, it will be noted that the knees of the $i_b$ vs. $e_b$ characteristics are gradual in change of slope and extend over an appreciable increment of plate voltage. Operating anywhere in this region will give appreciable distortion. The ideal amplifier tube would be a tube possessing straight line $i_b$ vs. $e_b$ characteristics over the entire range of plate voltage over which the tube is intended to operate. The gradual knee, which is characteristic of $i_b$ vs. $e_b$ curves for pentodes, is a result of the nonuniform control of secondary electrons by the suppressor grid. The ideal suppressor grid would produce a uniform electric field over the entire plane in which it is located, and thus would produce the same effect on electron flow over any area in this plane. A suppressor grid designed to give uniform field strength over the entire plane in which it is located would have to contain an infinite number of grid wires. Such a grid structure could not be penetrated by the electrons; thus there would be no flow of electrons from cathode to anode. It is obvious that a method of obtaining uniform suppressor action, other than using an infinite number of grid wires, must be devised if uniform suppression is to be realized.

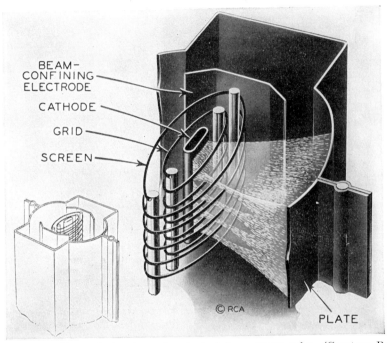

FIG. 2–48. Internal structure of a typical beam-power tube. (Courtesy Radio Corp. of America.)

A good approach to uniform suppressor action is obtained in the beam-power tube. This tube is designed so that the electrons flowing from the cathode to anode are concentrated in beams so as to give rise to a virtual cathode in the region near the anode. The internal structure of a typical beam-power tube is shown in Fig. 2–48.

The wires of the control grid are lined up with the screen-grid wires. This alignment causes the electrons to flow in sheets between the grid wires and allows very few to strike the screen grid, resulting in a relatively small screen-grid current, and some degree of concentration of the electrons into beams.

The sheets of electrons are further concentrated by use of an elliptical-shaped cathode which emits only in two general directions. The greatest factor in beaming the electrons is a set of beam-forming plates. These plates are illustrated clearly in Fig. 2–48. They are tied to the cathode and so repel electrons, forcing them into beams of high density. The high density of these beams results in a highly negative field near the anode which is substantially uniform over the entire area of current flow and gives rise to uniform suppressor action. It is interesting to study the potential distribution within a beam-power tube.

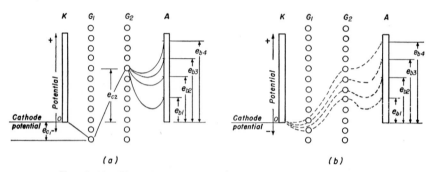

FIG. 2–49. Potential distribution curves for a beam-power tube.

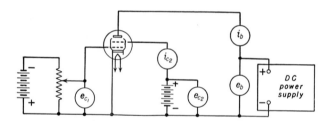

FIG. 2–50. Circuit for determining the characteristics of a beam-power tube.

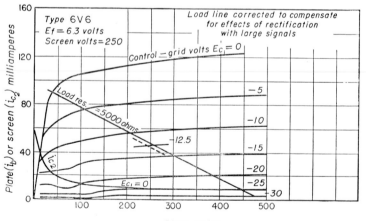

FIG. 2–51. Characteristics of a typical (6V6) beam-power tube. (Courtesy Radio Corp. of America.)

Consider Figs. 2–49a and 2–49b. From the sketches of either the average distribution curves of Fig. 2–49b or the distribution curves from individual grid-wires to the other electrodes as illustrated by Fig. 2–49a, it can be seen that the region near the cathode becomes increasingly more positive with increasing values of plate potential. Although the potential in this region does rise appreciably above zero under normal operating conditions, it is sufficiently negative to prevent most of the secondary electrons from returning to the screen grid. Because of the uniform suppressor action and the low screen-grid current, the beam-power tube has the following advantages when compared to the pentode: higher power output, high power sensitivity, higher efficiency and lower distortion. The plate characteristics of the beam-power tube can be obtained by employing the circuit of Fig. 2–50. Characteristics of a typical beam-power tube are illustrated by Fig. 2–51. The beam-power tube is used chiefly for power amplification.

## Miscellaneous Tubes

**2–16. Multiple-Unit Tubes.** Many modern high-vacuum tubes are comprised of two or more complete units within a single envelope; such tubes are known as multiple-unit tubes. Many different combinations of diodes, triodes, pentodes, and beam-power tubes are built in the same envelope. Typical examples of several types of multiple-unit tubes are listed in Table 2–2.

TABLE 2–2

| Type Multiple-Unit Tube | Manufacturer's Designation |
|---|---|
| Twin diode.................... | 6H6 |
| Twin triode................... | 6SN7 |
| Twin pentode................. | 1E7–G |
| Diode-triode................. | 1H5–G |
| Diode-pentode................ | 1S5 |
| Duplex diode-triode........... | 6SQ7 |
| Duplex diode-pentode.......... | 6B8–G |
| Diode-triode-pentode.......... | 3A8–GT |
| Diode beam-power tube........ | 70L7–GT |

The characteristics of each unit of a multiple-unit tube do not differ appreciably from the characteristics of similar units located in individual envelopes; thus, if the characteristics of each type of unit contained within such a tube are understood, an understanding of the operation of the complete tube follows.

**2–17. Pentagrid Converters and Mixers.** Pentagrid converters and mixers are high-vacuum tubes which are used primarily in connection with frequency conversion in superheterodyne radio receivers. An understanding of radio is necessary before the functions of the individual grids in either a pentagrid converter or mixer can be completely understood; thus they will not be discussed further at this time. Schematic diagrams showing the grid arrangements of both the pentagrid converter and the pentagrid

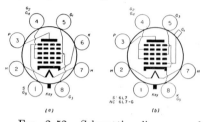

FIG. 2–52. Schematic diagrams of (a) pentagrid converter (6SA7) and (b) pentagrid mixer (6L7). (Courtesy Radio Corp. of America.)

mixer are shown in Figs. 2–52a and 2–52b, respectively.

**2–18. Acorn Tubes.** Most vacuum tubes of conventional design do not operate satisfactorily at very high frequencies (i.e., frequencies in the order of one hundred megacycles and higher). Inability of conventional vacuum tubes to operate at extremely high frequencies results because of interelectrode capacitance and transit time of the electrons between cathode and plate. At audio and ordinary radio frequencies (i.e., those well below 100 megacycles), the transit time of the electron is negligible compared to the period of one complete cycle of the frequency at which the tube is operating. If the frequency becomes so great that the transit time becomes appreciable with respect to the period of one complete cycle, the tube will not operate satisfactorily. The undesirable effects of interelectrode capacitance are more pronounced at high frequencies because of the decrease in reactance ($X_c = 1/2\pi f c$) which accompanies an increase in frequency.

One type of tube designed to operate at very high frequencies is the acorn tube. The dimensions of the acorn tube are very small, resulting in a marked decrease in interelectrode capacitance as well as a decrease in transit time. Acorn tubes are approximately $\frac{3}{4}$ inch in diameter and $1\frac{1}{2}$ inches in length. Because of their small size they are not capable of developing appreciable power and consequently are quite limited in their applications. Two types of acorn tubes (a triode and a pentode) are compared in size to a golf ball in Fig. 2–1.

FIG. 2–53. Typical lighthouse tube. (Courtesy Radio Corp. of America.)

**2–19. Lighthouse Tubes.** A fairly recently developed high-frequency triode which has become quite popular is the lighthouse tube, so named because of its resemblance to a lighthouse. Such tubes do not employ conventional lead wires and the electrodes are disk-like in structure. The unique arrangement in this type of tube results in low interelectrode capacitance, minimum lead inductance and short transit time. Such tubes will operate satisfactorily up to around 1,000 megacycles. Fig. 2–53 shows a modern lighthouse tube.

**2–20. Magnetrons.** A magnetron is a special type of high-vacuum transmitting tube in which the motion of electrons from cathode to anode is controlled by concurrent electric and magnetic fields. The magnetron oscillator is the only source of extremely high frequencies at high power levels. Magnetrons are commercially available in peak-pulse power ratings of from 100 kw at 10,000 megacycles to 700 kw at 3,000 megacycles. A typical magnetron is shown in Fig. 2–54.

FIG. 2–54. In this 10-cm magnetron the cavities, instead of being holes milled out of a solid block of copper, are formed by brazing vanes into a cylindrical shell. The tube delivers approximately 700–kw peak or pulse power. (Courtesy Westinghouse Electric Corp.)

**2–21. Klystrons.** The klystron is an ultra-high-frequency tube that operates on the principles of velocity modulation. Such tubes are employed in both receiving and transmitting circuits. Fig. 2–55 shows two typical klystrons. The klystron is used only in the field of extremely high frequency (1,000 to 30,000 megacycles).

**2–22. Electron-Ray Tubes.** Electron-ray tubes, also known as magic-eye and visual indicator tubes, have a wide variety of applications. Two of the more common uses include tuning indicators in certain makes of radio receivers and balance indicators for bridge circuits. A typical electron-ray tube is shown in Fig. 2–56.

The electron-ray tube is comprised of two sections; one is a high-mu triode section and the other is an electron-ray indicator which is located

Fig. 2–55. Two similar reflex klystrons designed for 3,000 and 10,000 megacycles, respectively. Conspicuous is the difference in the size of the cavities, which is the portion to which the coaxial output lines are connected. The cavities are tuned by adjusting the spacing between the two rings. In service the tube is tuned by a knob mechanism that acts on the lever, seen extending below the left of the spring-held rings. (Courtesy Westinghouse Electric Corp.)

directly above the triode section and consists of a cathode, a cone-shaped fluorescent target, a light shield and a blade-like ray-control electrode, often referred to as simply the control electrode. The control electrode is located between the cathode and target. The target is always operated at a positive potential with respect to the cathode; thus it attracts electrons emitted from the cathode. The target is coated with a fluorescent material (material capable of emitting a visible light when excited by an external source); therefore the area over which electrons strike it is illuminated.

If the control electrode is at the same potential as the target, the target will be lighted over its entire surface; but if the control electrode is made less positive than the target, electrons will not be distributed over the entire target surface because of the negative electrostatic field set up by the control electrode, and the region of the target over which electrons are not allowed to strike will not glow. This dark region is referred to as the shadow cast by the control electrode.

RCA—6E5
FLUORESCENT COATING
CATHODE LIGHT SHIELD
RAY-CONTROL ELECTRODE
TARGET
TRIODE PLATE
TRIODE GRID
CATHODE

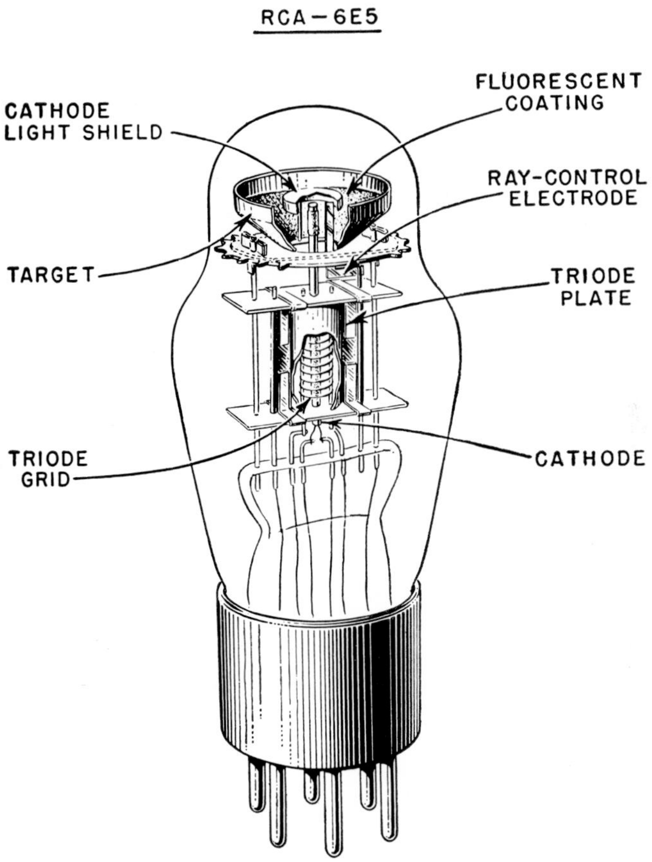

FIG. 2–56. Structure of a typical electron-ray tube. (Courtesy Radio Corp. of America.)

The geometry of the control electrode is of such a nature that the shadow appears as a perfect sector on the conic target. The approximate limits of

Fluorescent screen
Light shield over top of hot cathode
Shadow cast by control electrode

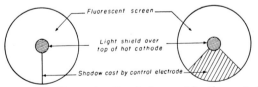

FIG. 2–57. Diagrams illustrating the shadow cast by the control electrode.

the shadow angle are 0 to 100° (Fig. 2–57). The zero angle occurs when the potential of the control electrode is equal to the target potential and the maximum angle occurs when the control electrode is much less positive than the target.

In most of its applications the electron-ray tube is employed to indicate visually a maximum or minimum value of voltage. A circuit illustrating the operation of an electron-ray tube and the characteristics of a typical tube is shown in Fig. 2–58.

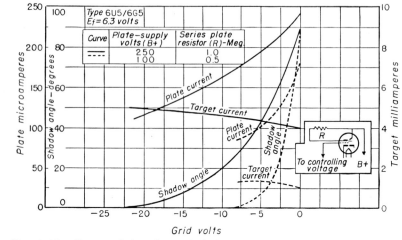

Fɪɢ. 2–58. Characteristics of a typical electron-ray tube. (Courtesy Radio Corp. of America.)

In the circuit of Fig. 2–58 the shadow angle will be a function of the input voltage to the grid; thus a visual indication of the change in input voltage is realized. If the grid is biased to cut off, no current will flow through the triode section of the electron-ray tube, and consequently no current will flow through the resistor R. This means that the target and the control electrode, which is connected to the anode of the triode section, will be at the same potential, and the resulting shadow angle will be zero. If the grid of the triode section is made less negative, the plate current through the triode section will increase, resulting in a greater voltage drop across the resistance R. This means that the plate of the triode section will become more negative with respect to the target and the shadow angle will increase as the grid voltage increases in a positive direction until it reaches its maximum value of around 100°. There are some electron-ray tubes that incorporate two control electrodes and give two shadow angles instead of one. The 6AF6–G is such a tube.

## PROBLEMS

**2–1.** The plate current for a given diode is expressed by the following equation:
$$i_b = 5 \times 10^{-6} e_b^{1.5} \text{ amp}$$
Determine the plate current $i_b$ and dynamic plate resistance $r_p$ when the plate voltage $e_b$ is 200 v.

**2-2.** Determine the total emission current from a pure tungsten wire $4 \times 10^{-2}$ m in length and $2 \times 10^{-4}$ m in diameter, when operated at a temperature of 2,490° K.

**2-3.** Determine the total emission current from a cylindrical barium-strontium oxide cathode with an effective emitting area of $2 \times 10^{-5}$ m² when operated at a temperature of 1,000° K.

**2-4.** Assuming that the current is not temperature limited, what is the maximum plate current that can be obtained from a diode, the cathode and anode of which may be considered as parallel planes $2 \times 10^{-3}$ m apart, if the area of the anode is $1 \times 10^{-4}$ m² and the difference in potential between electrodes is 100 v?

**2-5.** What is the maximum power that the anode of the diode of Prob. 2–4 must be capable of dissipating?

**2-6.** From the characteristics of a typical triode such as 6J5 (Refer to *RCA Receiving Tube Manual* for characteristics), determine an approximate equation for the plate current.

**2-7.** After obtaining the equation asked for in Prob. 2–6, calculate values of plate current for three different values of plate or grid voltages and check values of current thus obtained with corresponding values taken from characteristics curves.

**2-8.** Determine graphically at recommended operating conditions values of $\mu$, $g_m$ and $r_p$ for a typical triode such as a 6J5. (For characteristics and typical operating conditions of a 6J5 see *RCA Receiving Tube Manual*.)

**2-9.** If the radius of the grid of a given triode is decreased, how will $\mu$, $g_m$ and $r_p$ be affected?

**2-10.** The plate current of a certain triode is expressed by the following equation:

$$i_b = 3.33 \times 10^{-6}(e_b + \mu e_c)^{1.5} \text{ amp}$$

Determine the plate current $i_b$, dynamic plate resistance $r_p$, and grid plate transconductance $g_m$ when

$$e_b = 200 \text{ v}$$

$$e_c = -5 \text{ v}$$

$$\mu = 20.$$

## BIBLIOGRAPHY

ALBERT, A. L. *Fundamental Electronics and Vacuum Tubes.* New York: The Macmillan Co., 1947, pp. 81–91, 118–36, 159–88.

BENDZ, W. I. *Electronics for Industry.* New York: John Wiley & Sons, Inc., 1947, pp. 60–68, 83–114.

CHAFFEE, E. L. *Theory of Thermionic Vacuum Tubes.* New York: McGraw-Hill Book Co., Inc., 1933, pp. 95–135, 144–90, 588–621.

CRUFT LABORATORY STAFF. *Electronic Circuits and Tubes.* New York: McGraw-Hill Book Co., Inc., 1947, pp. 265–303.

DOW, W. G. *Fundamentals of Engineering Electronics.* New York: John Wiley & Sons, Inc., 1937, pp. 1–52, 121–45.

EASTMAN, A. V. *Fundamentals of Vacuum Tubes.* 2nd ed. New York: McGraw-Hill Book Co., Inc., 1941, pp. 34–91.

FINK, D. G. *Engineering Electronics.* New York: McGraw-Hill Book Co., Inc., 1938, pp. 93–131.

HENNEY, KEITH. *The Radio Engineering Handbook.* 3rd ed. New York: McGraw-Hill Book Co., Inc., 1941, pp. 231–68.

KLOEFFLER, R. G. *Industrial Electronics and Control.* New York: John Wiley & Sons, Inc., 1949, pp. 38–86.

————. *Principles of Electronics.* New York: John Wiley & Sons, Inc., 1942, pp. 44–54, 60–72, 96–102.

MCARTHUR, E. D. *Electronics and Electron Tubes.* New York: John Wiley & Sons, Inc., 1936, pp. 23–7, 59–79.

M.I.T. STAFF. *Applied Electronics.* New York: John Wiley & Sons, Inc., 1943, pp. 154–202.

MILLMAN, JACOB, and SEELY, SAMUEL. *Electronics.* New York: McGraw-Hill Book Co., Inc., 1941, pp. 204–30, 501–9, 551–69.

PENDER, HAROLD, and MCILWAIN, KNOX. *Electrical Engineers' Handbook — Electric-Communications and Electronics.* 3rd ed. Section 5. New York: John Wiley & Sons, Inc., 1936, pp. 2–39.

*RCA Receiving Tube Manual.* Harrison, New Jersey: R.C.A. Manufacturing Co., Inc., 1947.

REICH, H. J. *Theory and Applications of Electron Tubes.* 2nd ed. New York: McGraw-Hill Book Co., Inc., 1944, pp. 19–66.

RYDER, J. D. *Electronic Engineering Principles.* New York: Prentice-Hall, Inc., 1947, pp. 80–91, 128–38, 192–205.

SPANGENBERG, K. R. *Vacuum Tubes.* New York: McGraw-Hill Book Co., Inc., 1948, pp. 125–297.

TERMAN, F. E. *Radio Engineering.* 3rd ed. New York: McGraw-Hill Book Co., Inc., 1947, pp. 149–98.

————. *Radio Engineers Handbook.* New York: McGraw-Hill Book Co., Inc., 1943, pp. 285–321.

## CHAPTER 3

## GAS TUBES

For many years gas-filled tubes have been used in various types of rectifier units, particularly large power conversion units. Small glass-bulb gaseous rectifiers were used for battery charging as early as around 1906 and modern gas tubes * are still used extensively for this purpose. At the present time there are installed in the United States alone mercury-arc pool-type steel-tank conversion units totaling millions of kilowatts capacity which furnish direct current energy for railroads, local transportation systems, light-metal production, mining, etc. In recent years grid-controlled gas tubes have become almost indispensable to industry. Such tubes find their most extensive use in industrial control circuits.

Gas tubes can be classified as cold-cathode gas tubes, gas-filled thermionic tubes and mercury-arc pool-type rectifiers. The cold-cathode type is used a great deal in voltage regulator circuits for small power supplies such as those employed in various types of communications circuits. This type of tube does not have many industrial uses and will not be discussed in this text.

Gas-filled thermionic tubes have innumerable industrial applications. Such tubes have an oxide-coated filament and are made with from two to five active electrodes. Two-electrode tubes are referred to as diodes or phanotrons, three-electrode tubes as gas triodes or thyratrons, and tubes with additional grids are usually termed shield-grid thyratrons.

Mercury-arc pool-type rectifiers are used almost exclusively as power converters, i.e., for converting large amounts of alternating current to direct current. At present there are three types of mercury-arc rectifiers with pool-type cathodes. They are: the multi-anode steel-tank mercury-arc rectifier, the ignitron and the excitron. The multi-anode steel-tank mercury-arc rectifier is rapidly being superseded by the ignitron and the excitron.

## Gas-Filled Thermionic Tubes

**3-1. Gas Diodes.** Hot-cathode thermionic gas tubes (often referred to as phanotrons) contain mercury vapor or one of the inert gases such as

---

* A high pressure (pressure of about 0.05 meter of mercury) argon-filled tube with a thoriated-tungsten filament which is known by the trade names of Tungar or Rectigon is used in many battery charging units. Such tubes are made in current ratings from 0.5 to 15 amperes.

argon, helium, krypton, neon and xenon.   Mercury vapor is the most common gaseous medium, inert gases being employed mostly in small specialized tubes.   The reason that inert gases are used lies in the fact that they will not enter into chemical reaction with the electrodes within the tube. Thermionic cathodes used in gas tubes are oxide-coated and may take a

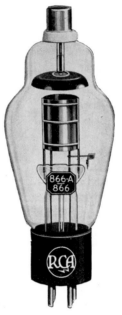

FIG. 3–1.  Typical light current mercury-vapor diode.  Rated at 0.25 ampere average plate current and 10,000 volts inverse peak.  (Courtesy Radio Corp. of America.)

number of different forms.  In general, the cathode takes the form of corrugated ribbon designed to give maximum emission surface and minimum heat loss.  Cathodes are often heat shielded in order to decrease radiation losses.  Heat shielding is applied to both filamentary and indirectly heated cathodes.  This type of construction not only improves the emitting efficiency immensely, but also increases the life of the emitter.  Anodes are usually made of carbonized metals or graphite and may take one of many forms.  The most common shapes are cylindrical and hemispherical; however, in the case of small tubes, anodes often take the shape of a flat disk. The spacing between the cathode and anode has little effect on the magnitude of the anode current; thus the spacing is usually quite large compared to the spacing in the case of a high-vacuum diode.  Decreasing the spacing between anode and cathode makes possible the handling of higher inverse peak voltages but decreases the heat radiation of the anode.  The tubes of Figs. 3–1 and 3–2 are typical mercury-vapor thermionic diodes.  The 866A/866 (Fig. 3–1) has an average current rating of 0.25 ampere and the 869B (Fig. 3–2) has an average current rating of 2.5 amperes.

Let it be assumed that the filament of the hot-cathode gas diode is at operating temperature and the anode is made positive with respect to the cathode. For extremely low values of anode potential (values below the ionization potential of the gas under consideration), the magnitude of the electron flow to the anode will be of essentially the same value as would

Fig. 3–2.  Typical medium current mercury-vapor diode. Rated at 2.5 amperes average plate current and 20,000 volts inverse peak. (Courtesy Radio Corp. of America.)

exist were the tube evacuated. However, for values of anode potential greater than the ionization potential of the gas under consideration, the current in the case of the gas tube will be many times larger than the current that would exist were the diode completely evacuated. The sketches of Figs. 3–3a and 3–3b illustrate the difference in the rectification characteristics of high-vacuum and gas diodes, respectively. The marked deviation of the rectification characteristics of the hot-cathode gas diode from those of the high-vacuum diode can best be understood by referring to the sketch of Fig. 3–4 (for simplicity, the cathode and anode are assumed to be parallel planes). If electrons are thermionically emitted from the hot-cathode $K$ of Fig. 3–4 and the anode is made positive with respect to the cathode, electrons will be attracted to the anode as in the case of the high-vacuum diode. The probability that these electrons will collide with gas atoms is extremely high. If an electron possesses sufficient kinetic energy when it collides with a gas atom, it will dislodge one or more electrons from the atom, producing free electrons. An atom which has lost one or more electrons will no longer be neutral but will possess a positive charge and is

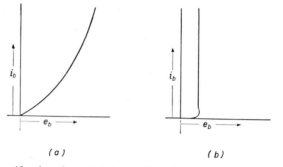

(a)                                          (b)

FIG. 3-3.   Rectification characteristics of (a) high-vacuum and (b) gas-filled diodes.

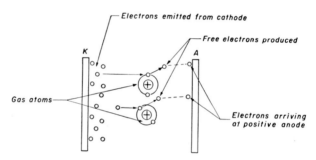

FIG. 3-4.   Sketch illustrating ionization in a gas tube.

usually referred to as a *positive ion*. The production of free electrons and positive ions in this manner is known as *ionization*. The *ionization potential* is the potential through which an electron must drop in order to produce ionization of the gas through which it is traveling. The anode potential necessary to produce ionization must exceed the ionization potential of the gas in order to start ionization, but once ionization is accomplished the tube drop will be approximately equal to the ionization potential. The ionization potentials of several gases employed in modern tubes are given in Table 3-1.

Once ionization is accomplished, the free electrons will be attracted to the anode giving rise to current flow. The positive ions will be attracted to the negative cathode and because of their positive charges they will tend to neutralize the space charge. This means that the current in a gas tube is never space-charge limited.

The positive ions also contributed to the total current flow, but due to the fact that the mass of an ion is several thousand times that of an electron, their velocity is very low compared to that of an electron and they do not add appreciably to the current flow.

TABLE  3–1

| Inert Gas | Ionization Potential (Volts) |
|---|---|
| Argon................. | 15.69 |
| Helium................ | 24.46 |
| Krypton............... | 13.94 |
| Neon.................. | 21.47 |
| Xenon................. | 12.08 |

It is interesting to compare the potential distribution curve for a typical high-vacuum diode with the potential distribution curve of a typical thermionic gas diode.  In the sketch of Fig. 3–5 the dotted line represents the potential distribution curve during conduction when the tube is evacuated, and the solid line represents the potential distribution curve during conduction when the same tube is filled with gas.

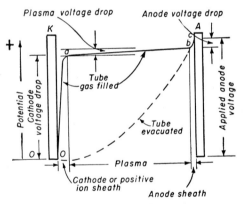

FIG. 3–5.  Potential distribution in a gas-filled diode.  Dotted line represents potential distribution of same diode if evacuated.

The potential distribution curve for a gas diode is quite different from that of a high-vacuum diode.  The region *oa* of curve *oabc* is called the *positive-ion sheath* and the region *ab* is called the *plasma*.  The voltage drop across the positive-ion sheath is approximately equal to the *tube drop* (voltage across tube during conduction), and the potential of the plasma is essentially constant at all points.  The positive-ion sheath is composed of the slow moving positive-ions and the magnitude of the positive space charge *oa* is due to the positively charged ions in that region.

There is one very important precaution that must be adhered to before putting hot-cathode gas diodes into operation. The cathode of the hot-cathode type of gas tube must be at operating temperature before anode potential is applied. The delay time (time filament must be on before anode potential is applied) varies from around 30 seconds to 30 minutes for various types of hot-cathode rectifier tubes. Application of anode potential before the cathode has reached normal emitting temperature can result in cathode disintegration. Consider what happens when an attempt is made to increase the anode current to a value greater than the emission current. This is the condition that will exist if anode potential is applied before the cathode reaches operating temperature. An increase in anode current above emission current will result in greater tube drop than normal; and if the tube drop exceeds the *disintegration voltage* (22 volts for a mercury-vapor diode), the cathode will be damaged as a result of positive-ion bombardment. The emitting properties of the cathode of a mercury-vapor diode can be determined by applying direct voltage to the tube, sending about one hundred and fifty percent rated current through it, and measuring the voltage drop across the tube. Normal tube drop should not exceed about 15 volts. A tube drop of greater than around 20 volts indicates that the cathode has lost most of its emitting surface.

Thermionic gas diodes are used extensively for supplying larger amounts of dc energy than are feasible with high-vacuum diodes. Such tubes are used to supply the dc voltage necessary for the operation of the high-power vacuum tubes in almost all radio transmitters, diathermy machines and large commercial oscillators. Thermionic gas diodes are also used to obtain the dc necessary for the operation of many types of industrial control circuits. The voltage drop between cathode and anode is very small compared to the voltage drop in a high-vacuum diode; consequently the efficiency of the gas diode as a rectifier will be much higher than that obtainable with a high-vacuum tube of the same power handling capacity. The tube drop is approximately constant for all values of anode current within the safe operating range of the tube; thus the regulation of power supplies

## TABLE 3–2

| G.E. Type No. | RCA Type No. | Westinghouse Type No. | Maximum Average Plate Amps | Maximum Peak Plate Amps | Maximum Peak Inverse Volts | Filament Voltage |
|---|---|---|---|---|---|---|
| GL–866A/866 | 866A/866 | WL–866A/866 | 0.25 | 1.0 | 10,000 | 2.5 |
| GL–872 | 872 | WL–872 | 1.25 | 5.0 | 7,500 | 5.0 |
| GL–872A | 872A | WL–872A | 1.25 | 5.0 | 10,000 | 5.0 |
| GL–869B | 869A–B | WL–869A | 2.50 | 10.0 | 20,000 | 5.0 |
| GL–870 | 870 | WL–870 | 75.0 | 450.0 | 16,000 | 5.0 |

employing gas tubes will be much better than that of power supplies of similar current capacity which employ high-vacuum tubes.

A few typical thermionic gas diodes, along with their respective voltage and current ratings, are listed in Table 3–2.

Thermionic gas diodes are used in single-phase half-wave rectifier circuits, single-phase full-wave rectifier circuits, three-phase half-wave rectifier circuits, three-phase full-wave rectifier circuits, six-phase rectifier circuits, etc. The rectifier circuits mentioned are discussed in Chapter 7.

**3–2. Gas Triodes.** Grid-controlled thermionic gas triodes, which are commonly known as thyratrons, find their most extensive use in industrial control circuits. A few of the more important applications include: temperature control of ovens, resistance welding, regulated power supplies, voltage regulation of alternators and direct current generators, frequency regulators for alternators, speed controllers for motors, parallel switching circuits, high-speed counting circuits, relay control, inverters for converting

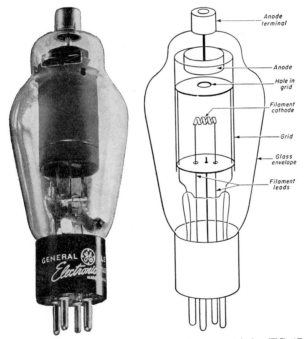

FIG. 3–6. External and internal structure of a gas triode (FG–17 thyratron). (Courtesy General Electric Co.)

direct current to alternating current, grid-controlled rectifiers, saw-tooth oscillators, frequency converters, and control of lighting in large theaters.

There is little similarity between the gas triode and the high-vacuum triode. As will be noted from the illustrations of Fig. 3–6, the outward appearance of a typical gas triode is not too different from the ordinary high-vacuum tube; however, the structure of the electrodes is quite different. The filament and anode are both essentially the same as those of the thermionic gas diode just described. The grid of a thyratron usually takes the form of a cylinder which completely surrounds both cathode and anode. There is a baffle between the cathode and anode which has a small hole through it in order to allow electron and ion passage when ionization is accomplished. In some cases the grid structure takes the form of a perforated cylinder; in such cases the baffle, which is also perforated, extends across the entire space between the anode and cathode. The holes in the baffle are of sufficient size to allow ample conduction. This type of grid structure is not so common as the grid structure previously mentioned.

The grid electrode of the thyratron functions as a one-way valve which has only two positions: completely open, and completely shut. It has the ability to initiate the flow of current; but once current begins to flow, a change in grid potential will have no influence on the magnitude of the plate current flowing. It is impossible to stop the plate current by making the grid negative with respect to the cathode. The only way to stop conduction is to open the plate circuit or to decrease the plate potential to a value lower than the *deionization potential* of the tube for a period sufficient for the tube to deionize. The *deionization time* is the time necessary for the gas to return to its neutral state after the excitation potential has been removed and is around 1,000 microseconds for most mercury vapor thyratrons. Inert gas tubes deionize more rapidly than mercury vapor tubes. The time required for ionization, which is known as the *ionization time*, is around 10 microseconds for most mercury vapor thyratrons.

The two gases that find widest usage in modern gas-filled triodes are argon and mercury vapor. Argon is generally used in the smaller higher frequency gas triodes and mercury vapor is used in all large gas triodes.

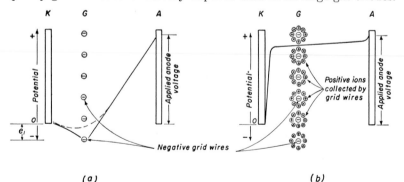

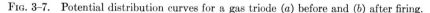

FIG. 3–7. Potential distribution curves for a gas triode (*a*) before and (*b*) after firing.

Fig. 3–7*a* illustrates the potential distribution curves between electrodes (dotted line is average potential distribution curve) when the grid bias is set at a value sufficiently negative to prevent current flow for the plate potential being applied; that is, when the grid potential is beyond cut-off for the plate potential in question. Now if the grid bias is gradually reduced, conduction will begin at the same value of negative grid voltage at which it would were the tube completely evacuated; but instead of remaining at a low value, which would be expected in the case of a high-vacuum triode, the current will jump instantaneously to a large value, the magnitude of which will be determined by the plate potential and load resistance. Eq. (3–1) expresses the anode current in a thyratron in terms of applied circuit voltage, tube drop and load resistance:

$$I_{dc} = \frac{V_{dc} - TD}{R_L} \tag{3-1}$$

where  $I_{dc}$ = average or direct current
$V_{dc}$ = average or direct potential difference applied between cathode and anode
$TD$ = tube drop between cathode and anode during conduction

If the electrons moving toward the anode are allowed to attain sufficient velocity to cause ionization when they collide with the gas atoms, the positive ions that result due to the loss of electrons in the outer orbits are attracted to the negative grid; in turn, the grid becomes surrounded by a sheath of positive ions that completely neutralizes the effects of the negative grid potential, leaving it ineffective as a control electrode. This condition is illustrated by the potential distribution curve of Fig. 3–7b. As mentioned previously, it is necessary to reduce the plate potential to a value below the deionization potential before a thyratron will cease to fire. The arc may be maintained by accumulative ionization at a slightly lower voltage than is necessary to initiate the arc; thus the ionization potential is greater than the tube drop or deionization potential. If the anode potential is reduced to such a value that ionization can no longer be accomplished (below the deionization potential), the electrons in the space between the cathode and anode will be returned to the cathode and the positive ions will return to the anode, thus conduction will cease. Current will continue to exist, however, if the plate potential is not held at zero for sufficient time for the ions to be removed from the space between the cathode and anode. This period, as already mentioned, is known as the deionization time. In the operation of hot-cathode gas triodes, as in the case of hot-cathode gas diodes, it is necessary that the cathode reach operating temperature before plate potential is applied. Most commercial applications incorporate time delay switches which do not allow plate potential to be applied before the cathode has had sufficient time to reach operating temperature. If anode potential is applied before normal cathode emission has been obtained, the voltage drop will increase above normal ionization potential, sending an excess of positive ions into the cathode with sufficient energy to cause it to disintegrate.

Several typical thyratrons along with their respective ratings are listed in Table 3–3.

TABLE  3–3

| Type No. | Peak Volts | Avg. Amps. | Peak Amps. | Filament Voltage |
| --- | --- | --- | --- | --- |
| KU–610..................... | 500 | 0.1 | 0.4 | 2.5 |
| FG–81A..................... | 500 | 0.5 | 2.0 | 2.5 |
| FG–17...................... | 2,500 | 0.5 | 2.0 | 2.5 |
| KU–627..................... | 2,500 | 0.64 | 2.5 | 2.5 |
| KU–628..................... | 2,500 | 2.0 | 8.0 | 5.0 |
| FG–27A..................... | 1,000 | 2.5 | 10.0 | 5.0 |
| FG–57...................... | 1,000 | 2.5 | 15.0 | 5.0 |
| KU–677..................... | 7,500 | 4.0 | 16.0 | 5.0 |
| FG–41...................... | 10,000 | 12.5 | 75.0 | 5.0 |

Thyratrons are classified as *positive-* or *negative-control* tubes, depending upon whether or not the grid must be made positive in order for the tube to fire.  The closer the grid structure encloses the cathode the greater is the effectiveness of the grid potential in preventing conduction.  In the case of positive-control gas triodes the grid structure is so near the cathode that a positive potential is necessary to cause conduction.

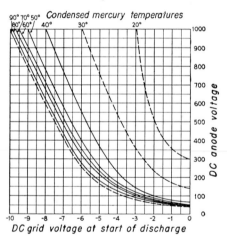

Fig.  3–8.   Control characteristics of a type FG–27A thyratron.  (Courtesy General Electric Co.)

The characteristic curves for a typical negative-grid mercury-vapor thyratron for several different values of ambient temperature are shown in Fig. 3–8.  It will be noticed that a large portion of each of these curves is almost a straight line.  If the projection of the straight line portion of the

*control characteristic*\* when projected toward the origin cuts fairly near
the origin, it is possible to define the ratio of plate potential to grid potential approximately as a constant $K$ which is somewhat similar to the amplification factor $\mu$ as defined in the case of a high-vacuum triode. $K$ is not
constant over the entire range of the tube. However, fairly accurate results are obtained if, in making calculations on circuits in which gas triodes
are used, $K$ is assumed to be constant. Control circuits employing gas
triodes are discussed in Chapter 12.

For mercury-vapor tubes the control characteristic varies greatly with
the ambient temperature of the tube. An increase in temperature results
in an increase in the number of gas atoms inside the tube; this means that
the probability of collision of electrons with gas atoms is greater, resulting
in conduction at a lower value of plate potential. For this reason it is
necessary that the temperature of thyratrons be controlled within fairly
close limits. In general, mercury-vapor thyratrons should not be operated
below 40° C or above 80° C.

The circuit of Fig. 3–9 can be used to determine the *control* or *starting*
*characteristic* of a gas triode. The control characteristic is obtained by
setting the grid potential at fixed values and determining the plate poten-

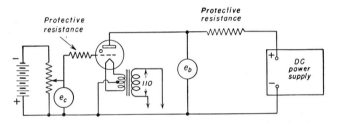

FIG. 3–9.   Circuit for determining the control characteristics of a thyratron.

tial necessary for firing at each value of grid voltage considered. The value
of plate voltage necessary to fire the tube for any specified value of grid
voltage can be readily determined by watching the voltmeter, inserted between the cathode and plate, as the plate potential is gradually increased
and noticing the maximum voltage registered by the voltmeter before the
tube conducts (or fires). At the instant the tube begins to conduct, the
reading of the voltmeter will drop back to a low value, equal to the voltage
drop between the cathode and anode during conduction. As mentioned
previously the voltage between cathode and anode during conduction is
termed the tube drop. Most thyratrons have a very low tube drop; those
employing mercury vapor have a tube drop of around 12 volts, while those
using inert gases have a somewhat higher tube drop.

---

\* A characteristic curve (for a given temperature) showing the relationship between
grid and anode voltages necessary for firing is often referred to as the control or starting characteristic.

At this point it is thought desirable to compare mercury-vapor and inert-gas thyratrons. Tubes filled with inert gases such as argon, which is the most common gas used, have more stable characteristics than mercury-vapor tubes. The characteristics are affected less by temperature. This means that over a fairly wide temperature range an argon tube with a given grid voltage will break down at approximately the same anode potential every time. Therefore, in applications where the ambient temperature cannot be controlled accurately, inert-gas-filled thyratrons are superior to mercury-vapor thyratrons. Another advantage of inert gas tubes is that the deionization time is shorter; thus argon-filled tubes may be used in much higher frequency circuits. An outstanding disadvantage of the inert-gas tube is that the tube drop is greater than in the case of the mercury-vapor tube. For this reason mercury-vapor tubes are much more efficient and are used in preference to inert-gas tubes in any application where the frequency and temperature are such as to allow them to operate satisfactorily. One important application of inert-gas-filled triodes is in the sweep circuit of cathode-ray oscillographs. Characteristics of a 6Q5, which is the type of gas triode used in most DuMont cathode-ray oscillographs as a sweep oscillator, are shown in Fig. 3–10.

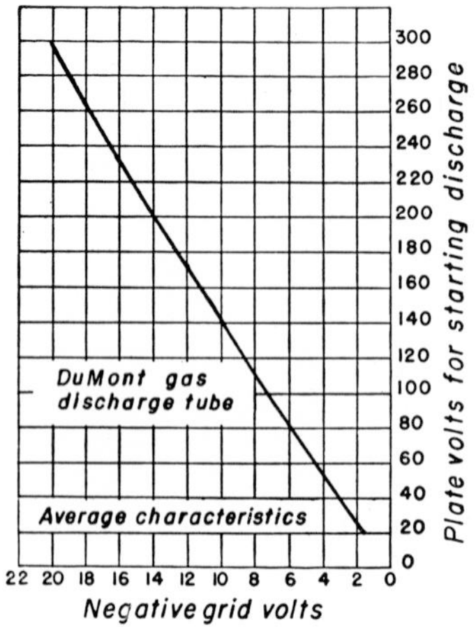

FIG. 3–10. Characteristics of a type 6Q5 gas triode. (Courtesy Allen B. DuMont Laboratories.)

**3–3. Shield-Grid Thyratrons.** The anode and cathode of a shield-grid thyratron are almost identical in structure to the anode and cathode of gas triodes of similar current ratings, but the grid structure is quite different. The structure of a typical shield-grid thyratron is illustrated by Fig. 3–11. In the case of the shield-grid thyratron, the control grid is nothing more than a small cylinder located between the anode and cathode. The shield grid is a large cylinder which completely surrounds cathode, anode and control grid. It has two baffles, one on either side of the control grid, shielding it from both anode and cathode. There is a small hole in each baffle to allow ample conduction. Electrically the screen grid is usually operated at cathode potential. The shield-grid thyratron has several advantages over the three-electrode thyratron: the capacitance and grid current are both reduced materially, the possibility of secondary emission from the grid is reduced and the cathode-emitting efficiency is increased. Because of these advantages the screen-grid thyratron is replacing the three-electrode thyratron for many applications. The characteristics of a typical shield-grid tube are shown in Fig. 3–12.

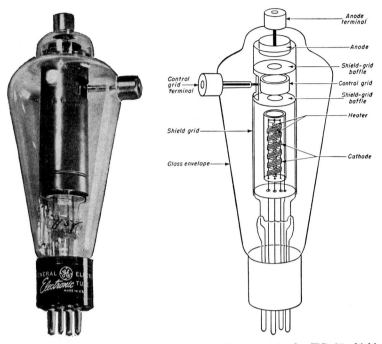

FIG. 3–11.  External and internal structure of a gas tetrode (FG–95 shield-grid thyratron). (Courtesy General Electric Co.)

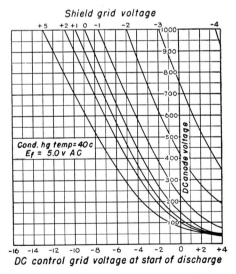

FIG. 3–12.  Control characteristics of a type FG–105 shield-grid thyratron. (Courtesy General Electric Co.)

## Pool-Type Mercury-Arc Rectifiers

Gas tubes using mercury-pool cathodes constitute the oldest and perhaps the most important group of gas-filled tubes. They handle, by far, more power for industrial electronic circuits than all other electronic devices combined. Small glass-bulb pool-type mercury-arc rectifiers found their first important use in connection with battery charging. The earliest type of mercury-arc rectifier tube consisted of a dome-shaped glass bulb with several arms and a pool of mercury in a small cavity at the bottom. Such a tube is sketched in Fig. 3–13. Although this type of tube is obsolete, it is important in that it represented the first step in the development of modern pool-type tubes. Today large steel-tank mercury-arc rectifiers are made in sizes capable of rectifying power measured in thousands of kilowatts. However, they are limited in the maximum voltage they can handle. Although pool-type tubes have been designed to handle potentials as high as 25,000 volts, most pool-type tubes operate at potentials well below 5,000 volts. The largest glass-bulb rectifiers built were capable of handling about 500 amperes at 500 volts. The limitation in the power-handling capacity of glass-bulb rectifiers lies in the fact that they are difficult to cool and are mechanically weak.

**3–4. Glass-Bulb Mercury-Arc Rectifiers.** The principle of the glass-bulb mercury-arc rectifier is the same as that of the steel-tank mercury-arc rectifier. The glass-bulb mercury-arc rectifier consists essentially of two main anodes and a mercury-pool cathode, enclosed in a large evacuated glass chamber (Fig. 3–13).

The mercury-pool cathode is in the base of the large glass bulb. It serves not only as the source of electrons, but also furnishes mercury vapor which is the gaseous medium in this type of tube. The dome of the large glass bulb acts as a condensing chamber. The mercury evaporated from the cathode by the heat of the arc at its surface is condensed on the inside of the large condensing chamber and runs back into the pool because of gravity. By virtue of this process the cathode is self-restoring. The current capacity of such a tube is limited only by the amount of heat that can be safely dissipated. If the temperature of the condensing chamber becomes too great, due to excessive current or improper cooling, the pressure of the mercury can become sufficiently high to cause conduction either from anode to anode, or in the reverse direction, i.e., from anode to cathode. Such conduction is termed *arc-back* or *backfire*. Arc-back is extremely undesirable and can result in injury to the tube as well as to the associated circuit parameters. Because the emission current is almost unlimited, such a tube can stand an extremely large over-load (many times normal current) for a short period of time. The time the over-load exists must not be great enough to allow the pressure in the tube to rise sufficiently to cause arc-back.

The mercury-pool tube of Fig. 3–13 is put into operation by applying ac voltage between the mercury pool and the anode and momentarily closing the circuit through the igniting or starting anode, labeled $I$. The circuit through the starting anode is closed by tilting the tube so the

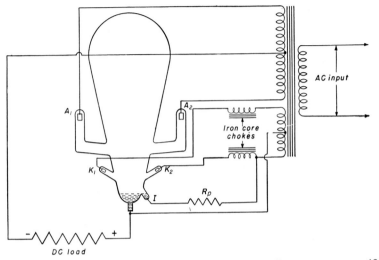

FIG. 3–13.   Full-wave rectifier circuit employing a glass-bulb mercury-arc rectifier.

mercury will make the connection between the starting anode and the pool; then, on breaking the connection, an arc will result. The forming of an arc results in what is known as a *cathode spot* on the surface of the pool of mercury, which acts as a source of electrons. Although electron emission from the surface of a mercury pool is not fully understood, it is thought to be due primarily to the high positive potential gradient at the surface of the pool.    McArthur makes the following statement concerning emission from a mercury pool:

The current density at the arc spot is about 4,000 amperes per square centimeter. The current can be delivered by one spot or from several spots, each delivering between 30 and 40 amperes. The temperature of the spot is about 200° C—a value much too low to permit the thermionic emission of electrons.*

The heat of the arc causes mercury atoms to be evaporated, resulting in mercury vapor which fills the chamber and serves as the gaseous medium within the tube. The glass bulb provides a cooling surface on which the mercury vapor is condensed and slides down the walls to the pool in the bottom. The electrons emitted from the cathode spot will be attracted to either anode $A_1$ or $A_2$, depending upon which is positive with respect to the cathode at the time the electrons in question are emitted. As in the case of

---

* Reprinted by permission from *Electronics and Electron Tubes* by E. D. McArthur, published by John Wiley & Sons, Inc., New York, 1936.

the hot-cathode gas tubes, the electrons moving toward the anodes collide with gas atoms, producing ionization. The positive ions which are formed as a result of the collisions of electrons with gas atoms are attracted to the cathode where they neutralize all existing space charge. The anodes labeled $K_1$ and $K_2$ are known as keep-alive electrodes. These anodes keep the arc alive during the short periods when neither of the main anodes is sufficiently positive to maintain ionization. If the load connected between the cathode and the anodes of the tube shown in Fig. 3–13 were reduced to zero for as much as a few thousandths of a second, the arc would go out and the tube would cease to conduct. Each keep-alive electrode has in series with it an iron-core inductance so that there will be conduction between the cathode and one or the other of the keep-alive electrodes at all times. Because of the small power dissipated in the keep-alive circuits, the reduction in efficiency due to the existence of these electrodes is almost negligible.

**3–5. Steel-Tank Multi-Anode Mercury-Arc Rectifiers.** Steel-enclosed mercury-arc rectifiers were built both in this country and in Europe as early as 1910. By 1908 Copper-Hewitt, in the United States, had built several small steel-enclosed rectifiers and in 1910 B. Schaefer, in Germany, designed a large water-cooled steel-enclosed rectifier which was used successfully for the rectification of currents up to 500 amperes. Both the General Electric Company and the Westinghouse Company developed several small steel-enclosed rectifiers during the period 1910–1912. However, very little developmental work was done on rectifiers in the United States during the following decade. In the meantime, considerable progress was made in Europe.

The first commercial rectifier unit, which consisted of two steel-tank rectifiers each containing 18 anodes and rated at 150 amperes at 230 volts, was installed in a foundry near Frankfurt, Germany, in 1911. In 1915, two 150-kw, 600-volt steel tank rectifiers were installed for street car service in Zurich, Switzerland. Early installations in this country included a rectifier which was installed on a motor car of the Pennsylvania Railroad in 1913. This rectifier supplied power for four 200-horsepower 600-volt dc motors. The car, which weighed 72 tons, pulled two 32-ton coaches over a 240-mile run and while in operation covered 13,400 miles of revenue service. Another early installation in this country was a 5,000-volt rectifier which was installed at a substation of the Michigan United Traction Company in 1915.*

By the middle twenties, a great many steel-tank rectifiers had been installed in Europe. However, such installations were not very common in the United States until the late twenties and early thirties. At present,

---

* For additional information on early mercury-arc rectifier installations, see O. K. Marti and H. Winograd, *Mercury-Arc Power Rectifiers* (New York: McGraw-Hill Book Co., Inc., 1930), pp. 1–9.

the combined rating of the mercury-arc rectifiers installed in the United States alone is millions of kilowatts.

The steel-tank multi-anode mercury-arc rectifier is much more rugged than the older glass-bulb type. It is water-cooled and has a much higher current capacity than the glass-bulb type. Shortly after its development this type rectifier began to replace the glass-bulb type. Steel-tank multi-anode mercury-arc rectifiers contain 3, 6, 12 or 18 anodes; the current capacity is between 10 and 500 amperes per anode. Regardless of the number of

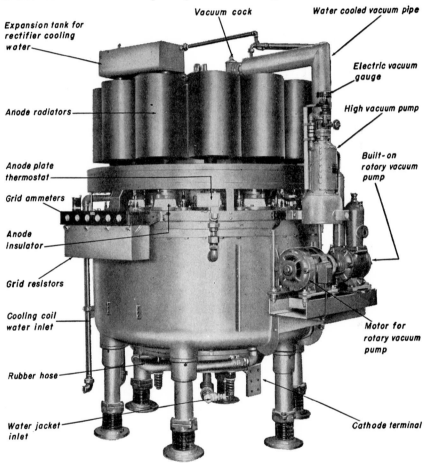

FIG. 3–14.   Typical multi-anode rectifier unit.   (Courtesy Allis-Chalmers Mfg. Co.)

anodes and consequently the number of phases, the power for polyphase rectifiers is supplied from a three-phase source; the three-phase is converted, by a suitable transformer arrangement, to the proper number of phases necessary for the number of anodes contained within the tube being used.

A typical multi-anode mercury-arc rectifier is shown in Fig. 3–14 and

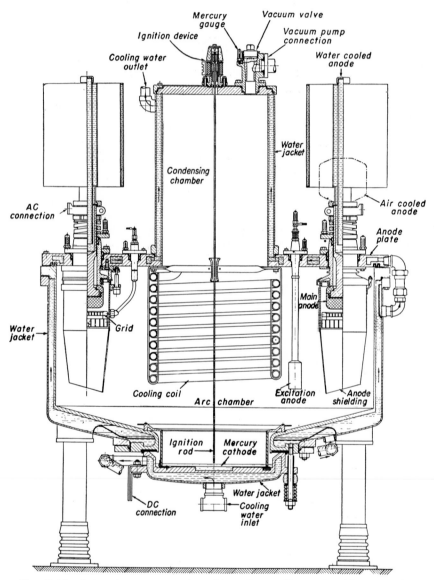

FIG. 3–15. Internal structure of multi-anode rectifier unit. (Courtesy Allis-Chalmers Mfg. Co.)

the internal structure of this type rectifier is shown in Fig. 3–15. The inside of the steel tank is made of stainless steel so that it will not be attacked by the mercury vapor. The mercury-pool cathode is located at the bottom of the steel tank. It is insulated from the steel tank by means of a porcelain or enameled steel ring or some other suitable arrangement. (The insulator can be seen in Fig. 3–15.) The anodes are rather large in size and are made of graphite. A grid structure in front of each anode makes possible control over the firing of the anodes. An elaborate shield surrounds each anode in order to cut down the possibility of arc-back.* Connections from each anode are brought through the top of the steel tank, from which they are well insulated. It is necessary to pump such tubes continuously in order to keep the necessary vacuum. There is a possibility of gas leaking in from the outside through the seals and there is also a possibility that gas will be liberated from the materials used in the construction of the tube. The vacuum pumps used are automatically controlled and are cut in when the gas pressure increases to a certain value. A starting or ignition electrode is necessary in order to start conduction. This takes the form of a solenoid-operated plunger which initiates the arc. Some mercury-arc rectifiers also incorporate an auxiliary anode which functions as a keep-alive mechanism. The arc, after being initiated, is picked up by the most positive anode and is transformed from anode to anode (each anode carrying the total load current while it is conducting) in the same order as the sequence of the potential applied to the anodes. The temperature of the steel-tank rectifier is held within proper limits by an elaborate water-cooling system. The multi-anode mercury-pool type tube just described has several undesirable features. Because of the number of anodes there is conduction within the chamber at all times and always a possibility of arc-back even though the anodes are surrounded by elaborate baffling. The baffling results in a higher tube drop (tube drop is usually around 20 volts) which decreases the over-all efficiency. The starting method is another feature which is not at all ideal.

**3–6. Ignitrons.** Slepian and Ludwig in 1933 developed an electrical device for initiating the arc in a mercury-pool tube.† The development of this new type of starting device, which is known as an *ignitor*, was an important step in the development of the modern ignitron, a mercury-pool tube which is at present rapidly displacing the mercury-arc multi-anode type as a high-power rectifier. Fig. 3–16 shows the internal structure of a typical low-power permanently evacuated ignitron.

The ignitron differs from the mercury-pool rectifier previously discussed

---

* Arc-back refers to the formation of cathode spots on anodes resulting in current flow from mercury-pool to anode, or from one anode to another. This phenomenon is discussed in some detail in Section 7–15.

† J. Slepian and L. R. Ludwig, A New Method for Initiating the Cathode of an Arc, *A.I.E.E. Trans.*, 1933, **52**, 693–700.

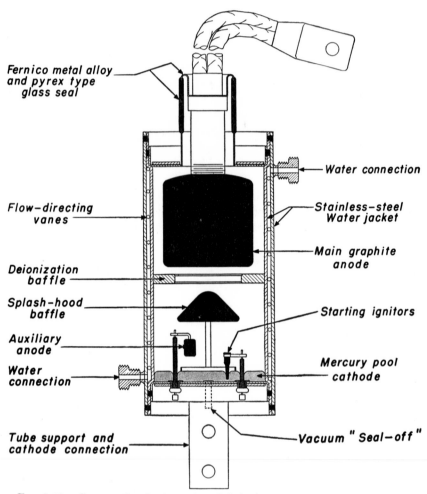

Fernico metal alloy
and pyrex type
glass seal

Flow-directing
vanes

Deionization
baffle

Splash-hood
baffle

Auxiliary
anode

Water
connection

Tube support and
cathode connection

Water connection

Stainless-steel
Water jacket

Main graphite
anode

Starting ignitors

Mercury pool
cathode

Vacuum " Seal-off "

FIG. 3–16.   Cross-sectional view of sealed ignitron for power-rectifier service. (Courtesy General Electric Co.)

in two main respects: the method of initiating the arc, and the number of electrodes. Aside from the ignitor electrode, the ignitron has only one main anode and may or may not have a small auxiliary anode, depending upon the type of service for which it is to be used. The ignitor is made of a material of very high resistivity; boron and silicon carbide are the two materials commonly used. The mercury does not wet the ignitor; therefore there is a very minute separation between the mercury and the rod.

When voltage is applied between the ignitor and the mercury pool, a very high potential gradient results across this small space. This gradient is great enough to ionize the vapor in this region, with subsequent production of an arc which is instantly picked up by the anode (providing the anode is positive with respect to the mercury pool). Ignitor currents vary considerably both with ignitor design and firing circuit used. Typical values are from 10 to 40 amperes. It might be concluded that the ignitor circuit would represent an appreciable loss of power and thus reduce the over-all efficiency appreciably. However, such is not the case. The ignitor circuit is only in operation for a very short interval of time during each cycle; consequently the power dissipated in the ignitor circuit, averaged over one cycle, is very small compared to the total power handled by the ignitron. During the interval of time the anode of an ignitron is negative with respect to the mercury pool, there is no conduction in the tube; therefore, the possibility of arc-back is much less than in the case of the multi-anode tube where there is conduction from the mercury pool to one of the anodes during the time the tube is in operation.

The inner surface of the ignitor envelope must be of such a nature that it will not corrode; stainless steel is used because it will stand up better under the influence of the mercury vapor than any other common construction material. As in the case of other steel-tank mercury-arc rectifiers, ignitrons are water-cooled. In smaller sizes the cooling system is a simple water jacket; in larger sizes regular cooling coils surround the tank. Small size ignitrons are permanently evacuated and sealed off at the factory. Such tubes are available in current ratings up to 400 amperes. Although commercially available ignitrons of higher current ratings are of the pumped type, a 400-ampere sealed ignitron has been developed recently.* The cross sections of typical sealed and pumped ignitrons are shown in Figs. 3–16 and 3–17, respectively. Pumped tubes require a fairly elaborate pumping setup. All the tubes of a given rectifier unit are generally connected to a common evacuation manifold. The pumps are automatically controlled and turn on when the pressure exceeds a given value. A typical ignitron is shown in Fig. 3–18, and a typical ignitron unit is shown in Fig. 3–19. Rectifier circuits employing ignitrons are discussed in Chapter 7.

---

* H. C. Steiner and H. N. Price, A 400-Ampere Sealed Ignitron, *A.I.E.E. Trans.,* 1946, **65,** 680–85.

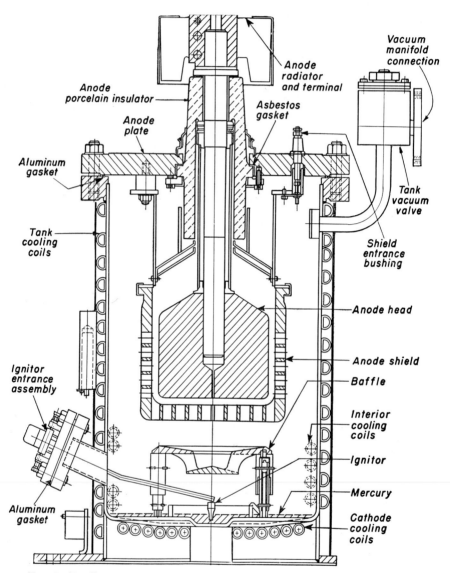

Fig. 3–17.　Cross section of pumped ignitron showing construction. (Courtesy Westinghouse Electric Corp.)

**3–7. Comparison of Ignitrons and Motor Generator Sets.** As a means of obtaining large blocks of dc energy, the ignitron unit has several important advantages over rotating machinery. The no-load losses are smaller, the overload capacity is greater, the voltage regulation is better and the over-all efficiency is greater. Because of these and other less important advantages, ignitron units are rapidly replacing rotating machinery as a means of obtaining large amounts of dc power for railroads, local

Fig. 3–18.  Typical pumped ignitron.  (Courtesy Westinghouse Electric Corp.)

transit systems, light metal refining, mining, etc. The ignitron unit also has some disadvantages. A more skilled technician is required to service an ignitron unit; this means that in an isolated location it may be some time before a serviceman can be obtained from the service department of the manufacturer of the equipment. This might prove a serious problem in some instances — for example, at an isolated coal mine. The ripple voltage of a three-phase half-wave rectifier unit is large enough to cause overheating of rotating machinery and usually requires some type of smoothing reactance; however most power rectifiers are six or twelve phase; thus the ripple is reduced to such a low value that its heating effects are negligible. Polyphase rectifier circuits are discussed in some detail in Chapter 7. The curves of Fig. 3–20 provide a comparison of ignitron units and motor generator sets based on efficiency and losses.

Fig. 3–19. 3,000-kw, 600-volt ignitron rectifier unit. (Courtesy Westinghouse Electric Corp.)

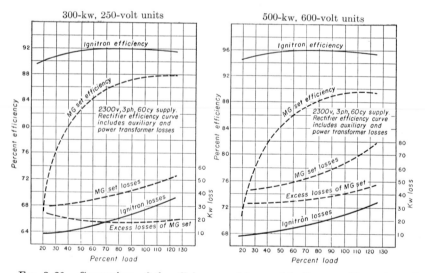

Fig. 3–20. Comparison of the efficiency and losses of ignitron rectifier units and MG sets. (Courtesy Westinghouse Electric Corp.)

**3–8. Ignitrons versus Multi-Anode Rectifiers.** Although eighteen ignitrons are required for an eighteen-phase rectifier unit, whereas an equal amount of output power of essentially the same wave form can be obtained from one multi-anode pool-type rectifier with eighteen anodes, the ignitron unit is superior in many respects. The possibility of arc-back is decreased; thus higher inverse-peak voltages can be handled. All multi-electrode units require pumping, whereas ignitron units are permanently sealed at the factory in sizes capable of carrying up to 400 amperes per anode. The firing of ignitrons can be controlled in almost any desirable manner by relatively simple ignitor circuits. One tube in an ignitron unit can be

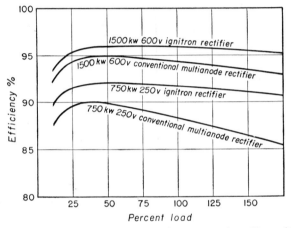

Fig. 3–21. Typical efficiency curves for various types of rectifier units. (Courtesy Westinghouse Electric Corp.)

taken out for repairs and the operation of the system of which it is a part can be made to continue; on the other hand, if trouble develops in a multi-anode unit, often the entire system must be shut down in order for repairs to be made. In general, the efficiency of the ignitron unit is somewhat higher than the efficiency of a multi-anode mercury-arc rectifier of the same rating. Fig. 3–21 gives the relative efficiencies of 1500-kw and 750-kw multi-anode and ignitron rectifier units. One factor which contributes to the higher efficiency of the ignitron unit is the lower tube or arc drop. Values of from 10 to 20 volts are typical for ignitrons.

Because the ignitron possesses most of the desirable features of the multi-anode pool-type tube and does not incorporate several of its undesirable features, it is rapidly replacing the older type unit in most large power rectification circuits.

**3–9. Excitrons.** A single-anode mercury-pool tube known as the excitron * is now being widely used in high-power polyphase rectifier cir-

---

* The excitron is manufactured only by the Allis-Chalmers Manufacturing Company.

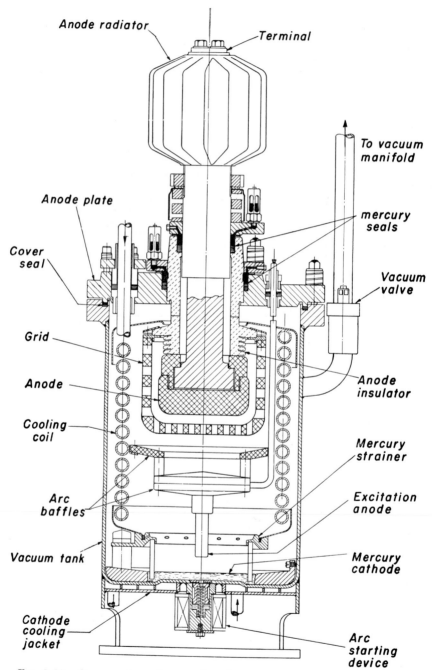

FIG. 3–22.  Cross section of pumped excitron showing construction. (Courtesy
Allis-Chalmers Mfg. Co.)

FIG. 3–23. Battery of twenty-four 12-tank excitron assemblies supplying power to two aluminum reduction circuits; high-speed anode breakers on left, cathode breakers on right. (Courtesy Allis-Chalmers Mfg. Co.)

cuits in a manner similar to ignitrons. Excitrons are used in conversion of ac to dc for transit systems, electrolytic refining, mining and for many other similar applications. Both sealed and pumped excitrons are manufactured. Sealed tubes are made in 200-ampere current ratings and pumped excitrons are made in 250- and 500-ampere current ratings. A cross-sectional view of an excitron is shown in Fig. 3–22. The main difference between the excitron and the ignitron lies in the method of starting and controlling the arc. In an excitron, the arc is initially made by a magnetic starting device which is quite similar in principle to devices used in multi-anode pool-type tubes. During the nonconducting period the arc is maintained by an excitation anode but is prevented from reaching the anode by a grid structure which surrounds the main anode. The grid structure shields the anode to such an extent that the arc cannot reach the anode unless the grid is made sufficiently positive to allow conduction.

No attempt will be made to compare the relative merits of the excitron and the ignitron. Both are widely used in industry and are rapidly replacing rotating machinery as a means of obtaining large amounts of dc energy. Both give a greater over-all efficiency than rotating converting machinery and in general their maintenance cost is much lower. A group of excitron assemblies used to supply power to an aluminum reduction plant is shown in Fig. 3–23.

## PROBLEMS

**3–1.** What is the minimum difference of potential between cathode and anode necessary to ionize (a) argon, (b) krypton and (c) neon?

**3–2.** What is the maximum value of the ac voltage (rms value) that can be rectified with a type 872A gas-filled diode?

**3–3.** Explain the precautions necessary when putting thermionic gas tubes into operation.

**3–4.** A thyratron type FG–27A is placed in series with a load resistance of 1,000 ohms and a dc voltage supply of 500 v. (Positive terminal of power supply connected to anode of tube.) If the tube drop is 12 v, the temperature of the condensed mercury 40° C, and the grid is negative with respect to the cathode by 5 v, determine the magnitude of the current in the plate circuit. Repeat for a grid potential of −7 v. (Characteristics of FG–27A are given in Fig. 3–8.)

**3–5.** Explain how the ambient temperature affects the characteristics of a mercury-vapor thyratron.

**3–6.** Compare the shield-grid thyratron with the three-electrode thyratron.

**3–7.** Explain why the number of anodes in a multi-anode mercury-arc rectifier is always some multiple of three.

**3–8.** Explain briefly the operation of the ignitron.

**3–9.** Explain briefly the operation of the excitron.

**3–10.** Compare briefly the ignitron unit and the MG set as a means of obtaining large blocks of dc power.

## BIBLIOGRAPHY

ALBERT, A. L. *Fundamental Electronics and Vacuum Tubes.* New York: The Macmillan Co., 1947, pp. 92–114.

BENDZ, W. I. *Electronics for Industry.* New York: John Wiley & Sons., Inc., 1947, pp. 68–81, 116–30, 168–92.

COBINE, J. D. *Gaseous Conductors.* New York: McGraw-Hill Book Co., Inc., 1941, pp. 417–71.

DOW, W. G. *Fundamentals of Engineering Electronics.* New York: John Wiley & Sons, Inc., 1937, pp. 458–504.

EASTMAN, A. V. *Fundamentals of Vacuum Tubes.* 2nd ed. New York: McGraw-Hill Book Co., Inc., 1941, pp. 92–120.

FINK, D. G. *Engineering Electronics.* New York: McGraw-Hill Book Co., Inc., 1938, pp. 133–58.

KLOEFFLER, R. G. *Industrial Electronics and Control.* New York: John Wiley & Sons, Inc., 1949, pp. 95–156.

MARTI, O. K., and WINOGRAD, HAROLD. *Mercury-Arc Power Rectifiers.* New York: McGraw-Hill Book Co., Inc., 1930, pp. 10–28, 210–41.

MCARTHUR, E. D. *Electronics and Electron Tubes.* New York: John Wiley & Sons, Inc., 1936, pp. 100–40.

M.I.T. STAFF. *Applied Electronics.* New York: John Wiley & Sons, Inc., 1943, pp. 205–45.

MILLMAN, JACOB, and SEELY, SAMUEL. *Electronics.* New York: McGraw-Hill Book Co., Inc., 1941, pp. 324–58.

MORECROFT, J. H. *Electron Tubes and Their Applications.* New York: John Wiley & Sons, Inc., 1933, pp. 117–30.

PRINCE, D. C., and VOGDES, F. B. *Principles of Mercury-Arc Rectifiers and Their Circuits.* New York: McGraw-Hill Book Co., Inc., 1937, pp. 3–63.

RYDER, J. D. *Electronic Engineering Principles.* New York: Prentice-Hall, Inc., 1947, pp. 280–93.

SLEPIAN, J., and LUDWIG, L. R. A New Method for Initiating the Cathode of an Arc. *A.I.E.E. Trans.*, 1933, **52**, 693–700.

STEINER, H. G., and PRICE, H. N. A 400-Ampere Sealed Ignitron. *A.I.E.E. Trans.*, 1946, **65**, 680–85.

WINOGRAD, H. Development of Excitron-Type Rectifier. *A.I.E.E. Trans.*, 1944, **63**, 969–78.

# CHAPTER 4

## PRINCIPLES OF CIRCUIT ANALYSIS

Although an elementary course in electrical engineering is ordinarily required as a prerequisite to a course of this type, many students—for one reason or another—may require the following brief review of basic circuit theory, advanced prior to study of the electronic circuits discussed in subsequent chapters.

## Direct Current Circuits

**4–1. Ohm's Law.** George Simon Ohm in 1827 evolved a basic law in electricity. He discovered that if a given metallic conductor is held at constant temperature the current through the conductor is directly proportional to the impressed voltage. Ohm's law may be expressed mathematically as follows:

$$I = \frac{E}{R} \qquad (4\text{--}1a)$$

or

$$R = \frac{E}{I} \qquad (4\text{--}1b)$$

or

$$E = RI \qquad (4\text{--}1c)$$

where $R$ = resistance of conductor
$I$ = current through conductor
$E$ = voltage impressed across conductor

**4–2. Resistors in Series.** By definition, a series circuit is one comprised of circuit elements so connected that the same current passes through each element. Such an arrangement is illustrated in Fig. 4–1.

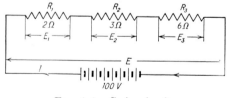

Fig. 4–1. Series circuit.

The *equivalent resistance* of this series circuit is the sum $R$ of the resistances of the individual resistors that make up the circuit.

$$R = R_1 + R_2 + R_3 \qquad (4\text{--}2)$$

102

The circuit current can be expressed as

$$I = \frac{E}{R} \tag{4-3}$$

Eq. (4–2) can be generalized to cover the case of an arbitrary number of resistors connected in series.

EXAMPLE.   If the impressed voltage $E$ is equal to 100 v and $R_1$, $R_2$ and $R_3$ are 2, 3 and 6 ohms, respectively, determine the current through the circuit and the voltage drop across each of the resistors in the circuit of Fig. 4–1.

*Solution:*

$$I = \frac{100}{2 + 3 + 6} = 9.09 \text{ amperes}$$

$E_1$ the voltage across $R_1 = IR_1 = (9.09)(2) = 18.18$ v
$E_2$ the voltage across $R_2 = IR_2 = (9.09)(3) = 27.27$ v
$E_3$ the voltage across $R_3 = IR_3 = (9.09)(6) = \underline{54.54 \text{ v}}$
$$E_1 + E_2 + E_3 = 99.99 \text{ v}$$

It is to be noticed that the numerical sum of $E_1$, $E_2$ and $E_3$ is equal to the impressed voltage $E$.

This example illustrates another important circuit principle, referred to as Kirchhoff's voltage law: "The algebraic sum of the products of the current and resistances in each of the conductors in any closed path in a network is equal to the algebraic sum of the electromotive forces in that path." *

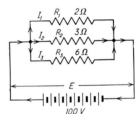

**4–3. Parallel Circuits.**   A parallel circuit is one comprised of circuit elements so connected that the same voltage exists across each element. A parallel circuit is illustrated in Fig. 4–2.

FIG. 4–2.   Parallel circuit.

In a circuit of this type, the equivalent resistance $R$ of the parallel resistors is equal to the reciprocal of the sum of the reciprocals of the resistances of each of the resistors, that is

$$\frac{1}{R} = \frac{1}{R_1} + \frac{1}{R_2} + \frac{1}{R_3} \tag{4-4a}$$

whence

$$R = \frac{R_1 R_2 R_3}{R_1 R_2 + R_2 R_3 + R_1 R_3} \tag{4-4b}$$

The total circuit current can be calculated by use of Eq. (4–3).   If there are $n$ resistors in parallel, it is evident that

$$\frac{1}{R} = \frac{1}{R_1} + \frac{1}{R_2} \cdots + \frac{1}{R_n} \tag{4-4c}$$

* *American Standard Definitions of Electrical Terms* (New York: American Institute of Electrical Engineers, 1941), p. 40.

If the $n$ resistors in parallel are identical, the equivalent resistance of the combination is equal to the resistance $R_x$ of one of the resistors divided by the number of resistors.

$$R = \frac{R_x}{n} \qquad (4\text{--}4d)$$

If only two resistors are in parallel, Eq. (4–4c) reduces to the following:

$$R = \frac{R_1 R_2}{R_1 + R_2} \qquad (4\text{--}4e)$$

EXAMPLE. If the impressed voltage across the parallel circuit of Fig. 4–2 is 100 v and $R_1$, $R_2$ and $R_3$ are 2, 3 and 6 ohms, respectively, determine the battery current $I_T$ and the branch currents $I_1$, $I_2$ and $I_3$.

*Solution:*

$$R = \frac{(2)(3)(6)}{(2)(3) + (2)(6) + (3)(6)}$$

$$= \tfrac{36}{36} = 1 \text{ ohm}$$

$$I_T = \tfrac{100}{1} = 100 \text{ amp}$$

Since the resistors are in parallel, the same voltage exists across each. Accordingly,

$$
\begin{aligned}
I_1 &= \tfrac{100}{2} = \phantom{0}50 \phantom{00} \text{amp} \\
I_2 &= \tfrac{100}{3} = \phantom{0}33.333 \text{ amp} \\
I_3 &= \tfrac{100}{6} = \phantom{0}\underline{16.667} \text{ amp} \\
I_1 + I_2 + I_3 &= \overline{100.000} \text{ amp}
\end{aligned}
$$

It is seen that $I_1 + I_2 + I_3 = I_T$

This example illustrates Kirchhoff's current law: "The algebraic sum of the currents flowing toward any point in a network is zero." *

It can be shown that the ratio of the currents in any two branches of a parallel circuit is inversely proportional to the ratio of the resistances of these two branches. Consider Fig. 4–2:

$$E = I_T R = I_1 R_1 = I_2 R_2 = I_3 R_3$$

or

$$\frac{I_T}{I_1} = \frac{R_1}{R}; \frac{I_T}{I_2} = \frac{R_2}{R}; \frac{I_T}{I_3} = \frac{R_3}{R} \qquad (4\text{--}5a)$$

whence

$$\frac{I_1}{I_2} = \frac{R_2}{R_1}; \frac{I_1}{I_3} = \frac{R_3}{R_1}; \frac{I_2}{I_3} = \frac{R_3}{R_2} \qquad (4\text{--}5b)$$

**4–4. Applications of Kirchhoff's Laws.** There are many types of circuits which cannot be solved merely by using Ohm's law. The network of Fig. 4–3 is an example of such a circuit. This network, however, can be readily solved by proper application of both Ohm's and Kirchhoff's laws.

---

* *American Standard Definitions of Electrical Terms* (New York: American Institute of Electrical Engineers, 1941), p. 40.

EXAMPLE. Let it be required to find the current in each of the branches of the circuit of Fig. 4–3.

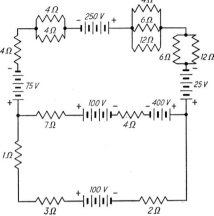

FIG. 4–3.  Complex network which can be readily solved by application of Kirchhoff's laws.

*Solution:* In analyzing a network of this type, it is usually good practice to replace each series and each parallel combination of resistors by its equivalent resistor. Thus, substituting equivalent values for all parallel combinations, the circuit may be reduced to the equivalent circuit shown in Fig. 4–4.

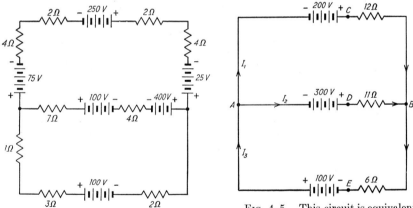

FIG. 4–4.  The circuit of Fig. 4–3 after each of the parallel branches has been reduced to an equivalent resistance.

FIG. 4–5.  This circuit is equivalent to the original circuit of Fig. 4–3. Resistors in series and batteries in series have been combined.

This circuit may be reduced further by combining the resistors which are in series and by combining the batteries which are in series. Batteries in series may be handled in the same manner as resistors, provided their polarity is taken into consideration. After some experience in reducing circuits to their simplest form, the circuit of Fig. 4–3 can be readily reduced to the circuit of Fig. 4–5 without going through intermediate steps.

To solve for the branch currents in the circuit of Fig. 4–5 with the aid of Kirchhoff's laws, the following procedure is used. First, arrows are placed on each branch to indicate current direction. Arrows need not necessarily be in the direction of the actual current, a fortunate circumstance since usually it is difficult, if not impossible, to determine the current direction by mere observation. If arrows are assumed in directions contrary to the actual current, solution will yield negative values for the currents in the corresponding branches—whence the rule that a negative value of current is indicative of the fact that the actual current is in the opposite direction to that assumed. After current directions have been decided on, they cannot be changed during the solution of the problem.

Kirchhoff's current law is applied at sufficient junctions to include each current at least once; in general, therefore, at all junctions save one, which can be specified at will. In the present example only one equation results, which can be written either at point $A$ or point $B$.

$$I_3 = I_1 + I_2 \tag{Ia}$$

or

$$I_2 = I_3 - I_1 \tag{Ib}$$

or

$$I_1 = I_3 - I_2 \tag{Ic}$$

Kirchhoff's voltage law is applied a sufficient number of times to include each branch at least once; in general, therefore, as many equations can be written as there are meshes (loops) of the given network. In the present example two equations result. In writing these equations it is immaterial in which direction a selected closed route is traversed so long as the correct algebraic signs are employed. The following method of assigning signs will be used: All potential drops will be preceded by negative signs and all potential rises will be preceded by positive signs.

Consider circuit $ACBA$:

$$+200 - 12I_1 + 11I_2 - 300 = 0 \tag{II}$$

From point $A$ to point $C$, a potential rise (negative to positive side of battery) is experienced; thus the 200 is preceded by a positive sign. If current flows from $C$ to $B$, then point $C$ must be at a higher potential than $B$ and there is a potential drop from $C$ to $B$; consequently a negative sign precedes the term $12I_1$. If current flows from $D$ to $B$ in the center section, then $D$ must be at a higher potential than $B$ and proceeding from $B$ to $D$ would represent an increase in potential; therefore, $11I_2$ is preceded by a positive sign. Point $D$ is at the positive terminal of the battery and point $A$ at the negative terminal; therefore there is a potential drop of 300 volts from $D$ to $A$, and the 300 is preceded by a negative sign. Since $A$ was the starting point, the algebraic sum of all terms in the equation must be equal to zero.

In a similar manner, the equation for circuit $ABEA$ is written:

$$+300 - 11I_2 - 6I_3 + 100 = 0 \tag{IIIa}$$

Now eliminate $I_3$ in equation (IIIa) by substituting $I_1 + I_2$ for $I_3$.

$$+300 - 11I_2 - 6(I_1 + I_2) + 100 = 0$$

Collecting terms

$$-6I_1 - 17I_2 + 400 = 0 \tag{IIIb}$$

Now solving Eq. (IIIb) simultaneously with Eq. (II)

$$6I_1 + 17I_2 = 400$$

$$-12I_1 + 11I_2 = 100$$

Multiplying Eq. (III$b$) by 2 and adding to Eq. (II)

$$12I_1 + 34I_2 = 800$$
$$\underline{-12I_1 + 11I_2 = 100}$$
$$45I_2 = 900$$

$$I_2 = 20 \text{ amp}$$

Now

$$6I_1 + 17I_2 = 400$$

whence

$$6I_1 + 17(20) = 400$$

$$6I_1 = 60$$

$$I_1 = 10 \text{ amp}$$

Again,

$$I_3 = I_1 + I_2$$

$$= 10 + 20 = 30 \text{ amp}$$

The solution may be checked by writing another voltage equation (one not used in the solution thus far) and substituting the values of current already obtained. If the values are correct, the equation will hold.

There is only one additional voltage equation that can be written, i.e., the equation around loop $ACBEA$

$$+200 - 12I_1 - 6I_3 + 100 = 0 \qquad\qquad \text{(IV}a\text{)}$$

The equation could be written around the circuit in the opposite direction, i.e., the equation around loop $AEBCA$

$$-100 + 6I_3 + 12I_1 - 200 = 0 \qquad\qquad \text{(IV}b\text{)}$$

Eq. (IV$b$) is the same as Eq. (IV$a$) except for signs which may be changed on each term without affecting the equality.

Substituting the values of $I_1$ and $I_3$ in Eq. (IV$a$)

$$+200 - 12(10) - 6(30) + 100 = 0$$
$$+200 - 120 - 180 + 100 = 0$$
$$0 = 0$$

Although many other circuit theorems can be employed to facilitate the solution of more complex circuits, any circuit, regardless of complexity, can be solved by proper application of Kirchhoff's laws.

## Inductance and Capacitance in Direct Current Circuits

There are three basic circuit parameters: *resistance, inductance* and *capacitance*. Inductance and capacitance do not enter into the computation unless the current varies with respect to time. In the circuits previously discussed the current was not a function of time; steady-state conditions existed in all cases. Resistance, which has already been discussed in Chapter 1, is the property of a circuit which determines for a given current the rate at which electric energy is converted into heat.

**4–5. Inductance.*** When current exists in a closed conductor, magnetic flux links the conductor. The strength of the magnetic field is a function of the current through the conductor. If the conductor is in the form of a coil of wire (Fig. 4–6), the total flux linking the coil will be proportional to

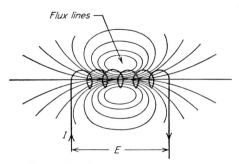

*Flux lines*

FIG. 4–6. Diagram illustrating flux pattern associated with a coil carrying direct current.

the square of the number of turns, provided the dimensions are held constant. Insertion of an iron core in the coil will result in the flux being increased in proportion to the permeability of the iron core. If the current through the coil is changed, the flux linking the coil will change and an electromotive force will be induced in the coil. In general, whenever the flux through a coil is changing, an emf is induced in the coil in such direction as to oppose the effect which produces the change; thus, if the change in flux is produced by change in the current through the coil, the induced voltage will be in such a direction as to tend to increase the current if it is actually decreasing, and vice versa.

Mathematically, the voltage induced in a coil of $N$ turns, each linked by the same flux $\phi$, is

$$e = -N \frac{d\phi}{dt} \tag{4-6a}$$

where $e$ will be expressed in volts if the rate of change of flux is expressed in webers per second.

Alternatively, if the permeability involved is constant, the induced voltage can be written in the form

$$e = -L \frac{di}{dt} \tag{4-6b}$$

where $L$ is termed the *self-inductance* of the coil. The unit of self-inductance is the henry, so named in honor of the American physicist, Joseph Henry. From Eq. (4–6b) it follows that the self-inductance of a coil is one

---

* It is to be emphasized that the discussion of self and mutual inductance given in this section is valid, in general, only for the case when each turn of a coil is linked by the same flux, and that the permeability involved is constant, hence is not a function of current.

henry, if an emf of one volt is induced in the coil when the current changes at the rate of one ampere per second.

From Eq. (4–6a) and (4–6b) it follows that

$$L = N \frac{d\phi}{di} \qquad (4\text{–}6c)$$

*If the permeability involved is constant, $d\phi/di = \phi/I$, whence*

$$L = N \frac{\phi}{I} \qquad (4\text{–}6d)$$

an equation sometimes used as the definition of inductance. If the flux linkages are changing at the rate of one weber per ampere, the inductance of the current is one henry.

Consider the two coils of Fig. 4–7. If the current through coil 1 is changed, a voltage will be induced in coil 2. This voltage is induced

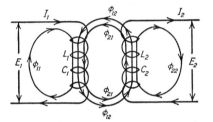

Fig. 4–7.  Diagram illustrating various flux components when mutual inductance exists between two coils.

because the flux linking coil 2 is changing in virtue of the changing current in coil 1.  With reference to Fig. 4–7, the following symbols will be used to represent the various components of flux.

$\phi_1$ = flux linking coil 1 due to current in coil 1

$\phi_2$ = flux linking coil 2 due to current in coil 2

$\phi_{12}$ = flux through coil 2 due to current in coil 1 or the portion of $\phi_1$ that links coil 2

$\phi_{21}$ = flux through coil 1 due to current in coil 2 or the portion of $\phi_2$ that links coil 1

$\phi_{11}$ = the portion of $\phi_1$ that links only coil 1

$\phi_{22}$ = the portion of $\phi_2$ that links only coil 2

From these definitions it follows that:

$$\phi_1 = \phi_{11} + \phi_{12} \qquad (4\text{–}7a)$$

$$\phi_2 = \phi_{22} + \phi_{21} \qquad (4\text{–}7b)$$

When two coils are so related that the voltage induced in one is due to change of current in the other, they are said to possess *mutual inductance*. When, as assumed in this section, the permeability of the medium is constant, the mutual inductance between two coils may be expressed mathematically as follows:

$$M = \frac{N_2\phi_{12}}{I_1} \qquad (4\text{--}8a)$$

$$M = \frac{N_1\phi_{21}}{I_2} \qquad (4\text{--}8b)$$

where all fluxes are in webers

and  $M$ = mutual inductance in henrys
   $N_1$ = number of turns in coil 1
   $N_2$ = number of turns in coil 2
   $I_1$ = current in coil 1 expressed in amperes
   $I_2$ = current in coil 2 expressed in amperes

Regardless of how close coils 1 and 2 are placed together, the flux $\phi_{12}$ which links coil 2 due to current in coil 1 cannot, in actuality, be equal to $\phi_1$, the flux that links coil 1 due to current in coil 1. Let the ratio of $\phi_{12}$, the flux produced in coil 2 due to current in coil 1, to $\phi_1$, the flux produced in coil 1 due to current in coil 1, be $K_{12}$. Likewise, let the ratio of $\phi_{21}$, the flux produced in coil 1 due to current in coil 2, to $\phi_2$, the flux produced in coil 2 due to current in coil 1, be $K_{21}$. Thus:

$$K_{12} = \frac{\phi_{12}}{\phi_1} \qquad (4\text{--}9a)$$

and

$$K_{21} = \frac{\phi_{21}}{\phi_2} \qquad (4\text{--}9b)$$

The quantity

$$K = \sqrt{K_{12}K_{21}} \qquad (4\text{--}10)$$

is termed the *coefficient of coupling*.* For constant permeability of medium as assumed in this section, $K_{12} = K_{21} = K$. It is easily established from the foregoing equations that the coefficient of coupling is related to the mutual and self-inductance of the two coils as follows:

$$K = \frac{M}{\sqrt{L_1L_2}} \qquad (4\text{--}11)$$

where  $M$ = mutual inductance in henrys
   $L_1$ = self-inductance of coil 1 in henrys
   $L_2$ = self-inductance of coil 2 in henrys

The coefficient of coupling between two coils can be readily determined from Eq. (4–11) if means are available for determining the inductance of $L_1$, $L_2$ and $M$. $L_1$ and $L_2$ can be measured with an inductance bridge. The mutual inductance existing between two coils can be determined with

---

* Although the coefficient of coupling is generally considerably less than unity if the medium in which the flux exists in nonmagnetic, in the case of iron-core transformers, the coefficient of coupling between primary and secondary is often as high as 0.99.

a mutual inductance bridge; or, if such a bridge is not available, by the following procedure. The two coils in question are connected in series as shown in Fig. 4–8 and the inductance between points $A$ and $D$ is measured. Terminals $B$ and $C$ should now be disconnected, terminal $B$ of coil 1 should

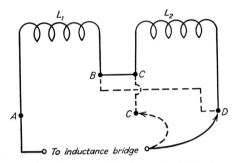

FIG. 4–8.   Connections for measuring the mutual inductance of two coils.

be connected to terminal $D$ of coil 2 as indicated by the dotted line and the inductance measured between points $A$ and $C$. The largest value of inductance will be obtained when the fluxes in the two coils aid each other and the smaller value will be obtained when the fluxes subtract from each other; for these two conditions the following relationships may be written:

$$L(\text{add}) = L_1 + L_2 + 2M$$
$$\underline{\qquad L(\text{sub}) = L_1 + L_2 - 2M \qquad}$$
$$L(\text{add}) - L(\text{sub}) = 4M$$
$$M = \frac{L(\text{add}) - L(\text{sub})}{4} \tag{4–12}$$

The mutual inductance $M$ and the coefficient of coupling $K$ between two given coils (or inductors) are functions of the geometry of the coils, their relative positions, and the permeability of the medium. If the permeability of the medium is not constant, but is a function of the currents in the coils, the foregoing definitions and discussion require modification.

**4–6. Current in an Inductive Circuit with Direct Voltage Applied.** Consider the circuit of Fig. 4–9a. When switch $S$ is closed, the current will not immediately reach its maximum value, but will gradually attain its maximum value as indicated by the curve of Fig. 4–9b. This is because as the current increases, a voltage which opposes the change is induced in the coil. Kirchhoff's voltage law can be written around the circuit as follows:

$$E = Ri + N\frac{d\phi}{dt} \tag{4–13a}$$

From earlier discussion it follows that

$$N\frac{d\phi}{dt} = L\frac{di}{dt}$$

Therefore Eq. (4–13a) can be rewritten as follows:

$$Ri + L\frac{di}{dt} = E \tag{4–13b}$$

where     $E$ = impressed voltage
$\quad Ri$ = voltage drop across $R$
$\quad L\,di/dt$ = voltage drop across $L$, equal to the negative of voltage $(e = -L\,di/dt)$ induced in the coil
$\quad N$ = number of turns
$\quad \phi$ = flux
$\quad L$ = inductance

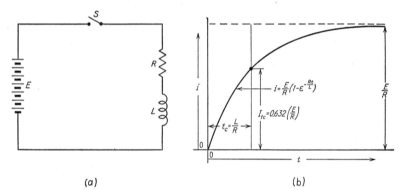

(a)                                   (b)

FIG. 4–9.  Increase of current in a circuit containing inductance, resistance and an emf in series.

Solving Eq. (4–13) for $i$ with boundary condition $i = 0$ when $t = 0$ yields

$$i = \frac{E}{R}(1 - \epsilon^{-Rt/L}) \tag{4–14}$$

where $t$ = time expressed in seconds
$\quad \epsilon$ = 2.718 · · · (base of natural logarithm)

From this equation it is to be seen that for $i$ to reach its Ohm's law value of $E/R$, $t$ would have to equal infinity. In practice, however, the current in most circuits reaches approximately its Ohm's law value in a small fraction of a second. The rapidity with which the current increases in an inductive circuit is expressed by what is termed the *time constant* $t_c$ of the circuit. The time constant of an $RL$ circuit is the ratio of $L$ to $R$. When $t = t_c = L/R$, the exponent of $\epsilon$ is unity, and—as readily computed—the current has risen to 63.2% of its final value of $E/R$.

Now consider the case where switch $S_1$ has been left closed until the current has reached its final value of $I_0$ and the inductive circuit is then short-circuited (by closing $S_2$) as indicated in Fig. 4–10a. A fuse is placed in series with this circuit so that when $S_2$ is closed the fuse will blow, thus protecting the battery from a short-circuit. The current in the circuit of Fig. 4–10a can be expressed as a function of time by writing Kirchhoff's voltage law around the circuit through $S_2$.

$$Ri + L\frac{di}{dt} = 0 \qquad (4\text{–}15)$$

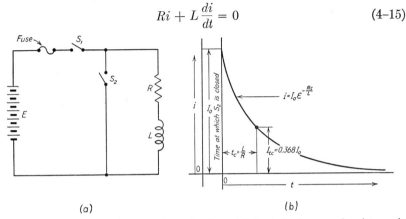

(a)	(b)

FIG. 4–10. Decrease of current in a circuit containing inductance and resistance in series.

Solving for $i$ with boundary condition $i = I_0$ when $t = 0$ yields

$$i = I_0(\epsilon^{-Rt/L}) \qquad (4\text{–}16)$$

where $I_0$ = value of $i$ at the time the circuit is short-circuited by switch $S_2$
$R$ = value of resistance through which current decreases. This may be different from the value of resistance through which the circuit is charged.

In this case, when $t = L/R$, the current has decreased to 36.8 percent of the initial value of $I_0$.

**4–7. Energy Stored in a Magnetic Field.** The energy stored in the magnetic field produced by the current flowing through an inductor can be evaluated by use of Eq. (4–13b). Multiplying both sides of Eq. (4–13b) by $i$ yields

$$Ri^2 + Li\frac{di}{dt} = Ei$$

where	$Ei$ = power input to the circuit at any instant
$Ri^2$ = rate at which energy is transformed into heat in the resistance at any instant
$Li\,di/dt$ = rate at which energy is being stored in the magnetic field associated with the coil

The total energy stored in the magnetic field from the instant the switch $S_1$ is closed (Fig. 4–9) until $i$ reaches its Ohm's law value of $E/R$ may be represented by the following equation:

$$W = \int_0^\infty Li\frac{di}{dt}\,dt \qquad (4\text{–}17)$$

Integrating

$$W = \frac{LI^2}{2}$$

(4–18)

where $W$ = energy in joules
$L$ = inductance in henrys
$I$ = current in amperes

**4–8. Capacitance.** When a potential difference is applied between two conductors separated by a dielectric, charge will be stored on the plates. Negative charge, due to accumulation of electrons, will exist on one plate; an equal amount of positive charge, due to a deficiency of electrons, will exist on the other. A device designed for so storing charge is known as a *capacitor*. Consider the circuit of Fig. 4–11. If switch $S$ is placed in position 1 there will be a momentary deflection of the meter in the circuit.

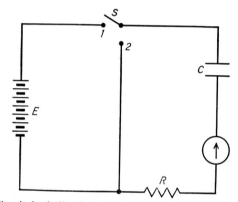

Fig. 4–11.   Circuit for indicating the charging and discharging of a capacitor.

After the capacitor has been completely charged (usually in a very short time) the pointer of the meter will return to zero, indicating that current has ceased to flow. When the capacitor is fully charged, the voltage across the capacitor will be equal to the battery voltage. If now the switch is moved into position 2, the charge will flow out of the capacitor (i.e., the excess of electrons on the negative plate will flow back to the positive plate) and the meter will deflect in the opposite direction. The pointer will drop back to zero as soon as the capacitor has had sufficient time to discharge completely. The ratio of the charge stored by a capacitor to the voltage impressed across the capacitor is termed the *capacitance* of the capacitor. The unit of capacitance, the farad, is named after the English physicist, Michael Faraday, and is equal to one coulomb per volt.

$$C = \frac{Q}{V}$$

(4–19)

where $C$ = capacity in farads
$Q$ = charge in coulombs
$V$ = voltage in volts

The capacitance of the commonly used parallel plate capacitor is expressed by Eq. (4–20).

$$C = \frac{kA \times 10^{-3}}{36\pi d} \qquad (4\text{–}20)$$

where $C$ = capacitance in microfarads. The capacitance is expressed in microfarads ($10^{-6}$ farads) instead of farads for numerical convenience; the great majority of capacitors used in practice are much smaller than one farad.

$A$ = area of one of the plates in square meters

$k$ = dielectric constant of the medium

$d$ = distance between the plates in meters

Capacitors are made with many different types of dielectrics and in many different forms; however, general discussion of capacitor design is beyond the scope of this text.

**4–9. Current in a Capacitive Circuit with Direct Voltage Applied.** Consider the circuit of Fig. 4–12a. Assume that with no initial charge on the capacitor switch $S$ is closed to position 1 at $t = 0$. Writing Kirchhoff's voltage law around the circuit

$$iR + \frac{q}{C} = E \qquad (4\text{–}21)$$

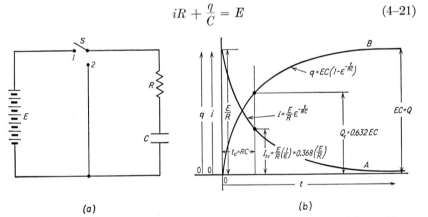

(a)                              (b)

FIG. 4–12.   Current and charge as a function of time in a circuit containing resistance and capacitance in series.

Solving for $i$ with boundary conditions $i = E/R$ when $t = 0$ yields

$$i = \frac{E}{R}\epsilon^{-t/RC} \qquad (4\text{–}22)$$

where  $i$ = instantaneous current

$E$ = impressed voltage

$R$ = resistance of circuit

$C$ = capacitance in farads

$t$ = time in seconds

At $t = 0$ the current is limited only by the resistance in the circuit, hence attains its maximum value at this instant. As the capacitor charges up, the rate of flow of charge—i.e., the current—decreases and becomes equal to zero when the voltage across the capacitor is equal to $E$, the impressed voltage. Eq. (4–22) indicates that this requires an infinite time; however, the current drops to a very small value in an extremely short time (curve $A$ of Fig. 4–12$b$). The time constant $RC$ is used as a criterion of the rate at which the capacitor is charged. Thus when $t = RC$, the exponent of $\epsilon$ is 1 and the current is equal to 36.8 percent of its initial value.

The charge $q$ on the capacitor at any time $t$ after the switch has been closed may be obtained as follows:

$$q = \int_0^t i \, dt \tag{4–23}$$

thus

$$q = \int_0^t \frac{E}{R} \epsilon^{-t/RC} \, dt$$

Integrating

$$q = EC(1 - \epsilon^{-t/RC}) \tag{4–24a}$$

$$= Q(1 - \epsilon^{-t/RC}) \tag{4–24b}$$

where $Q$ is the final charge. The charge as a function of time is indicated by curve $B$ of Fig. 4–12$b$.

If switch $S$ is changed to position 2 after the capacitor is fully charged, the capacitor will discharge through the circuit. An analysis of the discharge follows. Writing Kirchhoff's voltage law around the circuit with the switch in position 2:

$$iR + \frac{q}{C} = 0 \tag{4–25}$$

Solving for $i$ with boundary condition $i = -E/R$ at $t = 0$

$$i = -\frac{E}{R} \epsilon^{-t/RC} \tag{4–26}$$

Eq. (4–26) is identical to the equation for the charging of a capacitor through a resistor (Eq. 4–22), with the exception that the sign is negative. The difference in sign indicates that the discharge current, though of the same form as the charging current, is in the opposite direction. Solving for charge

$$q = \int_0^t i \, dt$$

gives

$$q = Q\epsilon^{-t/RC} \tag{4–27}$$

If the charge during discharge is plotted as a function of time the curve is of the same shape as the plot of current versus time during discharge.

**4–10. Energy Stored in a Capacitor.** Multiplying Eq. (4–21) by $i$ and substituting $dq/dt$ for $i$ in the second term of this equation gives

$$i^2R + \frac{q}{C}\left(\frac{dq}{dt}\right) = Ei$$

where $Ei$ is the rate at which energy is furnished by the battery, $i^2R$ is the rate at which energy is dissipated in the resistor, $(q/C)(dq/dt)$ is the rate at which energy is stored in the capacitor. The total energy stored in the capacitor during charging is

$$W = \int_{t=0}^{t=\infty} \frac{q}{C}\frac{dq}{dt}\,dt$$

$$= \int_{q=0}^{q=Q} \frac{q}{C}\,dq$$

$$= \frac{1}{2}\frac{Q^2}{C}$$

$$= \frac{1}{2}CE^2 \tag{4–28}$$

where $E$ = battery voltage = final voltage across capacitor

**4–11. Direct Current Circuits Containing Resistance, Capacitance and Inductance.** Consider the series $RLC$ circuit of Fig. 4–13. Writing Kirchhoff's voltage law around the circuit gives

$$Ri + L\frac{di}{dt} + \frac{q}{C} = E \tag{4–29}$$

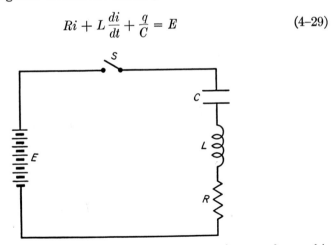

FIG. 4–13. Circuit containing resistance, inductance, capacitance and an emf in series.

A complete discussion of the solution of this equation would be lengthy and rather involved analytically; it suffices for present purposes to merely state the situation for the current when the circuit constants are such that $R^2/4L^2 < 1/LC$ and the initial charge on the capacitor is zero:

$$i = \frac{2CE\epsilon^{-\alpha t}}{\sqrt{4LC - R^2C^2}} \sin \beta t \qquad (4\text{-}30a)$$

where $\alpha = \dfrac{R}{2L}$ \hfill $(4\text{-}30b)$

$$\beta = \sqrt{\frac{1}{LC} - \frac{R^2}{4L^2}} \qquad (4\text{-}30c)$$

Because of the sinusoidal nature of the current, this solution for $R^2/4L^2 < 1/LC$ is termed the solution for the oscillatory case. If the circuit constants are such that $R^2/4L^2 = 1/LC$ or $R^2/4L^2 > 1/LC$, the nature of the current is non-sinusoidal; consequently these conditions comprise those for the

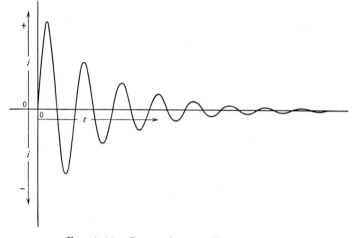

FIG. 4–14.   Current in an oscillatory $RLC$ circuit.

nonoscillatory cases. Fig. 4–14 shows the current as a function of time in a series $RLC$ circuit with circuit parameters adjusted for oscillation. The frequency of oscillation, or the natural frequency of the circuit $f_r$, is expressed as follows:

$$f_r = \frac{\beta}{2\pi} \qquad (4\text{-}31a)$$

$$= \frac{1}{2\pi} \sqrt{\frac{1}{LC} - \frac{R^2}{4L^2}} \qquad (4\text{-}31b)$$

As $R$ approaches zero, $f_r$ approaches as a limit the value

$$f_r = \frac{1}{2\pi\sqrt{LC}} \qquad (4\text{-}31c)$$

termed, for reasons discussed later, the resonant frequency of the circuit.

## Alternating Current Circuits

**4–12. Nature of Alternating Current.** "An alternating current is a periodic current the average value of which over a period is zero." * The most commonly used alternating current is that where the magnitude varies

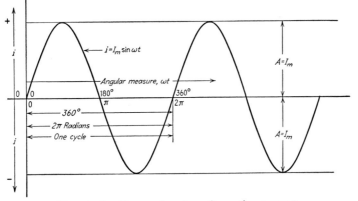

FIG. 4–15.   Two cycles of an alternating current.

sinusoidally (Fig. 4–15). Eq. (4–32) expresses the instantaneous magnitude of a sinusoidally varying current in terms of time and angular velocity.

$$i = I_m \sin \omega t \qquad (4\text{–}32)$$

where   $i$ = current at any time $t$
  $I_m$ = maximum value of current
  $\omega$ = angular velocity in radians/second
  $t$ = time in seconds
  $\omega t$ = angle in radians

*Amplitude.* The maximum displacement of a sinusoidal wave is known as the amplitude of the wave and is represented by the distance $A$ in Fig. 4–15. In the case under consideration the wave represents current; thus the maximum displacement is the maximum value of current and is represented by the symbol $I_m$. If this were a voltage wave, the maximum value would be designated by the symbol $E_m$.

*Period and Cycle.* The period is the time necessary for the current or voltage to change from a given value through all other possible values both positive and negative and return to its original value. A cycle is a complete series of values for the sinusoidal voltage current that occurs during one period. One cycle is indicated on Fig. 4–15 by 360° or $2\pi$ radians.

* *American Standard Definitions of Electrical Terms* (New York: American Institute of Electrical Engineers, 1941), p. 30.

*Frequency.* The frequency is the number of periods or cycles occurring in unit time and is generally expressed as cycles per second.

$$f = \frac{1}{T} \tag{4-33}$$

where $f$ = frequency in cycles/second

$T$ = time for one period

*Average Value.* With sign taken into account, the average value of a sinusoidal current or voltage over one complete cycle is zero. For this

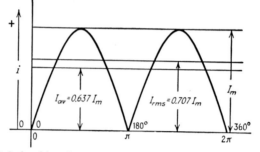

FIG. 4–16.  Relationship of average, effective and maximum values of a sinusoidal current.

reason the average value (Fig. 4–16) is defined as the value taken over one complete cycle of the rectified wave. Analytically, the average value is calculated as follows:

$$I_{av} = \int_0^\pi \frac{I_m \sin \omega t \, d\omega t}{\pi}$$

Solving

$$I_{av} = 0.637 I_m \tag{4-34}$$

*Effective Value.* The effective or *root-mean-square* (rms) value of a sinusoidal current or voltage is defined as the square root of the average of the square of the instantaneous values. This definition is employed so that with respect to a given resistance a current of one rms ampere through it will produce heat at the same rate as one dc ampere. Also applying one rms volt will produce heat at the same rate as one dc volt. It is the rms value that is indicated by the more commonly used types of ac ammeters and voltmeters.* Accordingly, unless otherwise specified, when ac current or voltage values are used, root-mean-square values are to be assumed. Analytically, the root-mean-square value is calculated as follows:

$$I_{rms} = \sqrt{\int_0^\pi \frac{I^2_m \sin^2 \omega t \, d\omega t}{\pi}}$$

Solving

$$I_{rms} = 0.707 I_m \tag{4-35}$$

* Although most ac instruments read the root-mean-square value of the wave, there are ac instruments which read crest or peak value of the wave.

**4–13. Circuits Containing Resistance Only.** When an alternating voltage is applied to the terminals of a resistive load, it follows from Ohm's law that the wave form of the current through the load is also sinusoidal and is in phase with the applied voltage, i.e., both waves will have their maximum and minimum values occurring at the same instant. The sketches of Fig. 4–17 indicate this phase relationship for a pure resistive load.

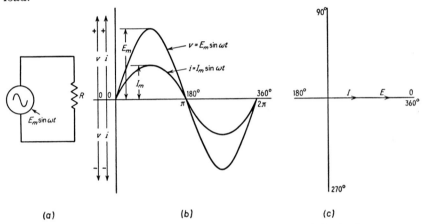

(a)                        (b)                        (c)

Fig. 4–17.   Current and voltage relations for a resistive load.

It is usually convenient in working with ac to represent the current and voltage by vectors of magnitudes equal to the corresponding rms values of the current and voltage and of relative position such that the angle between the vectors is equal to the phase angle between the current and voltage. The vector diagram in the case of a resistive load would be as indicated by the sketch of Fig. 4–17c.

The power input to an ac circuit is expressed as follows:

$$P = EI \cos \theta \qquad (4\text{–}36)$$

where $P$ = power in watts

$I$ = rms value of current through the circuit

$E$ = rms value of voltage across the terminals of the circuit

$\theta$ = angle between current and voltage

The term $\cos \theta$ is termed the *power factor* (*pf*) of the circuit.

If the circuit were more complicated, consisting of various combinations of resistors, the resistors could be combined in exactly the same manner as in the dc circuits already considered. The current through each resistor will be in phase with the voltage across it; thus $\theta = 0°$ and $\cos \theta = 1$.

**4–14. Circuits Containing Inductance Only.** Consider the case where an alternating voltage is impressed across pure inductance as indicated by

Fig. 4–18. From $e = -L \, di/dt$ it follows that the current through the inductor will lag the voltage drop $e = L \, di/dt$ across the inductor by 90°,

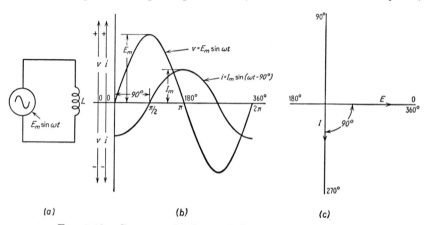

FIG. 4–18. Current and voltage relations for an inductive load.

as indicated graphically by Fig. 4–18b, and vectorially by Fig. 4–18c. In this case, the power consumed would be equal to zero:

$$P = EI \cos 90°$$

$$P = EI \, (0) = 0$$

It is not possible to make a coil without some resistance; thus any coil will take some power due to the resistance of its winding. In practice, however, the resistance of a well-designed coil can be made quite small.

The current in an inductive circuit is a function not only of the inductance, but also of the frequency. Let it be assumed that $E$ volts are applied to the terminals of the inductor $L$ of Fig. 4–18a. It can be derived from $e = -L \, di/dt$ that the current will then be expressed by the following equation:

$$I = \frac{E}{\omega L} \qquad (4\text{–}37a)$$

where $\omega = 2\pi f$

$f$ = frequency of impressed voltage

This equation is commonly written in the following form:

$$I = \frac{E}{X_L} \qquad (4\text{–}37b)$$

where $X_L = 2\pi f L$ is termed the *inductive reactance*.

Inductors in series or in parallel may be treated in a manner similar to that of resistors in series or in parallel. Thus, let it be required to obtain an expression for the total current in the circuit of Fig. 4–19. Then

$$I = \frac{E}{X_T}$$

where $X_T = X_{L1} + \dfrac{X_{L2}X_{L3}}{X_{L2} + X_{L3}} + X_{L4} + \dfrac{X_{L5}X_{L6}X_{L7}}{X_{L5}X_{L6} + X_{L5}X_{L7} + X_{L6}X_{L7}}$

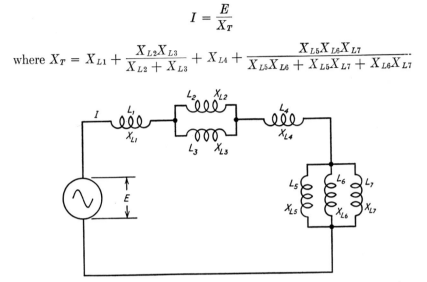

Fig. 4–19.    Circuit comprised of inductors in both series and parallel combinations.

**4-15. Circuits Containing Capacitance Only.** If an alternating voltage is applied to the terminals of a capacitor as indicated by Fig. 4–20, it follows from $q = eC$, whence $i = C\, de/dt$, that the current will lead the applied voltage by 90°. This condition is represented both graphically and

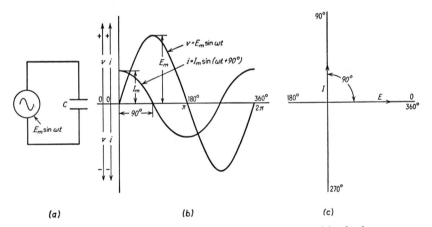

(a)                              (b)                              (c)

Fig. 4–20.    Current and voltage relations for a capacitive load.

vectorially by the sketches of Fig. 4–20. The power taken by a capacitor is equal to zero.

$$P = EI \cos \theta$$
$$P = EI(\cos 90°) = 0$$

It can be derived from $i = C\,de/dt$ that if $E$ volts are applied to the terminals of the capacitor $C$ of Fig. 4–20, the current $I$ will be expressed by

$$I = 2\pi fCE \qquad (4\text{–}38a)$$

$$= \frac{E}{X_C} \qquad (4\text{–}38b)$$

where $X_C = 1/2\pi fC$ is termed the *capacitive reactance*

Combinations of capacitive reactances can be combined in the same manner as combinations of inductive reactances or resistors. Thus, consider a circuit such as the one of Fig. 4–21 which has several series and parallel branches.

$$I = \frac{E}{X_T}$$

where $X_T = X_{C1} + \dfrac{X_{C2}X_{C3}}{X_{C2}+X_{C3}} + \dfrac{X_{C4}X_{C5}X_{C6}}{X_{C4}X_{C5}+X_{C5}X_{C6}+X_{C4}X_{C6}} + X_{C7} + X_{C8}$

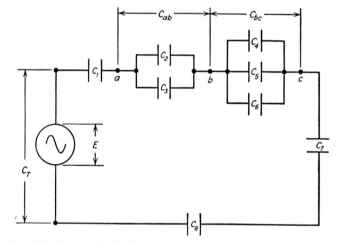

Fig. 4–21. Circuit comprised of capacitors in both series and parallel combinations.

However, if it is wished to combine capacitors in series or in parallel to obtain an equivalent capacitance, the procedure is quite different from that of combining capacitive reactances. It is to be recalled that capacitance in parallel is added and capacitance in series is combined in the same manner as resistance in parallel. In this fashion the total capacitance of the circuit of Fig. 4–21 may be replaced by an equivalent capacitance:

$$C_{ab} = C_3 + C_2$$

$$C_{bc} = C_6 + C_4 + C_5$$

$$\frac{1}{C_T} = \frac{1}{C_1} + \frac{1}{C_{ab}} + \frac{1}{C_{bc}} + \frac{1}{C_7} + \frac{1}{C_8}$$

or

$$\frac{1}{C_T} = \frac{1}{C_1} + \frac{1}{C_3 + C_2} + \frac{1}{C_6 + C_4 + C_5} + \frac{1}{C_7} + \frac{1}{C_8}$$

The current is

$$I = \frac{E}{X_{C_T}}$$

and the equivalent capacitive reactance,

$$X_{C_T} = \frac{1}{2\pi f C_T}$$

**4–16. Circuits Containing Inductance and Resistance.** Fig. 4–22a is a series circuit containing resistance and inductance with an alternating voltage of $E$ volts applied to its terminals. Since the current through the entire circuit is the same, current will be used as reference. As already shown, the

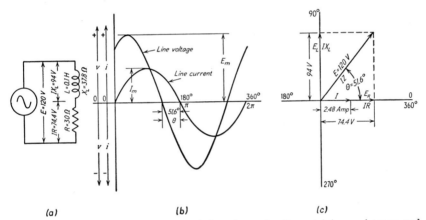

(a)                    (b)                    (c)

FIG. 4–22. Current and voltage relations in a circuit containing resistance and inductance in series.

voltage drop across the resistor $IR$ will be in phase with $I$; thus it is laid off along the same line (Fig. 4–22c). The voltage across $X_L$ will be equal to $IX_L$ and will lead $I$ by 90°; therefore it is laid off 90° ahead of $I$ on the diagram. The impressed voltage $E$ must then be equal to the vector sum of $E_L$ and $E_R$. The angle $\theta$ between $E$ and $I$ is the phase angle of the complete circuit. The input power to the circuit is $EI \cos \theta$; it is also equal to $I^2R$, since the resistance is the only element that dissipates power. A problem of this type can be analyzed as follows.

Since $E$ is the hypotenuse of a right triangle which has sides $E_L$ and $E_R$,

$$E = \sqrt{E_R{}^2 + E_L{}^2}$$
$$= \sqrt{(IR)^2 + (IX_L)^2}$$
$$= I\sqrt{R^2 + X_L{}^2}$$

and

$$I = \frac{E}{\sqrt{R^2 + X_L^2}} \tag{4-39a}$$

$\sqrt{R^2 + X_L^2}$ is known as the *impedance* of the circuit and is designated by the symbol $Z$. Eq. (4-39a) may be rewritten as

$$I = \frac{E}{Z} \tag{4-39b}$$

Returning to the diagram of Fig. 4-22c, $\theta$ may be determined as follows:

$$\tan \theta = \frac{E_L}{E_R} = \frac{IX_L}{IR} = \frac{X_L}{R} = \frac{2\pi fL}{R} \tag{4-40}$$

or

$$\cos \theta = \frac{E_R}{E} = \frac{IR}{IZ} = \frac{R}{Z} = \frac{R}{\sqrt{R^2 + X_L^2}} \tag{4-41}$$

or

$$\sin \theta = \frac{E_L}{E} = \frac{IX_L}{IZ} = \frac{X_L}{Z} = \frac{X_L}{\sqrt{R^2 + X_L^2}} \tag{4-42}$$

EXAMPLE. Assume the following parameters for the circuit of Fig. 4-22 and solve for $I$, $E_R$, $E_L$, $\theta$, $pf$ and $P$:

$E = 120$ v                 $L = 0.1$ henry

$f = 60$ cps               $R = 30$ ohms

*Solution:*    $X_L = 2\pi fL$

$$= 2\pi(60)(0.1)$$

$$= 37.7 \text{ ohms}$$

$$Z = \sqrt{R^2 + X_L^2}$$

$$= \sqrt{(30)^2 + (37.7)^2}$$

$$= 48.3 \text{ ohms}$$

$$I = \frac{120}{48.3} = 2.48 \text{ amp}$$

$$E_R = IR = (2.48)(30) = 74.4 \text{ v}$$

$$E_L = IX_L = (2.48)(37.7) = 93.5 \text{ v}$$

$$\tan \theta = \frac{X_L}{R} = \frac{37.7}{30} = 1.26$$

$$\theta = 51.6°$$

$$pf = \cos \theta = 0.6211$$

$$P = EI \cos \theta = (120)(2.48)(0.6211) = 185 \text{ watts}$$

The power may be checked by using the equation $(P = I^2R)$

$$P = I^2R = (2.48)^2(30) = 185 \text{ watts}$$

**4–17. Resistance and Capacitance in Series.** Consider à circuit containing capacitance and resistance in series (Fig. 4–23). Since this is a series circuit the current through the entire circuit is identical; thus it is logical to use the current as reference. The voltage drop across the resistance $E_R$

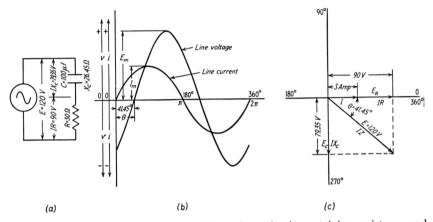

Fig. 4–23. Current and voltage relations in a circuit containing resistance and capacitance in series.

is in phase with the current and is represented as such by the vector diagram of Fig. 4–23. The voltage drop across the capacitor $E_C$ will lag the current by 90°, as shown by the diagram.

$$E = \sqrt{E_R{}^2 + E_C{}^2}$$
$$= \sqrt{(IR)^2 + (IX_C)^2}$$
$$= I\sqrt{R^2 + X_C{}^2}$$

and

$$I = \frac{E}{\sqrt{R^2 + X_C{}^2}} \qquad (4\text{–}43a)$$

$$= \frac{E}{Z} \qquad (4\text{–}43b)$$

where $Z = \sqrt{R^2 + X_C{}^2}$ is the impedance of the circuit.

The phase angle may be determined as follows:

$$\tan \theta = \frac{E_C}{E_R} = \frac{IX_C}{IR} = \frac{X_C}{R} \qquad (4\text{–}44)$$

or

$$\cos \theta = \frac{E_R}{E} = \frac{IR}{I\sqrt{R^2 + X_C{}^2}} = \frac{R}{Z} \qquad (4\text{–}45)$$

or

$$\sin \theta = \frac{E_C}{E} = \frac{IX_C}{I\sqrt{R^2 + X_C{}^2}} = \frac{X_C}{Z} \qquad (4\text{–}46)$$

EXAMPLE. Assume the following parameters for the circuit of Fig. 4–23, and solve for $I$, $E_R$, $E_C$, $\theta$, $pf$ and $P$:

$E = 120$ v  $\qquad\qquad\qquad$  $C = 100$ microfarads
$f = 60$ cps  $\qquad\qquad\qquad$  $R = 30$ ohms

Solution: $\qquad$ $X_C = \dfrac{1}{2\pi f C}$

$$= \frac{1}{2\pi(60)100 \times 10^{-6}}$$

$$= \frac{10 \times 10^5}{3.77 \times 10^4}$$

$$= 26.5 \text{ ohms}$$

$$Z = \sqrt{(30)^2 + (26.5)^2}$$

$$= 40 \text{ ohms}$$

$$I = \tfrac{120}{40} = 3 \text{ amp}$$

$$E_R = IR = (3)(30) = 90 \text{ v}$$

$$E_C = IX_C = (3)(26.5) = 79.5 \text{ v}$$

$$\tan \theta = \frac{X_C}{R} = \frac{26.5}{30} = 0.883$$

$$\theta = 41.45°$$

$$pf = \cos \theta = 0.75$$

$$P = EI \cos \theta$$

$$= (120)(3)(0.75) = 270 \text{ watts}$$

$$P = I^2R = (3)^2(30) = 270 \text{ watts (check)}$$

**4–18. Inductance, Capacitance and Resistance in Series.** Consider a circuit containing inductance, capacitance and resistance in series (Fig. 4–24a). In drawing the vector diagram for the circuit of Fig. 4–24, current will again be taken as reference. The voltage across $E_R$ will be in phase with $I$, $E_C$ will lag $I$ by 90° and $E_L$ will lead $I$ by 90°. The impressed voltage will be equal to the vector sum of the three voltages, $E_R$, $E_L$ and $E_C$. The voltage across the capacitor lags by 180° the voltage across the inductor; whence the net voltage across the series combination of capacitor and inductor will be the difference of $E_L$ and $E_C$.

$$E = \sqrt{E_R^2 + (E_L - E_C)^2}$$

$$= \sqrt{(IR)^2 + I^2(X_L - X_C)^2}$$

$$= I\sqrt{R^2 + (X_L - X_C)^2}$$

and

$$I = \frac{E}{\sqrt{R^2 + (X_L - X_C)^2}} \qquad (4\text{--}47a)$$

$$= \frac{E}{Z} \qquad (4\text{--}47b)$$

where $Z = \sqrt{R^2 + (X_L - X_C)^2}$

Eq. (4–47a) may be rewritten as follows:

$$I = \frac{E}{\sqrt{R^2 + \left(2\pi f L - \dfrac{1}{2\pi f C}\right)^2}} \qquad (4\text{--}47c)$$

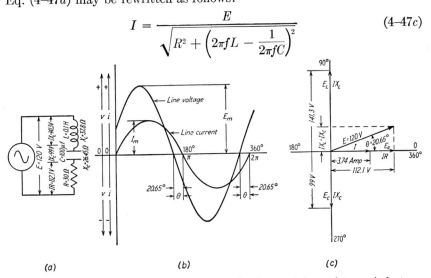

(a)          (b)          (c)

Fig. 4–24. Current and voltage relations in a circuit containing resistance, inductance and capacitance in series.

The phase angle may be determined as follows:

$$\cos \theta = \frac{R}{\sqrt{R^2 + (X_L - X_C)^2}} = \frac{R}{Z} \qquad (4\text{--}48)$$

or

$$\sin \theta = \frac{X_L - X_C}{Z} \qquad (4\text{--}49)$$

or

$$\tan \theta = \frac{X_L - X_C}{R} \qquad (4\text{--}50)$$

If $X_L$ is larger than $X_C$, the current lags the voltage; if $X_C$ is larger than $X_L$, the current leads the voltage.

EXAMPLE. Assume the following circuit parameters and solve for $I$, $E_R$, $E_C$, $E_L$, $\theta$, $pf$ and $P$.

$E = 120$ v                 $R = 30$ ohms

$f = 60$ cps                $X_C = 26.5$ ohms

$C = 100$ microfarads      $X_L = 37.7$ ohms

$L = 0.1$ henry

*Solution:*

$$Z = \sqrt{R^2 + (X_L - X_C)^2}$$
$$= \sqrt{(30)^2 + (37.7 - 26.5)^2}$$
$$= \sqrt{(30)^2 + (11.35)^2}$$
$$= 32.1 \text{ ohms}$$

$$I = \frac{120}{32.1} = 3.74 \text{ amp}$$

$$IR = E_R = (3.74)(30) = 112.2 \text{ v}$$
$$IX_L = E_L = (3.74)(37.7) = 141 \text{ v}$$
$$IX_C = E_C = (3.74)(26.5) = 99 \text{ v}$$

$$\tan \theta = \frac{X_L - X_C}{R} = \frac{11.2}{30} = 0.373$$

$$\theta = 20.47°$$

Since $X_L$ is greater than $X_C$, the line current lags the line voltage by 20.47°.

$$pf = \cos \theta = 0.937$$
$$P = EI \cos \theta$$
$$= (120)(3.74)(0.937)$$
$$= 420 \text{ watts}$$
$$P = I^2R = (3.74)^2(30) = 420 \text{ watts (check)}$$

**4–19. Parallel Circuits.** The parallel circuit of Fig. 4–25 consists of three branches, each branch being comprised of two different types of circuit parameters.

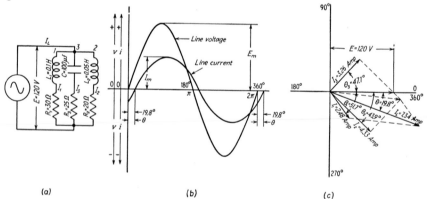

|     |     |     |
|-----|-----|-----|
| (a) | (b) | (c) |

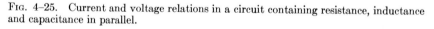

Fig. 4–25.   Current and voltage relations in a circuit containing resistance, inductance and capacitance in parallel.

In a parallel circuit, the impressed voltage is common to each branch and is usually taken as a reference. Since branch 1 is inductive, the current $I_1$ will lag the applied voltage $E$, as illustrated by the vector diagram of Fig. 4–25. Branch 2 is also inductive; thus $I_2$ will lag the applied voltage.

However, as branch 3 is capacitive, $I_3$ will lead the applied voltage.  The magnitude of the angle of lead or lag for each branch will be determined by the ratio of $R$ to $X_C$ or $R$ to $X_L$.  The expressions for the individual branch currents are as follows:

$$I_1 = \frac{E}{Z_1} = \frac{E}{\sqrt{R_1{}^2 + X_{L1}{}^2}} \qquad (4\text{-}51a)$$

$$I_2 = \frac{E}{Z_2} = \frac{E}{\sqrt{R_2{}^2 + X_{L2}{}^2}}$$

$$I_3 = \frac{E}{Z_3} = \frac{E}{\sqrt{R_3{}^2 + X_C{}^2}} \qquad (4\text{-}51b)$$

The total current $I_T$ is equal to the vector sum of $I_1$, $I_2$ and $I_3$.  Although the algebra of complex numbers affords the best means of combining vector quantities, it is thought undesirable to take time to cover, in a text of this type, the subject of complex notation.  The total current will be found by taking the summation of the vertical components and the summation of the horizontal components and adding the two resulting vectors which will be at right angles to each other.

| *Horizontal Components* | *Vertical Components* |
|---|---|
| $I_{h1} = I_1 \cos \theta_1 = I_1 \dfrac{R_1}{Z_1}$ | $I_{v1} = I_1 \sin \theta_1 = -I_1 \dfrac{X_{L1}}{Z_1}$ |
| $I_{h2} = I_2 \cos \theta_2 = I_2 \dfrac{R_2}{Z_2}$ | $I_{v2} = I_2 \sin \theta_2 = -I_2 \dfrac{X_{L2}}{Z_2}$ |
| $I_{h3} = I_3 \cos \theta_3 = I_3 \dfrac{R_3}{Z_3}$ | $I_{v3} = I_3 \sin \theta_3 = I_3 \dfrac{X_{C3}}{Z_3}$ |

The negative signs in the case of $I_{v1}$ and $I_{v2}$ occur because $\theta_1$ and $\theta_2$ are fourth quadrant angles.

$$I_T = \sqrt{(I_{h1} + I_{h2} + I_{h3})^2 + (I_{v1} + I_{v2} + I_{v3})^2} \qquad (4\text{-}52a)$$

Substituting values of the various components:

$$I_T = \sqrt{\left(I_1 \frac{R_1}{Z_1} + I_2 \frac{R_2}{Z_2} + I_3 \frac{R_3}{Z_3}\right)^2 + \left(-I_1 \frac{X_{L1}}{Z_1} - I_2 \frac{X_{L2}}{Z_2} + I_3 \frac{X_{C3}}{Z_3}\right)^2} \qquad (4\text{-}52b)$$

In place of $I_1$, $I_2$ and $I_3$, substitute $\dfrac{E}{Z_1}$, $\dfrac{E}{Z_2}$, and $\dfrac{E}{Z_3}$.  Then

$$I_T = E \sqrt{\left(\frac{R_1}{Z_1{}^2} + \frac{R_2}{Z_2{}^2} + \frac{R_3}{Z_3{}^2}\right)^2 + \left(-\frac{X_{L1}}{Z_1{}^2} - \frac{X_{L2}}{Z_2{}^2} + \frac{X_{C3}}{Z_3{}^2}\right)^2} \qquad (4\text{-}52c)$$

But

$$I_T = \frac{E}{Z}$$

Therefore

$$\frac{1}{Z} = \sqrt{\left(\frac{R_1}{Z_1^2} + \frac{R_2}{Z_2^2} + \frac{R_3}{Z_3^2}\right)^2 + \left(-\frac{X_{L1}}{Z_1^2} - \frac{X_{L2}}{Z_2^2} + \frac{X_{C3}}{Z_3^2}\right)^2} \qquad (4\text{-}53)$$

$1/Z$ is termed the *admittance* and is denoted by the symbol $Y$. The unit of admittance is the mho.*

Thus

$$I_T = EY \qquad (4\text{-}54)$$

The real or resistive component of the admittance is known as the *conductance* $G$; the imaginary or reactive component is known as the *susceptance* $B$. For the problem at hand

$$G = g_1 + g_2 + g_3 \qquad (4\text{-}55)$$

where $G$ = total conductance

and

$$g_1 = \frac{R_1}{Z_1^2}$$

$$g_2 = \frac{R_2}{Z_2^2}$$

$$g_3 = \frac{R_3}{Z_3^2}$$

also

$$B = b_1 + b_2 + b_3 \qquad (4\text{-}56)$$

where $B$ = total susceptance

and

$$b_1 = -\frac{X_{L1}}{Z_1^2}$$

$$b_2 = -\frac{X_{L2}}{Z_2^2}$$

$$b_3 = \frac{X_{C3}}{Z_3^2}$$

Accordingly, $Y$ may be written as follows:

$$Y = \sqrt{G^2 + B^2} \qquad (4\text{-}57)$$

If branch 1 were comprised of pure resistance, branch 2 pure inductance and branch 3 pure capacitance, the following relationships would exist:

$$g_1 = \frac{1}{R_1}; \; g_2 = 0; \; g_3 = 0$$

$$b_1 = -\frac{1}{X_{L1}}; \; b_2 = -\frac{1}{X_{L2}}; \; b_3 = \frac{1}{X_{C3}}$$

* Admittance is the reciprocal of impedance; thus it is quite fitting for the unit of admittance to be the mho—which is ohm spelled backwards.

If the circuit consisted of $n$ parallel branches, then

$$G = g_1 + g_2 \cdots + g_n$$
$$B = b_1 + b_2 \cdots + b_n$$

EXAMPLE. Assume the following circuit parameters for the circuit of Fig. 4–25 and solve for $I_T$, $\theta$, $pf$ and $P$:

$E = 120$ v                                    $L_2 = 0.05$ henry
$f = 60$ cps                                   $R_1 = 30$ ohms
$C = 100$ microfarads                          $R_2 = 20$ ohms
$L_1 = 0.1$ henry                              $R_3 = 25$ ohms

*Solution:*

$$X_C = \frac{1}{2\pi f C_3} = \frac{1}{2\pi 60(100) \times 10^{-6}} = 26.5 \text{ ohms}$$

$$X_{L1} = (2\pi f L_1) = (2\pi 60)(0.1) = 37.7 \text{ ohms}$$

$$X_{L2} = (2\pi f L_2) = (2\pi 60)(0.05) = 18.9 \text{ ohms}$$

$$g_1 = \frac{R_1}{Z_1^2} = \frac{30}{(30)^2 + (37.7)^2} = \frac{30}{2321} = 0.0129$$

$$g_2 = \frac{R_2}{Z_2^2} = \frac{20}{(20)^2 + (18.9)^2} = \frac{20}{770} = 0.0260$$

$$g_3 = \frac{R_3}{Z_3^2} = \frac{25}{(25)^2 + (26.5)^2} = \frac{25}{1355} = 0.0185$$

$$G = g_1 + g_2 + g_3 = \overline{0.0574} \text{ mho}$$

$$b_1 = -\frac{X_{L1}}{Z_1^2} = -\frac{37.7}{(30)^2 + (37.7)^2} = -\frac{37.7}{2321} = -0.01625$$

$$b_2 = -\frac{X_{L2}}{Z_2^2} = -\frac{18.9}{(20)^2 + (18.9)^2} = -\frac{18.9}{770} = -0.02460$$

$$b_3 = \frac{X_{C3}}{Z_3^2} = \frac{26.5}{(25)^2 + (26.5)^2} = \frac{26.5}{1355} = 0.01955$$

$$B = b_1 + b_2 + b_3 = -\overline{0.02130} \text{ mho}$$

$$Y = \sqrt{(0.0573)^2 + (-0.0213)^2} = 0.0611 \text{ mho}$$

$$I = EY$$

$$= (120)(0.0611) = 7.34 \text{ amp}$$

$$\tan \theta = \frac{B}{G} = -\frac{0.02120}{0.0573} = -0.37$$

$$\theta = -20.3°$$

Both $I$ and $\theta$ may be determined graphically by addition of $I_1$, $I_2$ and $I_3$, as indicated by the vector diagram of Fig. 4–25.

$$\cos \theta = 0.938$$

$$P = EI \cos \theta = (120)(7.34)(0.938) = 827 \text{ watts}$$

A check on this solution may be obtained by determining the $I^2R$ loss in each resistance in the circuit. This necessitates solving for each individual current.

$$I_1 = \frac{E}{Z_1} = \frac{120}{48.3} = 2.48 \text{ amp}$$

$$I_2 = \frac{E}{Z_2} = \frac{120}{27.75} = 4.33 \text{ amp}$$

$$I_3 = \frac{E}{Z_3} = \frac{120}{36.8} = 3.26 \text{ amp}$$

$$P_1 = I_1^2R_1 = (2.48)^2(30) = 184.5$$
$$P_2 = I_2^2R_2 = (4.33)^2(20) = 376.0$$
$$P_3 = I_3^2R_3 = (3.26)^2(25) = 266.0$$
$$P_T = P_1 + P_2 + P_3 \qquad = 826.5 \text{ watts (check)}$$

**4–20. Series Resonance.** If a fixed potential of varying frequency is applied to the terminals of the series $RLC$ circuit shown in Fig. 4–26, the impedance and current will be functions of the frequency.

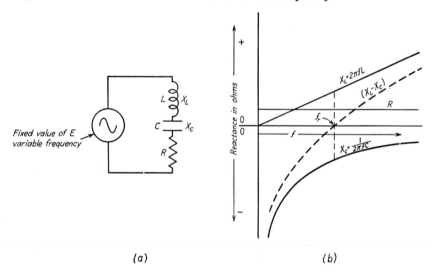

$$(a) \qquad\qquad\qquad\qquad (b)$$

FIG. 4–26. Variation of circuit parameters with frequency in a series $RLC$ circuit.

The inductive reactance $X_L$ is directly proportional to frequency, as is indicated by the straight line of Fig. 4–26b. The capacitive reactance $X_C$, which is opposite in sign from $X_L$ and tends to neutralize its effect when connected in series with it, increases hyperbolically when $f$ is increased. The total or net reactance of the circuit at any frequency is, as indicated by the dotted line of Fig. 4–26b, equal to the algebraic sum of $X_L$ and $X_C$. If the frequency is varied over a sufficiently wide range, a value of frequency will be passed through at which $X_L = X_C$. This is known as the *resonant* frequency of the $RLC$ series circuit and is denoted by the symbol

$f_r$ on the diagram. Obviously, $f_r$ may be determined by equating $X_L$ to $X_C$ and solving for $f$.

$$X_L = X_C$$

$$2\pi f L = \frac{1}{2\pi f C}$$

$$f_r^2 = \frac{1}{4\pi^2 LC}$$

$$f_r = \frac{1}{2\pi \sqrt{LC}} \qquad (4\text{-}58)$$

The impedance at resonance can be shown to be $R$.  Consider the general expression for impedance in a series $RLC$ circuit:

$$Z = \sqrt{R^2 + (X_L - X_C)^2}$$

When     $f = f_r$

$\qquad X_L = X_C$

Thus

$$Z = \sqrt{R^2 + (0)^2}$$

where     $Z = R$

Accordingly, the current at the resonant frequency is

$$I = \frac{E}{R} \qquad (4\text{-}59)$$

where $E$ = the impressed circuit voltage

The total impedance $Z$, if plotted as a function of frequency, will begin at a relatively high value ($Z = \infty$ and $f = 0$) and will approach a minimum as $f$ approaches $f_r$.  If $f$ is increased above $f_r$, the impedance $Z$ will increase and approach infinity as $f$ approaches infinity.  The current, of course, will vary inversely with $Z$ and will be equal to $E/R$ at $f_r$.  Typical curves are displayed in Fig. 4–27.

If the value of $R$ were increased to a larger value and the same frequency range covered, the curve for current versus frequency would be much flatter.  The sharpness of resonance, indicated by the steepness of the current curve in the neighborhood of the resonant frequency, is determined by the ratio of $X_L$ to $R$.  This ratio is known as the $Q$ of the circuit. Resonant curves for different values of $Q$ are sketched in Fig. 4–28.

$$Q = \frac{X_L}{R} = \frac{\omega L}{R} \qquad (4\text{-}60)$$

The voltage $E_R$ developed across the resistance at any frequency is equal to the product of $I$ and $R$:

$$E_R = IR$$

At resonance $I = \dfrac{E}{R}$

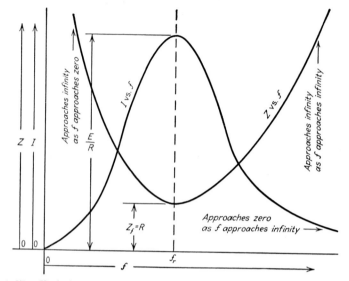

Fig. 4–27.  Variation of impedance and current with frequency in a series $RLC$ circuit.

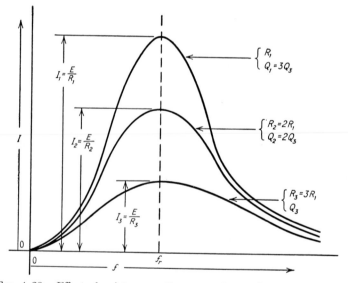

Fig. 4–28.  Effect of resistance on the current in a series resonant circuit.

Therefore, at resonance

$$E_R = E \qquad (4\text{--}61)$$

The voltage $E_L$ across the inductor is equal to the product of $I$ and $X_L$:

$$E_L = IX_L$$

At resonance $I = \dfrac{E}{R}$

Whence, at resonance

$$E_L = \frac{EX_L}{R}$$

or

$$E_L = EQ \qquad (4\text{--}62)$$

In radio frequency circuits, very high values of $Q$ are required; values of several hundred are not uncommon. From Eq. (4–62) it can be seen that a very high voltage may be developed in a series circuit with only a small applied voltage.

At resonance $X_L = X_C$; thus the voltage across $X_C$ is equal to the voltage across $X_L$. Thus

$$E_C = EQ \qquad (4\text{--}63)$$

Since $IX_L$ and $IX_C$ are equal and 180° out of phase, they cancel each other, with the result that the net voltage is, as shown previously, equal to $IR$ (vector diagram shown in Fig. 4–29). In practice it is impossible to

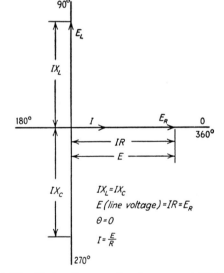

Fig. 4–29.   Vector diagram of series resonant $RLC$ circuit.

have a coil without some small amount of resistance. Therefore, the voltage drop across a coil is never exactly 180° out of phase with the voltage drop across a capacitor in series with it.

**4–21. Parallel Resonance.** A circuit consisting of inductive and capacitive branches in parallel exhibits characteristics that are quite different from those of a series circuit containing the same circuit parameters. Consider the circuit of Fig. 4–30.

$$Z = \frac{Z_1 Z_2}{Z_1 + Z_2} \tag{4-64}$$

where  $Z$ = total parallel impedance

$Z_1$ = impedance of capacitive branch

$Z_2$ = impedance of inductive branch

The denominator of this expression is:

$$Z_1 + Z_2 = \sqrt{(R_L + R_C)^2 + (X_L - X_C)^2}$$

Therefore, when the frequency is such that $X_L = X_C$, $Z_1 + Z_2$ will be a minimum and the parallel impedance will be a maximum.

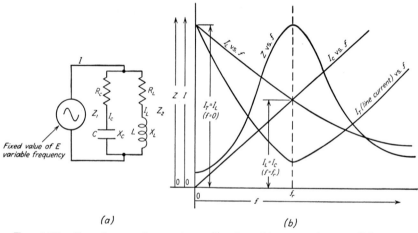

(a)        (b)

FIG. 4–30. Impedance and current as a function of frequency in a parallel resonant circuit.

For any value of frequency lower or higher than the frequency at which $X_L = X_C$, the parallel impedance will decrease; thus impedance plotted as a function of frequency will vary as indicated by Fig. 4–30. At the same time the total current will vary inversely with the impedance, reaching a minimum value when $f = f_r$. Although the line current at resonance may be very small, each branch current may be large.

The current through the inductive branch ($I_L = E/Z_1$) will start at a relatively high value ($I_L = E/R_L$) at $f = 0$, and will decrease as $f$ increases; on the other hand, the current through the capacitive branch ($I_C = E/Z_2$) will start at zero ($I = 0$) when $f = 0$, and will reach a maximum value of $E/R_C$ when $f$ is equal to infinity. The branch currents are shown as a function of frequency in Fig. 4–30.

Consider the vector diagram of Fig. 4–31.  Since $X_L = X_C$ at resonance, the vertical components of $I_L$ and $I_C$ will be equal; since they are in the opposite sense they will completely cancel each other.  The line current will then be only the sum of the horizontal or resistive components of the branch currents; in most practical parallel resonant circuits this value is small.

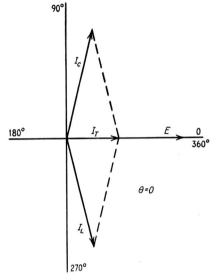

FIG. 4–31.   Vector diagram for a parallel resonant circuit.

In many circuits of this type the resistive components are small compared to $X_L$ and $X_C$, hence may be neglected in the numerator of Eq. (4–64) without serious error.  If $R_L$ and $R_C$ are neglected in the numerator, Eq. (4–64) reduces to the following form:

$$Z = \frac{(X_C)(X_L)}{Z_1 + Z_2} \qquad (4\text{–}65)$$

At resonance $X_L = X_C$
whence

$$Z = \frac{X_L{}^2}{R_L + R_C}$$

or

$$Z = \frac{(\omega L)^2}{R}$$

where $R = R_L + R_C$

Substituting $Q$ for $\omega L/R$ gives

$$Z = Q\omega L \qquad (4\text{–}66)$$

which is the approximate value of the impedance at resonance.

The line current $I_T$ at resonance is approximately

$$I_T = \frac{E}{Q\omega L} \tag{4-67}$$

At resonance $I_L = I_C = \dfrac{E}{\omega L}$

Therefore

$$I_L = I_C = QI_T \tag{4-68}$$

where $I_L$ = current through the inductive branch
$I_C$ = current through the capacitive branch
$I_T$ = line current

Parallel resonant circuits are usually high impedance circuits. They are widely used in electronic devices such as radios, oscillators, transmitters, etc.

**4–22. Coupled Circuits.** When the flow of current in one circuit affects another circuit, the circuits are said to be *coupled*. Coupled circuits may be classified as follows:

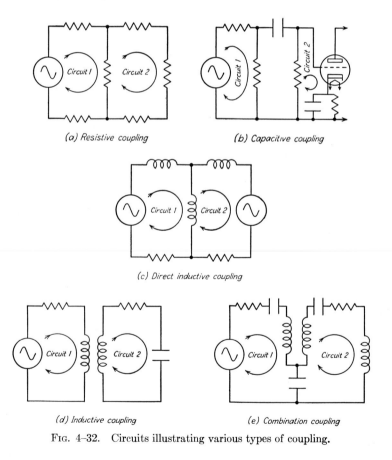

(a) Resistive coupling          (b) Capacitive coupling

(c) Direct inductive coupling

(d) Inductive coupling          (e) Combination coupling

Fig. 4–32.   Circuits illustrating various types of coupling.

1. Direct-coupled
   a) Resistive Coupling
   b) Capacitive Coupling
   c) Direct Inductive Coupling
2. Inductively-coupled
3. Combination-coupled

Circuits illustrating the various types of coupling are shown in Fig. 4–32. Each of the diagrams of Fig. 4–32 is comprised of two complete circuits, connected through a common coupling impedance.

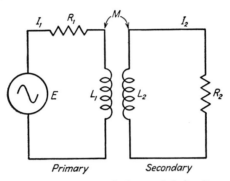

Fig. 4–33.  Inductively-coupled circuit.

The analysis of direct-coupled circuits is no different from the approach employed in previously considered problems; however, the analysis of inductively-coupled circuits offers a more complex problem.

Two circuits are said to be inductively coupled when they are coupled by magnetic flux. The coupling impedance between the two circuits is the mutual inductance.

Consider the inductively-coupled circuit of Fig. 4–33. In order to solve a circuit of this type it is necessary to determine the effect of the secondary circuit on the primary circuit. The equivalent impedance added to the primary circuit as a result of current in the secondary circuit is termed the *coupled impedance* and is defined as follows:

$$Z_{12} = \frac{Z_m{}^2}{Z_2} \tag{4-69}$$

where $Z_m = 2\pi f L_m = \omega L_m = X_{L_m}$
  $L_m$ = mutual inductance
  $Z_2$ = series impedance of the secondary
  $Z_2 = \sqrt{R_2 + X_{L_2}}$

The primary current $I_1$ is given by Eq. (4–70):

$$I_1 = \frac{E}{Z_1 + \dfrac{Z_m{}^2}{Z_2}} \tag{4-70}$$

The voltage induced in the secondary is expressed by Eq. (4–71):

$$E_2 = I_1 Z_m \qquad (4\text{–}71)$$

The secondary circuit $I_2$ is given by Eq. (4–72a):

$$I_2 = \frac{E_2}{Z_2} \qquad (4\text{–}72a)$$

Substituting $I_1 Z_m$ for $E_2$

$$I_2 = I_1 \frac{Z_m}{Z_2} \qquad (4\text{–}72b)$$

or substituting the value for $I_1$ given by Eq. (4–70) in Eq. (4–72a):

$$I_2 = \frac{E}{Z_1 + \dfrac{Z_m{}^2}{Z_2}} \left(\frac{Z_m}{Z_2}\right) \qquad (4\text{–}72c)$$

The more common inductively-coupled circuits fall into three main classes: untuned primary and untuned secondary; untuned primary and tuned secondary; and tuned primary and tuned secondary.* The circuit of Fig. 4–33 is a typical example of an untuned-primary and untuned-secondary coupled circuit. The circuits of Figs. 4–34a and 4–35a illustrate

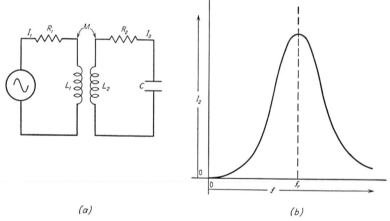

(a)                                    (b)

FIG. 4–34.   Untuned-primary tuned-secondary inductively coupled circuit.

untuned-primary tuned-secondary, and tuned-primary tuned-secondary coupled circuits, respectively. These circuits (Figs. 4–34a and 4–35a) are commonly encountered radio frequency circuits.

If the secondary current in the circuit of Fig. 4–34a is plotted as a function of frequency with constant voltage applied to the primary, its shape will be essentially that of a series resonance curve (Fig. 4–34b).

---

* A tuned circuit is a circuit the parameters of which are adjusted to be resonant at the frequency of the applied voltage.

The circuit of Fig. 4–35a is quite important in that it is the equivalent circuit of a band-pass filter.* The characteristics of this type circuit vary greatly depending upon the coefficient of coupling between the secondary

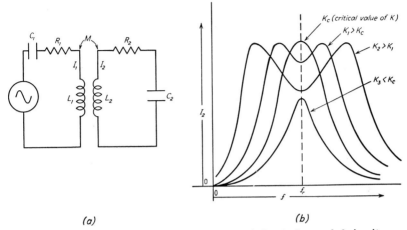

(a)                                                    (b)

Fig. 4–35. Tuned-primary tuned-secondary inductively coupled circuit.

and the primary. If the coefficient of coupling is of such a value that the equivalent resistance of the secondary coupled into the primary is equal to the primary resistance, *critical* coupling is said to exist. The curve of $I_2$ (secondary current) versus $f$ for critical coupling is sketched in Fig. 4–35b. It will be noted that for critical coupling $K_C$ the curve has a flat top. If the coefficient of coupling is larger than the critical value $K_1$, the curve will have peaks on both sides of resonance; and the larger the value of $K$ (coefficient of coupling) the farther the distance between the peaks. A value of coefficient of coupling $K_3$ lower than critical value $K_C$ results in one peak which is lower than the peak obtained for critical coupling.

**4–23. Polyphase Circuits.** Since the three-phase system is, by far, the most commonly used polyphase system, review of polyphase theory is confined to three-phase circuits. The circuits in three-phase generators, transformers, motors, etc., are usually connected in either $Y$ (wye) or $\Delta$ (delta). These two connections are illustrated by Figs. 4–36a and 4–36b, respectively. The dotted line in Fig. 4–36a represents the neutral wire which may or may not be included.

Most three-phase systems are balanced three-phase systems, that is, the phase or coil voltages (Fig. 4–36) are equal in magnitude and are displaced from each other by 120° and the phase impedances are identical. This balance gives rise to equal phase and line currents and equal power

---

* A band-pass filter is a circuit arrangement which will transmit all frequencies within a given band with little attenuation and give high attenuation to all other frequencies.

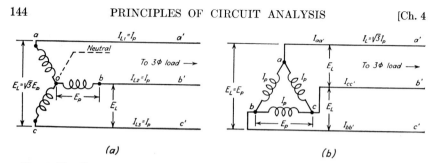

Fig. 4–36.  Common polyphase connections (a) three-phase wye connection, (b) three-phase delta connection.

per phase. The instantaneous values of line voltages (equal to phase voltages in the case of a delta connection) are illustrated graphically in Fig. 4–37. In the following treatment of polyphase circuits it will be assumed that balanced conditions exist.

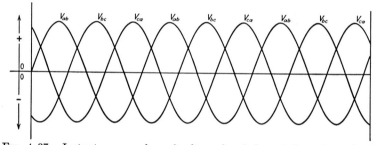

Fig. 4–37.   Instantaneous values of voltages in a balanced three-phase circuit.

Applying Kirchhoff's voltage law between terminals $a$, $b$ and $c$ of the wye-connected circuit of Fig. 4–36a, the following relationships are obtained: *

$$\mathbf{E}_{ab} = \mathbf{E}_{ao} + \mathbf{E}_{ob}$$

or

$$\mathbf{E}_{ab} = -\mathbf{E}_{oa} + \mathbf{E}_{ob}$$

$$\mathbf{E}_{bc} = \mathbf{E}_{bo} + \mathbf{E}_{oc}$$

or

$$\mathbf{E}_{bc} = -\mathbf{E}_{ob} + \mathbf{E}_{oc}$$

$$\mathbf{E}_{ca} = \mathbf{E}_{co} + \mathbf{E}_{oa}$$

or

$$\mathbf{E}_{ca} = -\mathbf{E}_{oc} + \mathbf{E}_{oa}$$

where $\mathbf{E}_{oa}$, $\mathbf{E}_{ob}$ and $\mathbf{E}_{oc}$ are phase or coil voltages and $\mathbf{E}_{ab}$, $\mathbf{E}_{bc}$ and $\mathbf{E}_{ca}$ are line voltages.

The subscripts indicate the direction in which the circuit is traced. For example, the voltage from $a$ to $b$ is designated as $\mathbf{E}_{ab}$, the voltage from $b$ to $c$ is designated as $\mathbf{E}_{bc}$ and the voltage from $c$ to $a$ is designated as $\mathbf{E}_{ca}$.

---

* Boldface type is used here and in Section 12–10 to indicate vectors.

Reversing the order of the subscripts is equivalent to reversing the sign preceding the voltage; thus $\mathbf{E}_{ao} = -\mathbf{E}_{oa}$, $\mathbf{E}_{bo} = -\mathbf{E}_{ob}$, etc.

By assuming three balanced phase voltages $\mathbf{E}_{oa}$, $\mathbf{E}_{ob}$ and $\mathbf{E}_{oc}$ displaced by 120 degrees and making the vector additions indicated to obtain line voltages $\mathbf{E}_{ab}$, $\mathbf{E}_{bc}$ and $\mathbf{E}_{ca}$, the vector diagram of Fig. 4–38a is constructed.

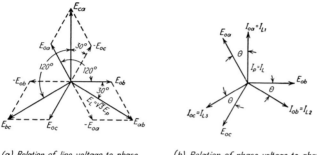

(a) Relation of line voltage to phase         (b) Relation of phase voltage to phase
       voltage in a wye system                        current in a wye system with inductive load

FIG. 4–38.   Current and voltage relations in a balanced wye-connected three-phase system.

The vector diagram of Fig. 4–38b shows the phase currents (which are identical to the line currents in the case of a wye connection) in relationship to the phase voltages for a three-phase inductive load. The vector sum of the currents meeting at the junction is equal to zero.

$$\mathbf{I}_{oa} + \mathbf{I}_{ob} + \mathbf{I}_{oc} = 0 \qquad (4\text{–}73)$$

Referring to the circuit and vector diagrams for a balanced wye-connected circuit, it is obvious that the following relationships exist:

$$E_L = \sqrt{3}E_p \qquad (4\text{–}74)$$

and

$$I_L = I_p$$

where $E_L$ = line voltage
$\quad\;\; E_p$ = phase voltage
$\quad\;\; I_L$ = line current
$\quad\;\; I_p$ = phase current

Applying Kirchhoff's current law to the delta-connected circuit of Fig. 4–36b, the following relationships are obtained.

$$\mathbf{I}_{aa'} = \mathbf{I}_{ba} + \mathbf{I}_{ca}$$

or

$$\mathbf{I}_{aa'} = -\mathbf{I}_{ab} + \mathbf{I}_{ca}$$

$$\mathbf{I}_{bb'} = \mathbf{I}_{cb} + \mathbf{I}_{ab}$$

or

$$\mathbf{I}_{bb'} = -\mathbf{I}_{bc} + \mathbf{I}_{ab}$$

$$\mathbf{I}_{cc'} = \mathbf{I}_{ac} + \mathbf{I}_{bc}$$

or

$$\mathbf{I}_{cc'} = -\mathbf{I}_{ca} + \mathbf{I}_{bc}$$

From the relationships, the vector diagrams of Fig. 4–39 are constructed. Referring to the circuit and vector diagrams for the balanced delta-connected circuit, it is obvious that the following relationships exist:

$$I_L = \sqrt{3}I_p \tag{4-75}$$

$$E_L = E_p$$

Symbols have the same significance as in the case of the wye-connected circuit.

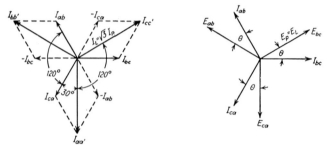

(a) Relation of line current to phase current in a delta system

(b) Relation of phase voltage to phase current in a delta system with inductive load

Fig. 4–39. Current and voltage relations in a balanced delta-connected three-phase system.

The power delivered by one phase of a three-phase alternator is

$$P' = I_p E_p \cos\theta$$

Therefore the total power delivered by a three-phase alternator is

$$P = 3I_p E_p \cos\theta \tag{4-76}$$

For a wye-connected alternator

$$I_p = I_L \quad \text{and} \quad E_p = \frac{E_L}{\sqrt{3}}$$

Therefore

$$P = 3I_L \frac{E_L}{\sqrt{3}} \cos\theta$$

$$= \sqrt{3}E_L I_L \cos\theta \tag{4-77}$$

For a delta-connected alternator,

$$I_p = \frac{I_L}{\sqrt{3}} \quad \text{and} \quad E_p = E_L$$

Thus

$$P = 3E_L \frac{E_L}{\sqrt{3}} \cos\theta$$

$$= \sqrt{3}E_L I_L \cos\theta$$

Accordingly, the power delivered by either a three-phase wye-connected alternator or a three-phase delta-connected alternator is equal to the product of line voltage, line current, the phase power factor and the square root of three. The power consumed by a balanced three-phase load is also expressed by Eq. (4–77).

## PROBLEMS

**4-1.** Resistors of 2, 3 and 6 ohms, respectively, are connected in parallel and the combination is connected in series with another combination consisting of a 2- and a 3-ohm resistor in parallel. Determine the current through each resistor and the total current that this circuit will draw when placed across the terminals of a 6-v battery.

**4-2.** Two resistors, when placed in series across a 96-v battery, draw 6 amp. When these resistors are placed in parallel across the same battery, the total current drawn from the battery is 32 amp. Find the value of each resistor.

**4-3.** A circuit consists of three main branches, $A$, $B$ and $C$. One end of each branch is connected to terminal $D$ and the other end of each branch is connected to terminal $E$. Branch $A$ is comprised of a 1-ohm resistor, a parallel combination of two 4-ohm resistors and a 6-v battery (negative battery terminal connected to terminal $E$) in series. Branch $B$ is comprised of a 10-v battery (positive battery terminal connected to terminal $D$), a combination of a 2-, a 3- and a 6-ohm resistor in parallel and an 8-v battery (positive battery terminal connected to terminal $E$) in series. Branch $C$ is comprised of a 2-v battery (positive battery terminal connected to terminal $D$), and a 4-ohm resistor in series. Determine the three main branch currents, $I_A$, $I_B$ and $I_C$.

**4-4.** The resistance of a relay is 100 ohms and the inductance is 0.1 henry. The relay is connected across a 120-v dc supply. Determine:

  *a)* The equation for the current.
  *b)* The rate at which the current begins to increase.
  *c)* The value of the current at $t = 0.0005$ sec.
  *d)* The time constant of the circuit.
  *e)* The value of current corresponding to the time constant of the circuit.
  *f)* The energy stored in the magnetic field at the time corresponding to the time constant.
  *g)* The energy stored in the magnetic field at the instant the switch is closed to connect the relay to the 120-v source.
  *h)* The maximum energy that can be stored in the magnetic field with only 120 v applied.

**4-5.** Give all the possible combinations of capacitance that can be obtained if only a 2-, a 3- and a 6-microfarad capacitor are available.

**4-6.** A circuit consisting of a 100-microfarad capacitor in series with a 2,000-ohm resistor is connected across a 120-v source. Determine:

  *a)* The initial charge on the capacitor.
  *b)* The initial value of the current.
  *c)* The equation of the current as a function of time.
  *d)* The value of current when $t = 0.1$ sec.
  *e)* The energy stored in the field when $t = 0.1$ sec.

**4–7.** A 0.25-henry inductor, a 50-ohm resistor and a 50-microfarad capacitor are connected in series across the terminals of a 120-v, 60-cycle generator. Determine:

a) The current.
b) The voltage across the inductor.
c) The voltage across the capacitor.
d) The voltage across the resistor.
e) The power factor of the circuit.
f) The total power consumed by the circuit.
g) The vector diagram of the circuit.

**4–8.** If the circuit parameters of Prob. 4–6 are placed in parallel across the generator, determine:

a) The current through the inductor.
b) The current through the capacitor.
c) The current through the resistor.
d) The total current from the generator.
e) The power factor of the circuit.
f) The total power consumed by the circuit.
g) The vector diagram of the circuit.

**4–9.** A variable capacitor is to be used for tuning a broadcast receiver which must have a frequency range of from 550 to 1,500 kilocycles. If the minimum capacitance cannot be made less than $30 \times 10^{-12}$ farads, determine the inductance of the coil and the maximum capacity of the variable capacitor necessary in order for resonant frequencies from 550 to 1,600 kilocycles to be covered.

**4–10.** a) Three heating units are connected across a 230-v, three-phase supply. Each unit is a 20-ohm resistor. Determine:

1) The voltage across each unit.
2) The current through each unit.
3) The current in each line.
4) The power taken by each unit.
5) The complete vector diagram.
6) The total power consumed.

b) Repeat Prob. 4–10a if the three heater units are connected in wye across the 230-v, three-phase supply.

## BIBLIOGRAPHY

BLALOCK, G. C. *Elements of Electrical Circuits and Machinery.* New York: McGraw-Hill Book Co., Inc., 1943, pp. 31–45, 74–103.
———. *Principles of Electrical Engineering.* 2nd ed. New York: McGraw-Hill Book Co., Inc., 1936, pp. 27–43, 222–310.
COOK, A. L., and CARR, C. C. *Elements of Electrical Engineering.* 5th ed. New York: John Wiley & Sons, Inc., 1947, pp. 65–97, 297–340.
CORCORAN, G. F. *Basic Electrical Engineering.* New York: John Wiley & Sons, Inc., 1949, pp. 92–150.
CREAMER, W. J. *Elements of Electrical Engineering.* New York: McGraw-Hill Book Co., Inc., 1948, pp. 16–33.
DAWES, C. L. *Direct Currents. Electrical Engineering, Vol. I.* 3rd ed. New York: McGraw-Hill Book Co., Inc., 1937, pp. 1–88, 347.

DAWES, C. L.  *Alternating Currents. Electrical Engineering, Vol. II.*  3rd ed.  New York: McGraw-Hill Book Co., Inc., 1934, pp. 1–59.

EVERITT, W. L.  *Communication Engineering.*  2nd ed.  New York: McGraw-Hill Book Co., Inc., 1937, pp. 59–92.

HESSLER, V. P., and CAREY, J. J.  *Fundamentals of Electrical Engineering.*  New York: McGraw-Hill Book Co., Inc., 1948, pp. 26–36, 64–78.

KERCHNER, R. M., and CORCORAN, G. F.  *Alternating Current Circuits.*  2nd ed.  New York: John Wiley & Sons, Inc., 1943, pp. 3–62, 93–122, 185–220, 225–62.

KIMBERLY, E. E.  *Electrical Engineering.*  Scranton, Pa.: International Textbook Co., 1939, pp. 15–53.

LAWRENCE, R. R.  *Principles of Alternating Currents.*  New York: McGraw-Hill Book Co., Inc., 1935, pp. 124–264.

LOEW, E. A.  *Direct and Alternating Currents.*  3rd ed.  New York: McGraw-Hill Book Co., Inc., 1946, pp. 26–51, 350–92.

M.I.T. STAFF.  *Electric Circuits.*  New York: John Wiley & Sons, Inc., 1940, pp. 121–228.

MUELLER, G. V.  *Introduction to Electrical Engineering.*  New York: McGraw-Hill Book Co., Inc., 1940, pp. 12–66.

PUMPHREY, F. H.  *Electrical Engineering.*  New York: Prentice-Hall, Inc., 1946, pp. 1–26, 75–117.

REED, M. B.  *Alternating-Current Circuit Theory.*  New York: Harper & Bros., 1948, pp. 65–178.

———.  *Fundamentals of Electrical Engineering.*  Scranton, Pa.: International Textbook Co., 1938, pp. 46–79.

TANG, K. Y.  *Alternating Current Circuits.*  Scranton, Pa.: International Textbook Co., 1940, pp. 68–94, 121–42.

TERMAN, F. E.  *Radio Engineering.*  3rd ed.  New York: McGraw-Hill Book Co., Inc., 1947, pp. 11–74.

TIMBIE, W. H., and BUSH, V. B.  *Principles of Electrical Engineering.*  3rd ed.  New York: John Wiley & Sons, Inc., 1940, pp. 28–67, 195–220, 304–26.

WARD, R. P.  *Introduction to Electrical Engineering.*  New York: Prentice-Hall, Inc., 1947, pp. 34–75.

# CHAPTER 5

## AMPLIFICATION

Long distance telephone, sound pictures, radio receivers, radio trans-mitters, television, radar, and most electronic control circuits would not be possible without amplification. The discovery of amplification was one of the most important advances in the field of electronics.

**5–1. Principle of Amplification.** Although most modern amplifier cir-cuits utilize pentodes or beam power tubes, all of the early amplifier cir-cuits used triodes.* Since the basic principle of amplification is the same regardless of whether the amplifier tube is triode, pentode, or beam power tube, for the sake of simplicity the analysis of an amplifier circuit using a triode will be given.

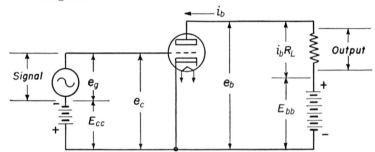

Fig. 5–1. Basic circuit diagram of a vacuum-tube amplifier.

A triode can be made to function as an amplifier by virtue of the fact that a given change in grid voltage results in a much larger change in plate current than the same change in plate voltage. The basic circuit diagram of a vacuum-tube amplifier is shown in Fig. 5–1. If an alternating signal is applied to the grid of the triode, a signal of increased magnitude but essen-tially unchanged in form will appear at the output of the amplifier. If the output signal is the exact duplicate of the input signal except for magni-

---

* Recently there has been developed the transistor which will function as an ampli-fier. The transistor consists of a small germanium block to which is attached three electrodes. One electrode is a low resistance plate which makes contact with the entire bottom surface and the other two electrodes, which are termed the emitter and collector, are point-contact electrodes placed very close together on the upper surface. Thus far the transistor has been used only in experimental work and its practical significance has yet to be determined. For a discussion of the transistor, see J. Bardeen and W. H. Brattain, Physical Principles Involved in Transistor Action, *The Bell System Technical Journal*, 1949, **28**, 239–76.

tude, the amplifier is said to be ideal.   It is impossible to design an amplifier which will develop an output voltage that is of exactly the same form as the input signal, but a well-designed amplifier develops an output voltage that is, for all practical purposes, identical in form to the input signal. The change in the wave form produced by an amplifier is known as distortion.   In the following analysis of the basic amplifier circuit of Fig. 5–1, distortion will be considered as negligible.

The symbols used are those recommended by the Institute of Radio Engineers * and are listed below for convenience.

$E_{bb}$ = plate supply voltage, called $B$ supply

$E_{cc}$ = control-grid supply, called $C$ bias

$E_g$ = effective value of varying component of grid voltage

$E_p$ = effective value of varying component of plate voltage

$I_p$ = effective value of varying component of plate current

$e_b$ = instantaneous total plate voltage

$e_c$ = instantaneous total grid voltage

$e_g$ = instantaneous value of varying component of grid voltage

$e_p$ = instantaneous value of varying component of plate voltage

$i_b$ = instantaneous total plate current

From the circuit of Fig. 5–1

$$e_c = e_g - E_{cc}$$

where $E_{cc}$ is the magnitude of the grid-supply voltage.

If                              $e_g = \sqrt{2} E_g \sin \omega t$

then                            $e_c = \sqrt{2} E_g \sin \omega t - E_{cc}$

The maximum value of $e_c$ exists when $\sin \omega t = 1$

$$e_c \text{ (max)} = \sqrt{2} E_g - E_{cc}$$

The minimum value of $e_c$ exists when $\sin \omega t = -1$

$$e_c \text{ (min)} = -\sqrt{2} E_g - E_{cc}$$

The amplification of the circuit under consideration is determined graphically as follows. Let it be assumed that the characteristic curves for the tube used in the amplifier are those sketched in Fig. 5–2. A *load line* which represents all possible points of operation for a given value of plate supply voltage $E_{bb}$ and load resistance $R_L$ is constructed on the family of plate characteristics. The method of locating the load line is described below:

Writing Kirchhoff's voltage law around the plate circuit

$$E_{bb} - i_b R_L - e_b = 0 \tag{5–1a}$$

or                          $$e_b = E_{bb} - i_b R_L \tag{5–1b}$$

---

* *Standards on Abbreviations, Graphical Symbols, Letter Symbols, and Mathematical Signs*, New York: Institute of Radio Engineers, 1948.

Solving for $i_b$,

$$i_b = \frac{E_{bb}}{R_L} - \frac{e_b}{R_L} \qquad (5\text{–}1c)$$

Taking the derivative of $i_b$ with respect to $e_b$,

$$\frac{di_b}{de_b} = -\frac{1}{R_L} = M_L \qquad (5\text{–}2)$$

where $M_L =$ slope of the load line.

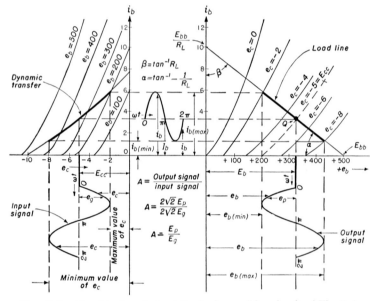

FIG. 5–2. Graphical analysis of the basic amplifier circuit of Fig. 5–1.

The slope can also be shown to be equal to $-\dfrac{1}{R_L}$ by geometry.

$$\text{Slope} = M_L = \frac{\dfrac{E_{bb}}{R_L}}{E_{bb}} = -\frac{1}{R_L}$$

Since Eq. (5–1) is that of a straight line, the load line can be drawn if two points are known or if one point and slope can be determined. Two points can be determined readily by use of Eq. (5–1c).

$$i_b = \frac{E_{bb}}{R_L} - \frac{e_b}{R_L}$$

When $\qquad\qquad i_b = 0$

then $\qquad\qquad e_b = E_{bb}$

When $\qquad\qquad e_b = 0$

then $\qquad\qquad i_b = \dfrac{E_{bb}}{R_L}$

By use of either of these two points or one point and the slope, the load line can be constructed.

The intersection of the load line with the curve $e_c = -E_{cc}$ is known as the *operating* or *quiescent point* Q. The *dynamic transfer characteristic* is obtained by transferring points from the load line to the $i_b$ vs. $e_c$ curves.

By assuming an input signal to the grid, it is now possible to determine both the magnitude and the wave form of the output signal. The construction is shown in some detail in Fig. 5–2.

The circuit amplification $A$ is equal to the ratio of the plate voltage swing to the grid voltage swing.

$$A = \frac{\text{plate swing}}{\text{grid swing}} = \frac{2\sqrt{2}E_p}{2\sqrt{2}E_g} \tag{5–3a}$$

or

$$A = \frac{E_p}{E_g} \tag{5–3b}$$

where $E_p$ = rms value of output voltage
$\quad\;\; E_g$ = rms value of input voltage
$\quad\;\; A$ = circuit amplification

An approximate expression for amplification can be determined analytically by considering the equivalent circuit of Fig. 5–3. In arriving at the equivalent circuit, the tube is replaced by a fictitious ac generator with an internal resistance $r_p$ (plate resistance of tube) and a generated voltage $\mu E_g$. To obtain the equivalent effect of the grid voltage change in terms of the plate circuit, the grid voltage must be multiplied by the amplification factor of the tube $\mu$. If $E_{bb}$ and $E_{cc}$ are both held constant, the only voltage that causes any change in current is the ac input to the grid; therefore it is the only voltage that is considered in the equivalent ac circuit. The resistance of the battery supplying the plate voltage is considered negligible; thus the fictitious generator $\mu E_g$ only has to work into the resistance offered by $r_p$ and $R_L$ in series.

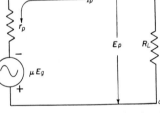

Fig. 5–3. Equivalent circuit of the amplifier of Fig. 5–1.

Writing Kirchhoff's voltage law around the equivalent circuit of Fig. 5–3,

$$I_p r_p + I_p R_L - \mu E_g = 0$$

$$I_p = \frac{\mu E_g}{R_L + r_p}$$

$$E_p' = I_p R_L = \frac{\mu E_g R_L}{R_L + r_p}$$

$$\text{Voltage amplification } A = \frac{E_p}{E_g} = \frac{-\mu R_L}{r_p + R_L} \tag{5-4}$$

where $E_p'$ = voltage from $a$ to $b$

$E_p$ = voltage from $b$ to $a$

$E_p = -E_p'$

From an examination of Eq. (5–4) it can be seen that the voltage amplification increases with an increase in load resistance $R_L$. As $R_L$ approaches

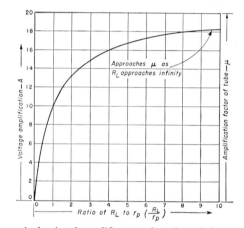

Fɪɢ. 5–4.   Theoretical gain of amplifier as a function of the ratio of load resistance of the circuit to the plate resistance of the amplifier tube.   Amplification factor of tube used is 20.

infinity, the circuit amplification $A$ approaches the amplification factor $\mu$ of the tube. Fig. 5–4 illustrates how the theoretical gain of an amplifier

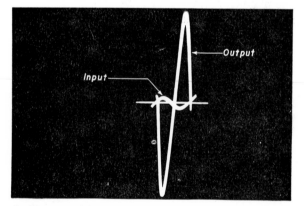

Fɪɢ. 5–5.   Oscillogram of input and output voltages of the amplifier of Fig. 5–1 when a load resistance $R_L$ of 100,000 ohms is used in conjunction with a 6C5 tube.

of this type is a function of load resistance. The oscillogram of Fig. 5–5 shows the input and output voltages of the amplifier circuit of Fig. 5–1 when a 6C5 (triode) is used with suitable circuit parameters. It will be noted that there is a 180° phase difference between the input and output voltages. This phase difference is indicated by the negative sign in Eq. (5–4).

**5–2. Classification of Amplifiers.** Amplifiers are classified according to their properties, applications and operation. They are classified as power or voltage amplifiers depending upon whether they are designed to develop maximum power or maximum voltage at the output. They are further classified as to the frequency range over which they are designed to operate. There are four divisions under this classification: dc amplifiers, audio-frequency amplifiers, video-frequency amplifiers, and radio-frequency amplifiers. Dc amplifiers amplify dc and also low frequency ac; audio-frequency amplifiers respond to frequencies that lie within the range of the human ear, i.e., frequencies from around 20 to 20,000 cycles per second. Video-frequency amplifiers are designed to respond to frequencies from well down in the audio range up to 5 megacycles or higher. Such an amplifier might be rightly classified as either an audio or radio-frequency amplifier since it amplifies frequencies that lie in both audio and radio-frequency range. (This type amplifier is common to television; thus the name video.) Amplifiers designed to amplify any frequency spectrum above the audio range to the maximum frequency obtainable by modern high-frequency vacuum tubes are classified as radio-frequency amplifiers.*

Amplifiers are also classified as to the portion of the cycle over which they operate and as to whether or not grid current flows during any portion of the cycle. Class A, Class AB, Class B and Class C amplifiers fall into this category. This classification applies primarily to power amplifiers, and is discussed in more detail in Section 5–8.

Amplifiers are also classified as to tuned or untuned, depending upon whether or not the output circuit consists of a tuned or an untuned circuit. In general, radio-frequency amplifiers are tuned amplifiers and audio-frequency amplifiers are untuned. Amplifiers are also classified as to band width. If the band of frequencies amplified is large compared to the mean frequency, such as in the case of audio and video amplifiers, the amplifier is said to be a wide-band amplifier. An audio amplifier might amplify frequencies from 20 to 10,000 cycles per second; thus the ratio of the frequency band to the mean frequency would be approximately two. Such an amplifier is classified as a wide-band amplifier. On the other hand, a type of radio-frequency amplifier used in superheterodyne radio receivers known as an intermediate frequency amplifier has a band width of around 10,000 cycles, while the mean frequency is around 455,000 cycles per second. In this case the ratio of the band width to the mean frequency

---

* Amplifiers designed to operate at extremely high radio frequencies are sometimes referred to as ultra-high frequency amplifiers.

would be approximately 0.02; therefore it would be considered a narrow-band amplifier.

## Audio-Frequency and DC Voltage Amplifiers

In general, amplifier circuits are much more complex than the basic circuit of Fig. 5–1 and usually consist of two or more stages. If one stage of amplification is not sufficient to give the desired output voltage, two or more stages may be connected in cascade in order to give the desired output voltage. If the gain of the first stage of a three-stage amplifier is 25, the gain of the second stage 40, and the gain of the third stage 50, then the over-all gain is equal to the product of 25, 40 and 50, which is 50,000. It might appear that by adding sufficient stages the gain of an amplifier could be made to approach infinity. This is not true, however, for as the number of stages increases the number of factors tending to cause a decrease in gain and an increase in distortion comes into the picture. There are several different methods of coupling used in audio amplifiers. The most common is resistance-capacitance coupling. This type of coupling is utilized in most audio-frequency voltage amplifiers.

**5–3. Resistance-Capacitance-Coupled Voltage Amplifiers.** Fig. 5–6 is a schematic circuit diagram of a two-stage resistance-capacitance-coupled amplifier (often referred to as simply a resistance-coupled amplifier). The first stage of this amplifier is essentially the same as the amplifier of Fig. 5–1. There has been added, however, a capacitor $C$ and a resistor $R_g$ to facilitate the feeding of the output of the first stage to the second stage. The coupling or blocking capacitor $C$ serves to prevent the large dc voltage due to $E_{bb}$ from being impressed on the grid of the following tube and driving it highly positive, which would make it inoperative as an amplifier tube. $R_g$ (grid-leak resistor) furnishes a means of maintaining grid potential for the following tube. This resistance must be very large so that it will not draw appreciable current through the capacitor $C$ and result in appreciable loss in gain due to $IX$ drop across the capacitor. The resistor $R_p$ is termed the coupling or plate resistor.* The equivalent load resistance $R_L$ in the circuit of Fig. 5–6, which corresponds to the load resistance $R_L$ in the basic amplifier circuit of Fig. 5–1, is equal to $R_p R_g/(R_p + R_g)$. The circuit of Fig. 5–7a is the general equivalent circuit of the first stage of the amplifier of Fig. 5–6. This general equivalent circuit is valid for all frequencies within the audio-frequency range. However, it may be simplified further for certain frequency bands.

**5–4. Frequency Response of Resistance-Capacitance-Coupled Amplifiers.** If the amplifier of Fig. 5–6 is correctly designed, there will be a rela-

---

* The symbol $R_p$ used to designate the plate resistor should not be confused with the symbol $r_p$ which is used to designate the plate resistance of the tube.

tively large frequency range over which the reactance $X_{C1}$ due to capacity $C_1$ (plate-cathode capacity plus capacity of wiring to left of coupling capacitor) and the reactance $X_{C2}$ due to capacity $C_2$ (input capacity to

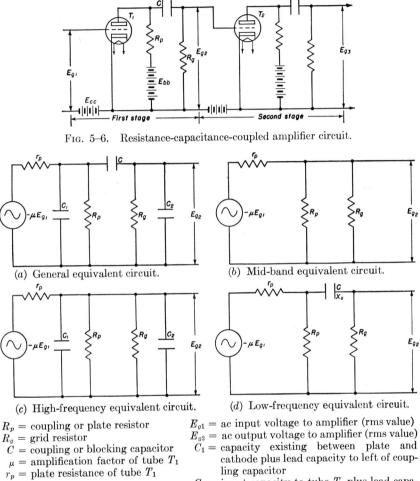

Fig. 5–6.    Resistance-capacitance-coupled amplifier circuit.

(a) General equivalent circuit.

(b) Mid-band equivalent circuit.

(c) High-frequency equivalent circuit.

(d) Low-frequency equivalent circuit.

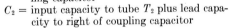

$R_p$ = coupling or plate resistor
$R_g$ = grid resistor
$C$ = coupling or blocking capacitor
$\mu$ = amplification factor of tube $T_1$
$r_p$ = plate resistance of tube $T_1$

$E_{g1}$ = ac input voltage to amplifier (rms value)
$E_{g2}$ = ac output voltage to amplifier (rms value)
$C_1$ = capacity existing between plate and cathode plus lead capacity to left of coupling capacitor
$C_2$ = input capacity to tube $T_2$ plus lead capacity to right of coupling capacitor

Fig. 5–7.    Equivalent circuits for resistance-capacitance-coupled amplifier for various frequency ranges.

next tube or load plus wiring capacity to right of coupling capacitor) are large compared with other circuit impedances and can be considered as negligibly large.  Over the same frequency range the reactance $X_x$ due to the coupling capacitor $C$ will be relatively small and can be considered as negligible.  Under the conditions cited, the general equivalent circuit of Fig. 5–7a may be reduced to the equivalent circuit of Fig. 5–7b.  This is called the mid-band equivalent circuit. From a mathematical analysis of the mid-band equivalent circuit, the relationship of Eq. (5–5a) is obtained.

$$\frac{E_{g2}}{E_{g1}} = -g_m R_e \tag{5–5a}$$

where  $g_m$ = grid-plate transconductance of tube
$R_e$ = equivalent resistance of $r_p$, $R_p$ and $R_g$ in parallel
$$= \frac{r_p R_p R_g}{r_p R_p + R_g R_p + r_p R_g}$$
$E_{g2}$ = output voltage
$E_{g1}$ = input voltage

The negative sign indicates the 180° phase shift between $E_{g1}$ and $E_{g2}$. The numerical voltage gain is given by Eq. (5–5b).

$$A_m = \left|\frac{E_{g2}}{E_{g1}}\right| = g_m R_e \tag{5–5b}$$

where $A_m$ = numerical voltage gain (or voltage amplification) for mid-band frequencies

Now consider the response of the amplifier to high frequencies. The higher the frequency handled by the amplifier, the lower the reactance of the coupling capacitor ($X_x = 1/2\pi f C$). Therefore if the reactance drop $X_x$ across the coupling capacitor is neglected at mid-band frequencies, there is even greater reason that it should be neglected at higher frequencies.

The greater the amount of current through capacitors $C_1$ and $C_2$ the poorer the frequency response. At high frequencies, $X_{C1}$ and $X_{C2}$ (reactance of $C_1$ and $C_2$, respectively) become smaller; thus the current through each cannot be considered as negligible and consequently it becomes necessary to include these capacitances in an equivalent circuit for high frequencies. Bearing in mind the above considerations, the general equivalent circuit of Fig. 5–7a can be reduced to the equivalent circuit of Fig. 5–7c. A mathematical analysis of the high-frequency equivalent circuit of Fig. 5–7c yields Eq. (5–6a).

$$\frac{E_{g2}}{E_{g1}} = \frac{-g_m R_e}{\sqrt{\frac{R_e^2}{X_t^2} + 1}} \left| -\tan^{-1}\frac{R_e}{X_t} \right. \tag{5–6a}$$

$$A_h = \left|\frac{E_{g2}}{E_{g1}}\right| = g_m R_e \left(\frac{1}{\sqrt{\frac{R_e^2}{X_t^2} + 1}}\right) \tag{5–6b}$$

where $A_h$ = numerical voltage gain for high frequencies
$X_t$ = reactance of the total shunting capacitance
$$= \frac{1}{2\pi f(C_1 + C_2)}$$

Other symbols have the same significance as in Eq. (5–5).

Examination of the expression under the radical sign, which might be conveniently termed the *high-frequency reduction factor*, will disclose that an increase in frequency gives a larger value for the radical which in turn results in lower voltage gain. It is also to be seen that when the frequency is increased to the value that makes $X_t = R_e$, the radical is equal to $\sqrt{2}$ and the voltage gain $A_h$ has dropped to $0.707 A_m$.

The low-frequency response of the first stage of the resistance-capacitance-coupled amplifier of Fig. 5–6 can be understood by studying the variation in circuit parameters with frequency. As the frequency of the signal to be amplified decreases, the reactance of the coupling capacitor increases, giving rise to greater voltage drop $IX_x$ which results in less output voltage for a given input voltage and consequently less voltage gain. For this reason it is necessary that a low frequency equivalent circuit include the coupling capacitance $C$. The equivalent circuit for mid-band frequencies does not require the inclusion of the shunting reactance $X_t$, due to the shunting capacitance $C_t$, and since $X_t$ becomes larger at low frequencies it is valid to consider $X_t$ as negligibly large for the low-frequency analysis. The equivalent circuit for low frequencies is as shown in Fig. 5–7d. A mathematical analysis of this equivalent circuit yields Eq. (5–7a).

$$\frac{E_{g2}}{E_{g1}} = \frac{-g_m R_e}{\sqrt{1 + \dfrac{X_x^2}{R_x^2}}} \left| \tan^{-1}\frac{X_x}{R_x} \right. \tag{5–7a}$$

$$A_L = \left| \frac{E_{g2}}{E_{g1}} \right| = g_m R_e \left( \frac{1}{\sqrt{1 + \dfrac{X_x^2}{R_x^2}}} \right) \tag{5–7b}$$

where $A_L$ = numerical voltage gain for low frequencies
$\phantom{where}$ $X_x$ = reactance of coupling capacitor $C$

$$R_x = R_g + \frac{r_p R_p}{r_p + R_p}$$

From Eq. (5–7b) it is obvious that an increase in $X_x$ which results from a decrease in frequency ($X_x = 1/2\pi f C$) results in a reduction in gain. It is also to be seen that when $f$ takes on a value such that $X_x = R_x$, the voltage gain $A_L = 0.707 A_m$. The expression under the radical sign will be called the *low-frequency reduction factor*.

A general equation which is valid at any frequency can be written for a resistance-coupled amplifier by combining Eqs. (5–5b), (5–6b) and (5–7b); the resulting equation is shown below.

$$A_g = \left| \frac{E_{g2}}{E_{g1}} \right| = g_m R_e \frac{1}{\sqrt{1 + \dfrac{X_x^2}{R_x^2}}} \cdot \frac{1}{\sqrt{1 + \dfrac{R_e^2}{X_t^2}}} \tag{5–8}$$

$$\underbrace{\phantom{\frac{1}{\sqrt{1+\dfrac{X_x^2}{R_x^2}}}}}_{\substack{\text{(Low-frequency}\\\text{reduction factor)}}} \quad \underbrace{\phantom{\frac{1}{\sqrt{1+\dfrac{R_e^2}{X_t^2}}}}}_{\substack{\text{(High-frequency}\\\text{reduction factor)}}}$$

Referring to the expression of Eq. (5–8), at mid-band frequencies both radicals will approach unity; at extremely low frequencies the radical to the left (low-frequency reduction factor) will become appreciably greater than unity while the radical to the right (high-frequency reduction factor) will more nearly approach unity. At extremely high frequencies the radical at the right will become appreciably greater than unity while the radical to the left will very nearly approach unity.

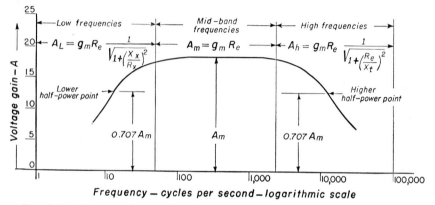

FIG. 5–8. Voltage gain as a function of frequency for a typical resistance-capacitance-coupled amplifier.

The response curve of a typical audio-frequency resistance-capacitance amplifier is shown in Fig. 5–8. The frequency below mid-band at which the gain drops to 70.7 percent of the mid-band gain is the frequency which gives the *lower half-power point*.* An examination of Eq. (5–7b) will show that the lower half-power point is reached when the frequency is such that $X_x = R_x$. The frequency at which the *higher half-power point* occurs is the frequency above mid-band that results in a gain of 70.7 percent of the mid-band gain. Eq. (5–6b) shows that the higher half-power point occurs when $X_t = R_e$. The useful frequency range of an amplifier of this type is usually considered to constitute the band of frequencies that lie between the two half-power points.

The useful frequency range of a resistance-coupled amplifier can be increased by making certain changes in circuit constants. Consider the low-frequency reduction factor $\sqrt{1 + X_x^2/R_x^2}$. If this radical were equal to unity, ideal low-frequency response would be realized. This, of course, is impossible; but by careful design it is possible to make this radical very near unity except for extremely low frequencies. The greater the capacitance of the coupling capacitor $C$, the lower will be the value of $X_x$ and the better the low-frequency response. However, due to the fact that the cost of good

---

* Since power in a given circuit varies as the square of the voltage, a reduction of the voltage to 70.7 percent of its original value will result in one-half of the original power.

capacitors increases rapidly with size and in most cases good response at extremely low frequencies is not required, practical values of $C$ are not generally greater than around 0.025 microfarad. An increase in $R_x$ will improve the low-frequency response $[R_x = R_g + r_pR_p/(r_p + R_p)]$. An increase in either the value of $R_g$ or $R_p$ will result in an increase in $R_x$; however, an increase in the value of $R_g$ will result in a greater increase in $R_x$ than the same incremental increase in $R_p$. The value of $R_g$ cannot be increased indefinitely, however, for an increase in $R_g$ changes other characteristics of the amplifier circuit; usually practical values of $R_g$ do not exceed one megohm.*

Now consider the high-frequency reduction factor $\sqrt{1 + R_e{}^2/X_t{}^2}$. It can be seen that an increase in $X_t$ will reduce the value of the high-frequency reduction factor and thereby results in an improvement in the high-frequency response of a given amplifier. By careful design $C_t$ can be reduced to a minimum, thereby making $X_t$ a maximum. There is a limit,

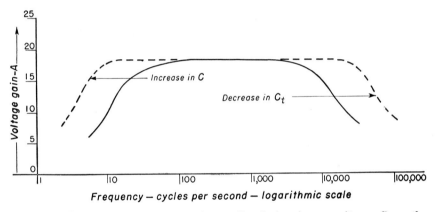

FIG. 5–9. Effect of coupling capacitance $C$ and shunting capacitance $C_t$ on the frequency response of a resistance-capacitance-coupled amplifier.

of course, to the minimum value of $C_t$ that can be obtained. The next factor to consider is $R_e$. A reduction in $R_e$ will reduce the value of the expression under the radical sign but at the same time will reduce the midband gain. The sketches of Fig. 5–9 illustrate how the frequency response is affected by various changes in circuit parameters.

Resistance-coupled amplifiers using pentodes are analyzed in a similar manner to those using triodes; however, the maximum gain of amplifiers using pentodes is usually much higher than that of amplifiers using triodes while the frequency response is poorer.

---

* Although the values of $C$ and $R_g$ given here are the largest values which are generally recommended by tube manufacturers, amplifier circuits utilizing values of $R_g$ as high as 10 megohms and values of $C$ as high as 10 microfarads have been designed.

**5–5. Circuit Parameters of Resistance-Coupled Amplifiers.** The circuits of Figs. 5–10 and 5–11 are typical working circuits for triode and

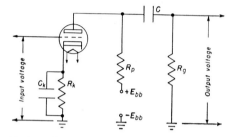

FIG. 5–10.  Circuit of a resistance-capacitance-coupled amplifier employing a triode.

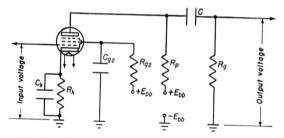

FIG. 5–11.  Circuit of a resistance-capacitance-coupled amplifier employing a pentode.

pentode resistance-coupled amplifiers, respectively.  In the above circuits, the plate-supply voltage instead of being obtained from a $B$ battery, as indicated by the basic circuit diagram of Fig. 5–6, is obtained from the output of a vacuum tube rectifier, that is, after the output of the rectifier has been properly filtered.  The resistor $R_k$ furnishes the dc grid bias.  The grid is negative with respect to the cathode by an amount equal to the $IR_k$ drop across the resistor $R_k$.  The capacitor $C_k$ which is in parallel with $R_k$ has a relatively large capacitance and is employed to by-pass the ac so that a relatively pure dc grid bias will be realized.  Additional circuit parameters, $R_{g2}$ and $C_{g2}$ are employed in the circuit of Fig. 5–11.  $R_{g2}$ is a dropping resistor which furnishes screen-grid voltage and $C_{g2}$ is employed to by-pass the ac component existing on the screen grid so that it will not flow through $R_{g2}$.  Typical circuit parameters for several resistance-coupled amplifiers are given in Tables 5–1 and 5–2.

The symbols employed in Tables 5–1 and 5–2 are indicated on the circuit diagrams of Figs. 5–10 and 5–11 and are defined below:

$C$ = Blocking capacitor (microfarads)
$C_k$ = Cathode by-pass capacitor (microfarads)
$C_{g2}$ = Screen by-pass capacitor (microfarads)

$E_{bb}$ = Plate-supply voltage (dc volts)
$E_o$ = Voltage output (peak volts)
$R_k$ = Cathode resistor (ohms)
$R_{g2}$ = Screen resistor (megohms)
$R_g$ = Grid resistor (megohms)
$R_p$ = Plate resistor (megohms)
$V.G.$ = Voltage gain at 5 v (rms) output unless otherwise specified.

TABLE 5–1*

TRIODES

6F5, 6F5–GT, 6SF5, 6SF5–GT, 12F5–GT, 12SF5

| $E_{bb}$ | $R_p$ | $R_g$ | $R_{g2}$ | $R_k$ | $C_{g2}$ | $C_k$ | $C$ | $E_o$ | $V.G.$ |
|---|---|---|---|---|---|---|---|---|---|
| | | 0.1 | – | 4,400 | – | 2.5 | 0.02 | 4 | 28† |
| | 0.1 | 0.25 | – | 4,800 | – | 2.1 | 0.01 | 5 | 34‡ |
| | | 0.5 | – | 5,000 | – | 1.8 | 0.005 | 6 | 35§ |
| | | 0.25 | – | 8,000 | – | 1.33 | 0.01 | 6 | 39† |
| 90 | 0.25 | 0.5 | – | 8,800 | – | 1.18 | 0.005 | 7 | 43§ |
| | | 1.0 | – | 9,000 | – | 0.9 | 0.003 | 10 | 44 |
| | | 0.5 | – | 12,200 | – | 0.76 | 0.005 | 8 | 43 |
| | 0.5 | 1.0 | – | 13,500 | – | 0.67 | 0.003 | 10 | 46 |
| | | 2.0 | – | 14,700 | – | 0.58 | 0.0015 | 12 | 48 |
| | | 0.1 | – | 1,800 | – | 4.4 | 0.025 | 16 | 37 |
| | 0.1 | 0.25 | – | 2,000 | – | 3.3 | 0.015 | 23 | 44 |
| | | 0.5 | – | 2,200 | – | 2.9 | 0.006 | 25 | 46 |
| | | 0.25 | – | 3,500 | – | 2.3 | 0.01 | 21 | 48 |
| 180 | 0.25 | 0.5 | – | 4,100 | – | 1.8 | 0.006 | 26 | 53 |
| | | 1.0 | – | 4,500 | – | 1.7 | 0.004 | 32 | 57 |
| | | 0.5 | – | 6,100 | – | 1.3 | 0.006 | 24 | 53 |
| | 0.5 | 1.0 | – | 6,900 | – | 0.9 | 0.003 | 33 | 63 |
| | | 2.0 | – | 7,700 | – | 0.83 | 0.0015 | 37 | 66 |
| | | 0.1 | – | 1,300 | – | 5.0 | 0.025 | 33 | 42 |
| | 0.1 | 0.25 | – | 1,600 | – | 3.7 | 0.01 | 43 | 49 |
| | | 0.5 | – | 1,700 | – | 3.2 | 0.006 | 48 | 52 |
| | | 0.25 | – | 2,600 | – | 2.5 | 0.01 | 41 | 56 |
| 300 | 0.25 | 0.5 | – | 3,200 | – | 2.1 | 0.007 | 54 | 63 |
| | | 1.0 | – | 3,500 | – | 2.0 | 0.004 | 63 | 67 |
| | | 0.5 | – | 4,500 | – | 1.5 | 0.006 | 50 | 65 |
| | 0.5 | 1.0 | – | 5,400 | – | 1.2 | 0.004 | 62 | 70 |
| | | 2.0 | – | 6,100 | – | 0.93 | 0.002 | 70 | 70 |

* Values taken by permission from *RCA Receiving Tube Manual*, RCA Manufacturing Company, Harrison, New Jersey, 1949.
† At 2 volts (RMS) output.  ‡ At 3 volts (RMS) output.  § At 4 volts (RMS) output.

TABLE 5–2*

PENTODES

6SJ7, 6SJ7–GT, 12SJ7, 12SJ7–GT

| $E_{bb}$ | $R_p$ | $R_g$ | $R_{g2}$ | $R_k$ | $C_{g2}$ | $C_k$ | $C$ | $E_o$ | V.G. |
|---|---|---|---|---|---|---|---|---|---|
| | | 0.1 | 0.29 | 820 | 0.09 | 8.8 | 0.02 | 18 | 41 |
| | 0.1 | 0.25 | 0.29 | 880 | 0.085 | 7.4 | 0.016 | 23 | 68 |
| | | 0.5 | 0.31 | 1,000 | 0.075 | 6.6 | 0.007 | 28 | 70 |
| | | 0.25 | 0.69 | 1,680 | 0.06 | 5.0 | 0.012 | 16 | 75 |
| 90 | 0.25 | 0.5 | 0.92 | 1,700 | 0.045 | 4.5 | 0.005 | 18 | 93 |
| | | 1.0 | 0.82 | 1,800 | 0.04 | 4.0 | 0.003 | 22 | 104 |
| | | 0.5 | 1.5 | 3,600 | 0.045 | 2.4 | 0.003 | 18 | 91 |
| | 0.5 | 1.0 | 1.7 | 3,800 | 0.30 | 2.4 | 0.002 | 22 | 119 |
| | | 2.0 | 1.9 | 4,050 | 0.028 | 2.35 | 0.0015 | 24 | 139 |
| | | 0.1 | 0.29 | 760 | 0.10 | 9.1 | 0.019 | 49 | 55 |
| | 0.1 | 0.25 | 0.31 | 800 | 0.09 | 8.0 | 0.015 | 60 | 82 |
| | | 0.5 | 0.37 | 860 | 0.09 | 7.8 | 0.007 | 62 | 91 |
| | | 0.25 | 0.83 | 1,050 | 0.06 | 6.8 | 0.001 | 38 | 109 |
| 180 | 0.25 | 0.5 | 0.94 | 1,060 | 0.06 | 6.6 | 0.004 | 47 | 131 |
| | | 1.0 | 0.94 | 1,100 | 0.07 | 6.1 | 0.003 | 54 | 161 |
| | | 0.5 | 1.85 | 2,000 | 0.05 | 4.0 | 0.003 | 37 | 151 |
| | 0.5 | 1.0 | 2.2 | 2,180 | 0.04 | 3.8 | 0.002 | 44 | 192 |
| | | 2.0 | 2.4 | 2,410 | 0.035 | 3.6 | 0.0015 | 54 | 208 |
| | | 0.1 | 0.35 | 500 | 0.10 | 11.6 | 0.019 | 72 | 67 |
| | 0.1 | 0.25 | 0.37 | 530 | 0.09 | 10.9 | 0.016 | 96 | 98 |
| | | 0.5 | 0.47 | 590 | 0.09 | 9.9 | 0.007 | 101 | 104 |
| | | 0.25 | 0.89 | 850 | 0.07 | 8.5 | 0.011 | 79 | 139 |
| 300 | 0.25 | 0.5 | 1.10 | 860 | 0.06 | 7.4 | 0.004 | 88 | 167 |
| | | 1.0 | 1.18 | 910 | 0.06 | 6.9 | 0.003 | 98 | 185 |
| | | 0.5 | 2.0 | 1,300 | 0.06 | 6.0 | 0.004 | 64 | 200 |
| | 0.5 | 1.0 | 2.2 | 1,410 | 0.05 | 5.8 | 0.002 | 79 | 238 |
| | | 2.0 | 2.5 | 1,530 | 0.04 | 5.2 | 0.0015 | 79 | 263 |

**5–6. Transformer-Coupled Voltage Amplifiers.** In the early development of amplifiers, tubes with high amplification factors were not available and the transformer-coupled amplifier became popular as a means of obtaining fairly high voltage gain with the amplifier tubes available at that time. Audio-frequency transformers usually employ cores made of silicon steel which have an extremely short air gap. The air gap enables the transformer to remain unsaturated at much higher values of dc current than would be possible if it did not have an air gap; therefore, the incremental inductance is larger for a given amount of steel. Most transformers

---

* Values taken by permission from *RCA Receiving Tube Manual*, RCA Manufacturing Company, Harrison, New Jersey, 1947.

of this type have a turns ratio of 2, 2.5, 3 or 4. The maximum gain obtained from a well-designed transformer-coupled amplifier can be made to approach the product of the amplification factor of the tube and the turns ratio of the transformer.

The circuit of a typical transformer-coupled voltage amplifier is shown in Fig. 5–12. In the transformer-coupled amplifier the primary of the coupling transformer constitutes all of the dc resistance in series with the plate and plate-supply voltage of the triode; thus the dc drop in the plate circuit is much lower than it would be for the resistance-coupled amplifier. This results in higher undistorted output for a given dc supply voltage.

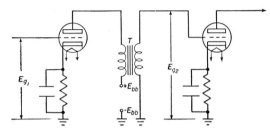

Fig. 5–12.   Circuit of a transformer-coupled amplifier.

Pentodes can be used in transformer-coupled amplifiers; however, they require special consideration, give rise to more distortion and are usually more expensive; thus they are seldom used in this connection.

A changing magnetic field will induce a voltage in the coupling transformer; therefore, transformer-coupled amplifiers are more likely to pick up stray signals than resistance-coupled amplifiers. They are more expensive, have poorer frequency response and give less voltage gain than resistance-coupled amplifiers employing modern high-gain tubes. For these reasons they are not generally used except for applications where the particular type of circuit arrangement makes them more suitable. One common application of transformer coupling is driving push-pull power amplifiers.

The general equivalent circuit of a transformer-coupled voltage amplifier is shown in Fig. 5–13a. By combining circuit constants and referring everything to the primary, the general equivalent circuit of Fig. 5–13a can be reduced to the equivalent circuit of Fig. 5–13b.

By making assumptions similar to those made for the resistance-capacitance-coupled amplifier for different frequency ranges, the equivalent circuits of Figs. 5–13c, 5–13d and 5–13e for mid-band, low-frequency and high-frequency response, respectively, may be employed with a reasonable degree of accuracy. An analysis of the mid-band equivalent circuit yields Eq. (5–9a).

$$A_m = \left| \frac{E_{g2}}{E_{g1}} \right| = ag_m R_e \qquad (5\text{–}9a)$$

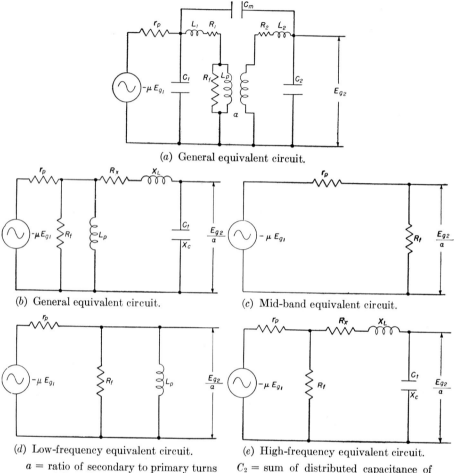

(a) General equivalent circuit.

(b) General equivalent circuit.   (c) Mid-band equivalent circuit.

(d) Low-frequency equivalent circuit.   (e) High-frequency equivalent circuit.

$a$ = ratio of secondary to primary turns
$r_p$ = plate resistance of triode employed
$R_1$ = ohmic resistance of primary
$R_2$ = ohmic resistance of secondary
$R_f$ = resistance representing the eddy current and hysteresis loss
$L_1$ = leakage inductance of primary
$L_2$ = leakage inductance of secondary
$L_p$ = incremental primary inductance
$E_{g2}$ = output voltage
$E_{g1}$ = input voltage
$\mu$ = amplification factor of the tube
$C_1$ = sum of cathode-plate capacitance of triode employed, distributed capacitance of leads between tube and transformer and distributed capacitance of the primary of the transformer.

$C_2$ = sum of distributed capacitance of the secondary of transformer, and distributed capacitance of leads between secondary of transformer and tube to which voltage is delivered, and input capacity of the tube to which voltage is being delivered.

$C_m$ = capacitance existing between the transformer windings

$$C_t = C_1 + a^2 C_2 + (a \pm 1)^2 C_m$$

$$X_c = \frac{1}{2\pi f [C_1 + a^2 C_2 + (a \pm 1)^2 C_m]}$$

$$X_L = 2\pi f \left( L_1 + \frac{L_2}{a^2} \right)$$

$$R_x = R_1 + \frac{R_2}{a^2}$$

Fig. 5-13.   Equivalent circuits for a transformer-coupled amplifier.

where $A_m$ = numerical voltage gain at mid-band frequency

$R_e = \dfrac{r_p R_f}{r_p + R_f}$

$R_f$ = resistance representing the eddy current and hysteresis of transformer

$a$ = turns ratio of transformer

An examination of Eq. (5–9a) shows that if $R_f$ is very large compared to $r_p$ (which is usually the case for a well-designed transformer), $R_e$ is approximately equal to $r_p$, and $A_m$ is approximately equal to the product of amplification factor $\mu$ and turns ratio $a$.

$$A_m \approx a\mu \tag{5–9b}$$

An analysis of the low-frequency equivalent circuit yields Eq. 5–10.

$$A_L = ag_m R_e \cdot \frac{1}{\sqrt{\left(\dfrac{R_e}{X_p}\right)^2 + 1}} \tag{5–10}$$

where $A_L$ = numerical voltage gain at low frequencies

$X_p = 2\pi f L p$

$L_p$ = incremental primary inductance

The term under the radical sign might be called the low-frequency reduction factor. An examination of Eq. (5–10) shows that a decrease in frequency results in a reduction in gain.

An analysis of the high-frequency equivalent circuit yields Eq. (5–11).

$$A_h = ag_m R_e \cdot \frac{1}{\sqrt{\dfrac{(R_e + R_x)^2}{X_c{}^2} + \dfrac{(X_L - X_C)^2}{X_c{}^2}}} \tag{5–11}$$

where $A_h$ = numerical voltage gain at high frequencies

$R_x$ = total ohmic resistance referred to primary

$X_L$ = total leakage inductance referred to primary

$X_C$ = total shunting reactance referred to primary

Careful examination of the term under the radical sign in Eq. (5–11) will show that as the frequency increases, a frequency will eventually be reached at which $X_L = X_C$. At this frequency the radical will be less than unity and the gain will be greater than the gain at mid-band frequencies. This is the frequency at which the leakage inductance of the transformer is in resonance with the distributed capacitance of the circuit. Typical frequency response curves for a transformer-coupled amplifier are shown in Fig. 5–14.

Eq. (5–12) gives the gain of a transformer-coupled amplifier for any frequency in terms of circuit parameters.

$$A_g = ag_m R_e \cdot \frac{1}{\sqrt{\left(\dfrac{R_e}{X_p}\right)^2 + 1}} \cdot \frac{1}{\sqrt{\dfrac{(R_e + R_x)^2}{X_c{}^2} + \dfrac{(X_L - X_C)^2}{X_c{}^2}}} \tag{5–12}$$

The hump in the curve $a$ of Fig. 5–14 is undesirable; however, it can be reduced by shunting the secondary of the transformer with a high resistance which in effect lowers the $Q$ of the circuit. At the same time the addition of this resistance lowers the maximum gain of the amplifier as indicated

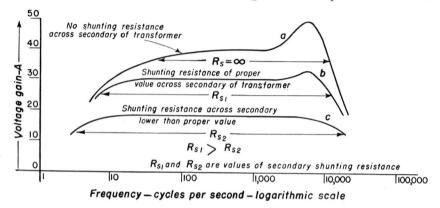

Fig. 5–14. Voltage gain as a function of frequency for a transformer-coupled amplifier.

by curves $b$ and $c$ of Fig. 5–14. At present, transformers are available which are designed so that no appreciable hump is noticeable.

**5–7. DC Amplifiers.** The circuit diagram of the simplest type of dc amplifier capable of amplifying direct voltage is shown in Fig. 5–15. Such an amplifier is known as a direct-current or direct-coupled amplifier. It will be noticed that this circuit is essentially the same as that of the resistance-capacitance-coupled voltage amplifier of Fig. 5–6, with the exception that the coupling capacitor is replaced by a battery and the resistance $R_g$ has been eliminated.

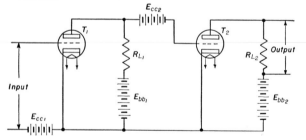

Fig. 5–15. Circuit of a direct-coupled amplifier

It might seem logical to eliminate the battery $E_{cc2}$ and make a connection from the plate of tube $T_1$ directly to the grid of tube $T_2$. This, however, would put a high positive potential on the grid of the second tube which would make it inoperative. The magnitude of $E_{cc2}$ must be large enough to reduce the voltage on the grid of tube $T_2$ to its required bias. The value of $E_{cc2}$ for a given value of grid bias $E_{c2}$ is defined by Eq. (5–13).

$$E_{cc2} = -E_{bb1} + I_{b1}R_{L1} + E_{c2} \qquad (5\text{–}13)$$

where $E_{bb1}$ = plate-supply voltage for tube $T_1$

$I_{b1}$ = dc to the plate of tube $T_1$

$R_{L1}$ = load resistance of first stage

The operation of this amplifier is quite simple. Any change in the grid potential of the first tube will cause a change in the current through $R_L$ which will result in a corresponding voltage drop across $R_L$. This voltage will be applied to the grid of the second tube; however, due to the 180° phase difference the current in the second tube will change in the opposite direction from the first. If a third stage is added, the current in the third stage will change in the same way as the current in the first. The voltage gain of one stage of a dc amplifier is expressed by Eq. (5–14).

$$A = \frac{\mu R_L}{r_p + R_L} \qquad (5\text{–}14)$$

Where there are several stages, the over-all gain is equal to the product of the gains of the individual stages. An amplifier of this type will amplify dc and ac voltages equally well, provided the frequencies involved are not high enough to cause the reactances due to the tubes and wiring to become

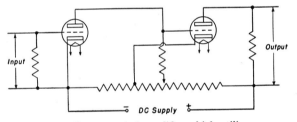

Fig. 5–16.   Circuit of a direct-coupled amplifier which utilizes a common dc supply voltage.

appreciable. Because of the separate dc sources required for each grid and plate, the dc amplifier circuit of Fig. 5–15 is both bulky and expensive. A more common type of dc amplifier circuit which utilizes a common dc supply is shown in Fig. 5–16. Direct-coupled amplifiers have the disadvantage of being extremely sensitive to a dc voltage change anywhere in the circuit. Any voltage drift which occurs in one of the first stages will be amplified throughout the circuit, resulting in a large variation in the output. For this reason it is essential that an extremely well-regulated dc supply be used to supply tube voltages for dc amplifiers.

Direct-coupled amplifiers are used to some extent for the amplification of audio frequencies; however, because of the extremely well-regulated power source required and the cost involved, they are not very widely used for this purpose. Dc amplifiers can be designed to give uniform amplification from zero frequency up through the audio-frequency range and are applicable where excellent audio-frequency response is required. The resistance-capacitance-coupled amplifier which was discussed in Sections 5–3, 5–4 and 5–5 is by far the most common circuit for the amplification of frequencies within the audio range.

## Audio-Frequency Power Amplifiers

**5–8. Basic Considerations.** In contrast with voltage amplifiers, power amplifiers are designed to develop maximum undistorted power across the load impedance. As used here, the word "undistorted" indicates an amplitude distortion of 5 percent or less. A distortion of 5 percent is not appreciable to the average human ear and thus can be readily tolerated in most common applications. The audio-frequency power amplifier finds wide usage in industrial control circuits, as well as in all types of communications circuits such as radio receivers, radio transmitters, public address systems and telephone systems.

As mentioned previously, power amplifiers are classified as Class A, Class AB, Class B or Class C, according to the portion of the cycle over which plate current flows. These terms are defined as follows: *

*Class A Amplifier.* "A Class A amplifier is an amplifier in which the grid bias and alternating grid voltages are such that plate current in a specific tube flows at all times." (Fig. 5–17a)

*Class AB Amplifier.* "A Class AB amplifier is an amplifier in which the grid bias and alternating grid voltages are such that plate current in a specific tube flows for appreciably more than half but less than the entire electrical cycle." (Fig. 5–17b)

*Class B Amplifier.* "A Class B amplifier is an amplifier in which the grid bias is approximately equal to the cut-off value so that the plate current is approximately zero when no exciting grid voltage is applied, and so that plate current in a specific tube flows for approximately one-half of each cycle when an alternating grid voltage is applied." (Fig. 5–17c)

*Class C Amplifier.* "A Class C amplifier is an amplifier in which the grid bias is appreciably greater than the cut-off value so that the plate current in each tube is zero when no alternating grid voltage is applied, and so that plate current flows in a specific tube for appreciably less than one-half of each cycle when an alternating grid voltage is applied." (Fig. 5–17d)

NOTE: (applicable to all classes) "To denote that grid current does not flow during any part of the input cycle, the suffix 1 may be added to the letter or letters of the class identification. The suffix 2 may be used to denote that grid current flows during some part of the cycle."

---

* *American Standard Definitions of Electrical Terms*, New York: American Institute of Electrical Engineers, 1941, p. 234.

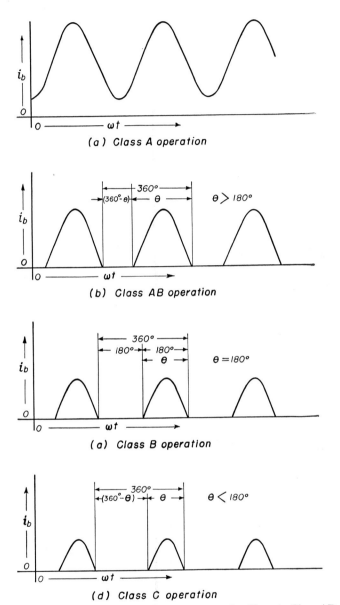

(a) Class A operation

(b) Class AB operation

(a) Class B operation

(d) Class C operation

Fig. 5–17.   Diagrams illustrating the plate current for Class A, Class AB, Class B and Class C operation.

Radio-frequency power amplifiers are usually Class $B_2$ or $C_2$; audio-frequency amplifiers employing one tube are Class $A_1$, while push-pull audio-frequency amplifiers are usually operated as Class $AB_1$ or Class $AB_2$. Driving the grid of a power amplifier tube positive results in much higher efficiency and, at the same time, greater distortion.

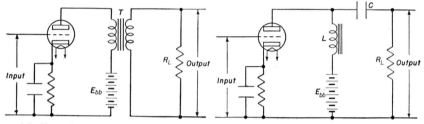

(a) Class A power amplifier with output transformer.

(b) Class A power amplifier with shunt feed.

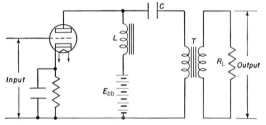

(c) Class A power amplifier with shunt feed and output transformer.

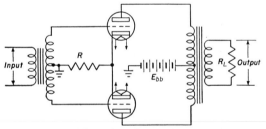

(d) Push-pull amplifier.

Fig. 5–18.   Typical audio-frequency power-amplifier circuits.

Several typical audio-frequency power-amplifier circuits are shown in Fig. 5–18. Fig. 5–18a is the circuit of a single-tube power-amplifier employing transformer coupling; Fig. 5–18b is the circuit of a single-tube power amplifier employing shunt feed; Fig. 5–18c is the circuit of a single-tube power amplifier employing transformer coupling in conjunction with shunt feed; and Fig. 5–18d is the circuit of a push-pull power amplifier. A push-pull amplifier always necessitates the use of two tubes, or the equivalent of two tubes, in one envelope; but two tubes does not always indicate push-pull operation for two amplifier tubes are sometimes operated in parallel.

There are three very important aspects that must be considered when dealing with power amplifiers: power output, percent distortion, and efficiency. Although voltage output and distortion are important in the case of a voltage amplifier, due to the small amount of power handled by a voltage amplifier as compared to the power handled by a power amplifier, the efficiency does not have the same significance in the voltage amplifier that it does in 'the power amplifier.

As the power output of a given amplifier is increased, it usually follows that the efficiency also increases, but at the same time an increase in power output results in greater distortion which is usually very undesirable; thus, in the design of a power amplifier a careful balance between efficiency, power output, and maximum permissible distortion must be obtained. In some applications it is advantageous to sacrifice power in favor of fidelity and in others, fidelity in favor of power. There are design equations that show how the various characteristics of a power amplifier are functions of circuit parameters and voltages but the development of these is, for the most part, rather complex and since most of them cannot be employed intelligently without an understanding of their development, they will not be included here. Instead of giving equations, typical operating values for several of the more common types of small power tubes are given in Table 5–3.

At present, the beam power tube is the most used power-amplifier tube for low-power * applications. Beam power tubes give greater sensitivity, more power output and higher efficiency than pentodes or triodes. The distortion in amplifier circuits employing beam power tubes is somewhat greater than that encountered in equivalent circuits in which triodes are used but less than in the case of equivalent pentode-amplifier circuits. For most applications, beam power tubes, if operated properly, do not give enough distortion to cause appreciable trouble. Pentodes give greater output and higher sensitivity than triodes but are less suitable for most low-power applications than beam power tubes. Triodes, since they give less distortion and low efficiency as well as low sensitivity, are generally used (for low-power applications) only where extremely high fidelity is necessary.

**5–9. Efficiency.** A properly designed Class A power amplifier using a single triode will give up to around 15 percent plate efficiency without appreciable distortion, while the same type of operation of the pentode will give a maximum efficiency of about 30 percent. The beam power tube will give plate efficiencies as high as 40 percent. The plate efficiency of an

---

* By low-power applications is meant power amplifiers used in radio receivers, phonographs, public address systems, etc. In high-power applications such as radio transmitters, triodes are used for amplification. Beam power tubes, pentodes and tetrodes are not available in power ratings comparable to large transmitting triodes.

TABLE 5-3

| Type Tube | Class Operation | Control Grid Voltage | Screen Grid Voltage | Plate Voltage | Plate[1] Current Milliamperes | Screen[2] Current Milliamperes | Load[3] Resistance Ohms | Percent Total Harmonic Distortion | Power Output Watts |
|---|---|---|---|---|---|---|---|---|---|
| 2A3 Triode | Class A₁ Single tube | −45 | − | 250 | 60 | − | 2,500 | 0 | 3.5 |
| | Class AB₁ Two Tubes Push-Pull | −62 | − | 300 | 80 | − | 3,000 | 2.5 | 15 |
| 6F6 Pentode | Class A₁ Single Tube | −16.5 | 250 | 250 | 34 | 6.5 | 7,000 | 8 | 3.2 |
| | Class A₁ Two Tubes Push-Pull | −24 | 285 | 315 | 62 | 12 | 10,000 | 4 | 11 |
| | Class AB₂ Two Tubes Push-Pull | −26 | 250 | 375 | 82 | 5 | 10,000 | 3.5 | 18.5 |
| 6L6 Beam Power Tube | Class A₁ Single Tube | −14 | 250 | 250 | 72 | 5 | 2,500 | 10 | 6.5 |
| | Class A₁ Two Tubes Push-Pull | −16 | 250 | 250 | 120 | 10 | 5,000 | 2 | 14.5 |
| | Class AB₁ Two Tubes Push-Pull | −22.5 | 270 | 360 | 132 | 5 | 6,600 | 2 | 26.5 |
| 6V6 Beam Power Tube | Class A₁ Single Tube | −12.5 | 250 | 250 | 45 | 4.5 | 5,000 | 8 | 4.5 |
| | Class AB₁ Two Tubes Push-Pull | −15 | 250 | 315 | 70 | 5 | 10,000 | 5 | 10 |

[1] Only value of zero-signal plate current given     [2] Only value of zero-signal screen current given
[3] In the case of push-pull operation resistance is the effective resistance from plate to plate. Additional information may be obtained by consulting the *RCA Receiving Tube Manual*, RCA Manufacturing Company, Harrison, New Jersey, 1947.

amplifier utilizing either a triode, pentode or beam power tube is defined as follows:

$$\text{Plate efficiency} = \frac{I_{ac}^2 R_L}{I_{dc} E_{dc}} \qquad (5\text{--}15)$$

where $R_L$ = load resistance

   $I_{ac}$ = rms value of output current

   $I_{dc}$ = direct plate current

   $E_{dc}$ = direct plate voltage

At the present time, the circuit of Fig. 5–18$d$ is a very popular type of power-amplifier circuit. As previously mentioned, this circuit is known as a push-pull power amplifier. Although small inexpensive radio receivers usually employ single tube power amplifiers, almost all audio-frequency power amplifiers designed to handle appreciable power are of the push-pull type. Push-pull amplifiers are commonly used in public address systems, and better phonographs and radio receivers.

**5–10. Advantages of Push-Pull Operation.*** The advantages of push-pull operation over single tube operation are as follows:

1. No hum voltages exist due to improper filtering of the plate power supply.
2. All even harmonics (2nd, 4th, 6th, 8th, etc.) are balanced out in the output circuit; thus, two tubes in push-pull can be made to handle much more distortionless power than the same two tubes in parallel or much more distortionless power than one tube with twice the power rating of either of the tubes in a push-pull circuit.
3. There is no dc saturation of the plate transformer.
4. There is no current of signal frequency through the power supply; thus this tendency to produce feed-back is almost completely eliminated.

These advantages apply to push-pull amplifiers employing either power triodes, power pentodes, or beam power tubes. Beam power tubes are more common in push-pull circuits than pentodes or triodes but triodes are used where a premium is placed on fidelity.

Consider the push-pull amplifier circuit of Fig. 5–18$d$. The grids of the two tubes are excited by a center tapped transformer secondary (this is not the only method of excitation); thus the voltages on the individual grids are always 180° out of phase. The output of each tube is connected to opposite ends of the primary of the plate transformer which is center tapped, the dc being applied at the center. The output appears across the secondary of the plate transformer. The resistance $R$ furnishes grid bias and since there is no current of signal frequency flowing through $R$ (if the

---

* For a discussion of these advantages, see F. E. Terman, *Radio Engineering*, 3rd ed. (New York: McGraw-Hill Book Co., Inc., 1947), pp. 299–301.

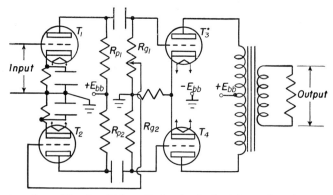

(a) Push-pull amplifier in which excitation is obtained from phase-inverter circuit.

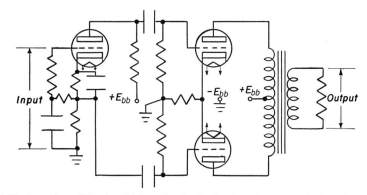

(b) Push-pull amplifier in which excitation is obtained from a cathode resistor.

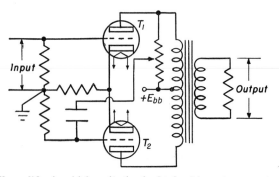

(c) Push-pull amplifier in which excitation is obtained from tap on output transformer

Fig. 5–19.   Several methods of exciting push-pull amplifiers.

circuit is properly balanced), it is not, under ideal conditions, necessary to by-pass it with a capacitor.

**5–11. Excitation Circuits for Push-Pull Amplifiers.** In the push-pull amplifier of Fig. 5–18$d$, a transformer is utilized to obtain proper grid excitation (180° phase difference between grids). Although this type of feed is widely used, it has some disadvantages. The input transformer is expensive, it tends to reduce the frequency response and there is a possibility that it will pick up signals due to stray magnetic fields in the vicinity. Often push-pull amplifiers are fed with phase inverter circuits such as the one shown in Fig. 5–19$a$. In this case the push-pull amplifier is fed by two resistance-coupled voltage amplifiers arranged so that they constitute what is termed a phase inverter circuit.

The operation of this circuit is as follows: The input signal is impressed upon the grid of the voltage amplifier tube $T_1$; this signal is amplified and appears across $R_{g1}$ after experiencing a 180° phase shift. The excitation for the grid of tube $T_2$ is obtained from a tap on $R_{g1}$; thus the signal applied to the grid of tube $T_2$ is 180° out of phase with the signal applied to the grid of tube $T_1$. This means that the output of tube $T_2$ which appears across $R_{g2}$ will be 180° out of phase with the signal across $R_{g1}$. The voltage across $R_{g1}$ is applied to the grid of the power tube $T_3$ and the voltage across $R_{g2}$ is applied to the grid of power tube $T_4$ resulting in the two power tubes being excited 180° out of phase which is required for push-pull operation.

Instead of using two triodes in a phase-inverter circuit, often a twin triode such as 6N7 is employed. There are several other methods of obtaining the proper excitation for push-pull amplifiers. One such method consists of taking the signal for driving one of the push-pull tubes from the output circuit of a voltage amplifier and the signal for the other from an unby-passed cathode resistor in the same voltage amplifier circuit (Fig. 5–19$b$). Another arrangement consists of taking a tap off the output transformer and feeding the signal thus obtained back to the grid of the opposite power amplifier tube (Fig. 5–19$c$).

## Radio-Frequency Amplifiers

Since radio-frequency amplifiers are employed primarily in radio receivers and transmitters, they will be discussed only very briefly in this text. In general, radio-frequency amplifiers, whether they be designed for power or voltage amplification, are of the tuned circuit type and respond to a narrow band of frequencies.

**5–12. Radio-Frequency Voltage Amplifiers.*** Tuned radio-frequency voltage amplifiers are employed to amplify radio-frequency signals which

---

* For a more complete treatment of radio-frequency voltage amplifiers, see F. E. Terman, *Radio Engineering*, 3rd ed. (New York: McGraw-Hill Book Co., Inc., 1947), pp. 338–74.

are picked up by the antenna of a radio. They are also employed to amplify the intermediate frequency voltages in superheterodyne receivers. However, when used in this connection they are known as intermediate-frequency (IF) amplifiers. The IF amplifier is a radio-frequency amplifier which is designed to be tuned to only one frequency, the intermediate frequency, which in regular broadcast receivers is around 450 kilocycles.

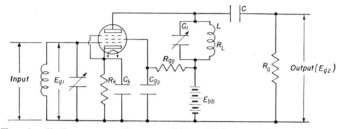

(a) Tuned-radio-frequency voltage amplifier utilizing capacitive coupling.

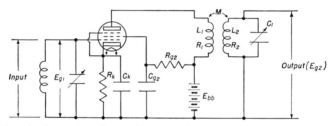

(b) Untuned-primary tuned-secondary transformer-coupled radio-frequency voltage amplifier.

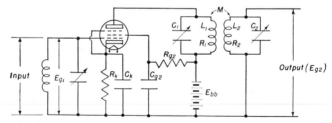

(c) Tuned-primary tuned-secondary transformer-coupled radio-frequency voltage amplifier.

FIG. 5–20.   Basic radio-frequency voltage-amplifier circuits.

Tuned-radio-frequency (TRF) amplifiers, on the other hand, may be tuned to any frequency within the range of the radio receiver. In the case of a regular broadcast receiver the TRF amplifier should be capable of being tuned to any frequency between 550 kilocycles and 1600 kilocycles. There are many types of tuned radio-frequency voltage amplifiers; the circuits of three of the more basic types are shown in Figs. 5–20a, 5–20b and 5–20c. The simplest type of TRF amplifier is shown in Fig. 5–20a. This amplifier is comprised of a single resonant circuit, capacitance coupling and a radio-frequency pentode. Because of their high gain and low grid-plate capacitance, pentodes are more widely used in radio-frequency voltage amplifier circuits than triodes. The gain of the circuit of Fig. 5–20a at resonance is expressed by Eqs. (5–16a) and (5–16b).

$$A_r = \left| \frac{E_{g2}}{E_{g1}} \right| = \frac{g_m \omega_r L Q_r}{1 + \omega_r L Q_r \left( \dfrac{1}{r_p} + \dfrac{1}{R_g} \right)} \tag{5–16a}$$

where $g_m$ = transconductance of tube employed
$\quad r_p$ = plate resistance of tube employed
$\quad R_g$ = grid-leak resistance
$\quad A_r$ = voltage amplification at resonance
$\quad Q_r$ = Q for the circuit at resonance = $\omega_r L / R_L$
$\quad \omega_r = 2\pi f_r$
$\quad f_r$ = resonant frequency

In the practical case, $r_p$ and $R_g$ are both very large compared to the resonant circuit impedance $\omega_r L Q_r$; thus Eq. (5–16a) may be reduced to the form of (5–16b).

$$A_r \approx g_m \omega_r L Q_r \tag{5–16b}$$

The circuit of Fig. 5–20b is that of a typical TRF amplifier employed in radio receivers. This is an untuned-primary tuned-secondary transformer-coupled type circuit. The amplification of this circuit at resonance is expressed by Eqs. (5–17a) and (5–17b).

$$A_r = \left| \frac{E_{g2}}{E_{g1}} \right| = \frac{g_m \omega_r M Q_r}{1 + \dfrac{(\omega_r M)^2}{r_p R_2}} \tag{5–17a}$$

where $M$ = mutual inductance between transformer windings
$\quad R_2$ = resistance of secondary of transformer

In the case of a pentode, $r_p$ is extremely high and

$$A_r \approx g_m \omega M Q \tag{5–17b}$$

The circuit of Fig. 5–20c is a tuned-primary tuned-secondary transformer-coupled amplifier. This type of circuit is commonly used as an IF amplifier in superheterodyne receivers. Such a circuit gives a band-pass characteristic, the width of the band being a function of the coefficient of coupling. The way in which the characteristics of a coupled circuit of this type varies with the coefficient of coupling is discussed in Section 4–22.

If both tuned circuits are resonant at the same frequency, the gain at resonance is expressed by Eq. (5–18a).

$$A_r = g_m k \frac{\omega_r \sqrt{L_1 L_2}}{k^2 + \dfrac{1}{Q_1 Q_2}} \tag{5–18a}$$

where $g_m$ = grid-plate transconductance of tube

$k$ = coefficient of coupling between transformer windings

$L_1$ = inductance of primary

$L_2$ = inductance of secondary

$Q_1$ = effective $Q$ of primary = $\omega_r L_1 r_p / [R_1 r_p + (1/\omega_r C_1)^2]$

$Q_2$ = $Q$ of secondary = $\omega_r L_2 / R_2$

$R_2$ = resistance of secondary of transformer

$C_1$ = capacitance of secondary

When $k = 1/\sqrt{Q_1 Q_2}$ (critical value), the maximum gain is realized.

$$A_{(max)} = g_m \frac{\omega(\sqrt{L_1 L_2})(\sqrt{Q_1 Q_2})}{2} \qquad (5\text{--}18b)$$

**5–13. Radio-Frequency Power Amplifiers.**\* Radio-frequency power amplifiers are employed for obtaining large amounts of radio-frequency power for the output stages of transmitters. They are operated as Class B or Class C, the latter type of operation being the more common. Class $C_2$ operation is generally preferred to other types of operation because it en-

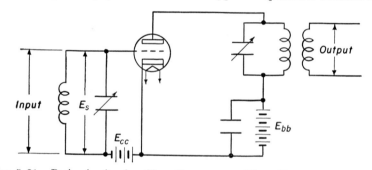

Fig. 5–21. Basic circuit of a Class C power amplifier. (Neutralizing circuit not shown.)

ables a given tube or tubes to handle more power at a higher efficiency than any other type of operation. The basic circuit diagram of a Class C power amplifier is shown in Fig. 5–21. Although there are numerous variations of Class C amplifier circuits, consideration of each type is beyond the scope of this text.

As defined previously, Class C operation means that the grid is biased so that the plate current flows for less than 180°, i.e., less than one-half of each cycle. Under normal Class C operating conditions, the signal input $E_s$ is sufficiently large to drive the grid positive on the positive half cycle; thus there is grid-current flow over a portion of each cycle, resulting in Class $C_2$ operation. The sketches of Fig. 5–22 illustrate the current voltage relationships in a Class $C_2$ amplifier.

---

\* For a more complete discussion of power amplifiers, see F. E. Terman, *Radio Engineering*, 3rd ed. (New York: McGraw-Hill Book Co., Inc., 1947), pp. 374–400.

Although the plate current in the case of a Class C amplifier flows only in pulses as indicated by Fig. 5–22c, a sinusoidal voltage is developed across the load (usually referred to as a tank circuit) which is comprised of inductance and capacitance in parallel. The sine wave is developed due to the

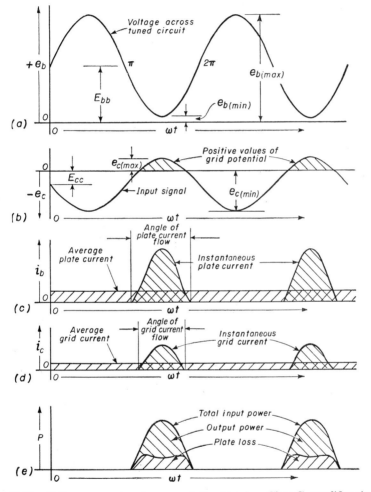

Fig. 5–22.   Voltage, current and power relationships in a Class C₂ amplifier circuit.

transfer of energy between the inductance and capacitance and is somewhat analogous to the "fly-wheel effect" in the case of a gasoline engine. Although a mathematical discussion of this is beyond the scope of this text, the reader who is interested in such a treatment is referred elsewhere.*

* B. Van der Pol, The Nonlinear Theory of Electric Oscillations, *I.R.E. Proc.*, 1934, **22**, pp. 1051–86.

**5–14. Efficiency and Power Relations.** The high efficiency obtainable from a Class $C_2$ amplifier results from the fact that the plate current flows only during periods when the plate voltage is very low, representing a minimum of plate dissipation (Figs. 5–22a, 5–22c and 5–22e). The plate efficiency obtainable is generally in the order of 70 percent although under certain conditions it may go as high as 85 percent. The grid is usually so that plate current flows for about one third of the complete cycle, representing from 120 to 150 electrical degrees.

The power output of a Class C amplifier is expressed by Eq. (5–19).

$$P = \frac{(E_{max} - E_{min})I_{m1}}{4} \tag{5–19}$$

where $E_{max}$ = maximum value of plate voltage

$E_{min}$ = minimum value of plate voltage

$I_{m1}$ = peak value of fundamental component of ac plate current

The dc input power is equal to the product of the dc plate current and the plate-supply voltage; thus

$$P_{dc} = E_{bb}I_b \tag{5–20}$$

where $E_{bb}$ = dc plate voltage

$I_b$ = dc plate current

Thus the plate efficiency is defined by Eq. (5–21).

$$\% \text{ Eff} = \frac{(E_{max} - E_{min})I_{m1}}{4E_{bb}I_b} \tag{5–21}$$

The effective voltage across the tank circuit is

$$E = \sqrt{P\omega_r LQ} \tag{5–22}$$

where $P$ = power delivered to tank circuit

$\omega_r = 2\pi f_r$

$L$ = inductance of the tank circuit

$Q$ = effective $Q$ of the tank circuit

**5–15. Neutralization of Class C Amplifiers.** Because of the relatively large grid-plate capacitance of a triode, there is usually at radio frequencies enough energy fed from the plate circuit through this capacitance to supply the grid circuit losses. If such be the case, the Class C amplifier will be converted into an oscillator, oscillating at the frequency to which the tuned grid and plate circuits are resonant. As pointed out in Chapter 2, pentodes and tetrodes have very little grid-plate capacitance, and when used in connection with Class C amplification, except at very high frequencies, are not likely to result in oscillation. However, many difficulties are involved in the design and construction of high-power tetrodes and pentodes (one big problem is the dissipation of the screen-grid power). Thus triodes are generally employed if the power involved is greater than several hundred watts.

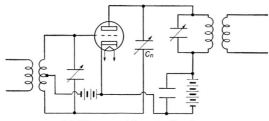

(*a*) Rice or grid neutralization.

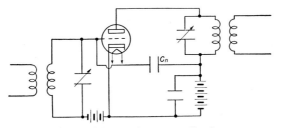

(*b*) Hazeltine or plate neutralization.

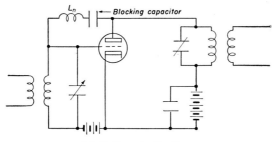

(*c*) Coil neutralization.

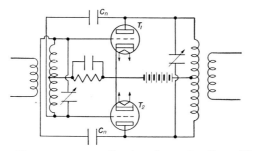

(*d*) Bridge or cross neutralization of a push-pull amplifier.

Fig. 5–23.　Typical neutralization circuits for Class C amplifiers.

It is possible to neutralize the effects of the grid-plate capacitance of a triode by using a circuit arrangement whereby a current which is equal in magnitude to the grid-plate current and 180° out of phase with it is introduced into the circuit. There are many different circuit arrangements for neutralizing grid-plate capacitance; several typical circuit arrangements are illustrated in Fig. 5–23. The neutralization circuits of Figs. 5–23a and 5–23b are known as the Rice (or grid) and the Hazeltine (or plate) systems, respectively.

The capacitor $C_n$ in each of these circuits is known as the neutralization capacitor and should be adjusted for complete neutralization if the amplifier is to operate properly. In the arrangement of Fig. 5–23c the grid circuit is connected to the plate circuit through an inductance and blocking capacitor. In this circuit, the neutralizing inductance is of such a magnitude as to resonate with the grid-plate capacitance at the frequency at which the circuit is to be neutralized. Thus a very high impedance is obtained and the current flow between control grid and plate is essentially zero. This system is termed coil neutralization. In the case of push-pull amplifiers, neutralization can be accomplished by the circuit of Fig. 2–23d.

**5–16. Harmonic Generators.** It is often desirable to obtain an output frequency which is some multiple of the frequency of the input signal to a Class C amplifier. This may readily be accomplished by adjusting the tank circuit so it is resonant at the desired frequency, provided of course that this frequency is some harmonic of the signal frequency. Harmonic generators are employed as frequency multipliers in radio transmitters and frequency meters. Generally, harmonics above the seventh are not utilized except in the case of frequency meters.

## PROBLEMS

**5–1.** Determine the theoretical voltage amplification of an amplifier circuit in which the following circuit parameters are used.

Load Resistance $R_L = 30,000$ ohms
Dynamic Plate Resistance of tube $r_p = 10,000$ ohms
Amplification factor of tube $\mu = 20$
Grid-plate transconductance of tube $g_m = 2,000$ micromhos

**5–2.** For the amplifier circuit described in Prob. 5–1, plot a curve of theoretical voltage gain versus load resistance as the load resistance is varied in 10,000 ohm steps from 10,000 ohms to 100,000 ohms.

**5–3.** Starting with the equivalent circuit of Fig. 5–7b, develop Eq. (5–5b).

**5–4.** A resistance-capacitance-coupled amplifier which employs a triode is comprised of the following components:

Blocking capacitor $C = 0.00222$ microfarad
Cathode-bypass capacitor $C_k = 5$ microfarads
Grid resistor $R_g = 0.5$ megohm

Coupling or plate resistor $R_p = 0.25$ megohm

Plate supply voltage $E_{bb} = 300$ v

Plate resistance of tube $r_p = 0.1$ megohm

Grid-plate transconductance of tube $g_m = 1,000$ micromhos

Amplification factor $\mu = 100$

a) Give the actual circuit diagram and label all components.

b) Give the general equivalent circuit and label all components.

c) Give the mid-band equivalent circuit and label all components.

**5-5.** If the amplification or voltage gain of the amplifier circuit of Prob. 5–4 drops to 70.7% of the mid-band value when the frequency reaches 10,000 cps, determine:

a) The value of the shunting capacitance $C_t$.

b) The mid-band amplification $A_m$.

c) The amplification at 100 cps $A_L$.

**5-6.** a) Determine the value to which the blocking capacitor $C$ should be increased in order for the low-frequency response of the amplifier of Prob. 5–4 to be as good at 10 cps as formerly at 100 cps.

b) Determine the value to which the shunting capacitance $C_t$ must be reduced in order for the high-frequency response to be as good at 20,000 cps as formerly at 10,000 cps.

**5-7.** Give the circuit diagram and specify values of all circuit parameters for a resistance-capacitance-coupled amplifier that will give a voltage gain of not less than 50 over the entire operating range. See Tables 5–1 and 5–2 or *RCA Receiving Tube Manual*.

**5-8.** Repeat Prob. 5–7 if the required voltage gain is 100.

**5-9.** a) Give the circuit diagram of a transformer-coupled voltage amplifier employing a triode.

b) If the coupling transformer has a turns ratio of 3:1 and the tube employed is a 6C5 (See *RCA Receiving Tube Manual* for characteristics), determine the approximate voltage gain at mid-band frequencies. Assume that the resistance $R_f$ representing the eddy current and hysteresis loss of the transformer is negligibly large.

**5-10.** a) Determine the efficiency of a Class $A_1$ power amplifier which employs a 6L6 and operates according to the conditions listed in Table 5–3.

b) Repeat Prob. 5–10a for two 6L6's operating Class $AB_1$ push-pull. See Table 5–3 for typical operating conditions.

## BIBLIOGRAPHY

Albert, A. L. *Fundamental Electronics and Vacuum Tubes.* New York: The Macmillan Co., 1947, pp. 233–85.

*American Standard Definitions of Electrical Terms.* New York: American Institute of Electrical Engineers, 1941, p. 234.

Arguimbau, L. B. *Vacuum Tube Circuits.* New York: John Wiley & Sons, Inc., 1948, pp. 49–99.

Bardeen, J., and Brattain, W. H. Physical Principles Involved in Transistor Action, *The Bell Sys. Tech. J.* 1949, **28**, 239–76.

Cruft Laboratory Staff. *Electronic Circuits and Tubes.* New York: McGraw-Hill Book Co., Inc., 1947, pp. 325–422.

EASTMAN, A. V. *Fundamentals of Vacuum Tubes.* 2nd ed. New York: McGraw-Hill Book Co., Inc., 1941, pp. 249–337, 352–71.

HENNEY, KEITH. *The Radio Engineering Handbook.* 3rd ed. New York: McGraw-Hill Book Co., Inc., 1941, pp. 359–422.

M.I.T. STAFF. *Applied Electronics.* New York: John Wiley & Sons, Inc., 1943, pp. 378–518.

MILLMAN, JACOB, and SEELY, SAMUEL. *Electronics.* New York: McGraw-Hill Book Co., Inc., 1941, pp. 512–23, 573–670.

*RCA Receiving Tube Manual.* Harrison, N. J.: RCA Manufacturing Co., Inc., 1947.

REICH, H. J. *Theory and Applications of Electron Tubes.* 2nd ed. New York: McGraw-Hill Book Co., Inc., 1944, pp. 124–62, 174–94, 222–81.

RYDER, J. D. *Electronic Engineering Principles.* New York: Prentice-Hall, Inc., 1947, pp. 128–242.

*Standards on Electronics—Definition of Terms, Symbols.* New York: Institute of Radio Engineers. 1943, pp. 5–6.

TERMAN, F. E. *Radio Engineering.* 3rd ed. New York: McGraw-Hill Book Co., Inc., 1947, pp. 223–50, 268–76, 287–307, 338–409.

———. *Radio Engineers Handbook.* New York: McGraw-Hill Book Co., Inc., 1943, pp. 353–413, 434–59.

VAN DER POL, B. The Nonlinear Theory of Electric Oscillations. *I.R.E. Proc.* 1934, **22**, 1051–86.

WESTINGHOUSE ELECTRIC CORPORATION. *Industrial Electronics Reference Book.* New York: John Wiley & Sons, Inc., 1948, pp. 228–35, 246–60.

## CHAPTER 6

## OSCILLATION, MODULATION AND DETECTION

### Oscillators

"An oscillator is a nonrotating device for producing alternating current, the output frequency of which is determined by the characteristics of the device." * Vacuum-tube oscillators are common to all radio transmitters and most radio receivers.† In recent years, vacuum-tube oscillators have found widespread usage in the fast-growing field of high-frequency heating. There are numerous other less common applications of vacuum-tube oscillators, such as various types of instruments and testing devices.

By virtue of the fact that the input signal to the grid of an amplifier tube constitutes less power than is developed across the load impedance, it is possible, with the proper circuit arrangement, to make an amplifier furnish its own excitation and thus develop *self-sustained oscillations*.

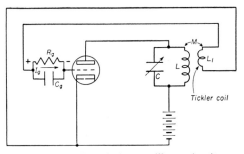

Fig. 6–1.   Tuned-plate oscillator circuit.

Consider the circuit of Fig. 6–1. This is essentially the circuit of a Class C amplifier with the exception that the grid signal is obtained from the output of the circuit rather than from an outside source. When plate voltage is applied to the tube of Fig. 6–1 there will be a pulse of current in the plate circuit; this will cause a sinusoidal voltage to be developed across the tank circuit,§ the frequency of which will be equal to the resonant fre-

---

\* *Standards on Transmitters and Antennas*, New York: Institute of Radio Engineers, 1938.

† Superheterodyne receivers utilize oscillators and essentially all broadcast radio receivers are of this type. Most of the earlier broadcast receivers were of the tuned radio-frequency type, a circuit arrangement that does not make use of an oscillator. However, due to the superiority of the superheterodyne receiver, the tuned radio-frequency receiver is practically obsolete as a broadcast receiver.

§ See Section 4–11 for a discussion of oscillatory circuits.

quency of the tank circuit. A part of this energy will be fed through the coupling network back into the grid circuit; thus it will be amplified and appear again across the output circuit. The cycle will repeat itself so long as the circuit is intact and sustained oscillation will result. In general, two conditions must be fulfilled before a circuit of this type will develop self-sustained oscillations. The energy returned to the grid circuit from the tank circuit must be greater than the grid-circuit losses and the voltage across the tank circuit must be approximately 180° out of phase with the grid excitation.

It will be noticed that the grid bias is obtained differently from the methods of cathode bias and fixed bias, which were previously discussed in connection with amplifiers. In this case, grid-leak bias is employed. This type of bias can only be employed when the grid is made to go positive for a part of each cycle. When the grid goes positive, the grid and cathode simulate a diode and pulsating dc flows through $R_g$. The capacitor filters out the pulsations, giving a suitable dc bias. Since vacuum tubes employed in oscillators are operated Class $C_2$, the tube is biased past cut-off; thus if fixed bias were employed (battery used for bias voltage) no current could flow through the circuit and the oscillator would not be self-starting. For this reason, grid-leak bias is commonly employed in oscillator circuits.

Although there are many types of vacuum-tube oscillators, in general most types can be classified either as power or frequency-controlling oscillators. Power oscillators generally develop the required amount of radio-frequency energy for a given application without amplification, but are suitable only for applications which do not require high-frequency stability. One important application of power oscillators is high-frequency heating. Frequency-controlling oscillators develop very little power; thus the output of such oscillators must, in most cases, be amplified before the required amount of radio-frequency power is available. Frequency-controlling oscillators are employed in radio transmitters and various types of precision timing devices.

**6–1. Power Oscillators.** There are numerous types of power oscillator circuits, all of which depend upon amplification, storage and feedback of energy into the grid circuit. There are, however, only three basic circuits which are generally used in connection with high-frequency heating: Hartley, Colpitts and tuned-plate circuits. There are many different variations of each of these circuits.

*Tuned-Plate Oscillators.* The basic circuit of a tuned-plate oscillator is shown in Fig. 6–1. As already explained, the grid excitation is obtained by feeding back a portion of the output into the grid circuit by means of the "tickler coil" $L_1$ through the mutual inductance existing between $L_1$ and $L$. Although the frequency of this circuit is, to some extent, a function of the resistance of the tank circuit, it is expressed approximately by

Eq. (6–1) where $L$ and $C$ are the inductance and capacitance of the tank circuit.

*Hartley Oscillators.* Fig. 6–2 is a basic Hartley oscillator circuit which employs shunt feed. The Hartley oscillator circuit employs inductive coupling as a means of obtaining feedback. Coupling is obtained between

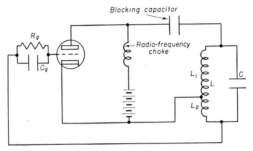

FIG. 6–2.   Hartley oscillator circuit.

the two sections of coil in the tank circuit $L_1$ and $L_2$. The frequency of oscillation is defined approximately by Eq. (6–1):

$$f = \frac{1}{2\pi\sqrt{LC}} \qquad (6\text{–}1)$$

where $C$ = capacitance of the tank circuit in farads
$L$ = total inductance of the tank circuit in henrys
$\quad = L_1 + L_2$

The Hartley circuit is not as critical as most other oscillator circuits, hence is easier to adjust for oscillation. The amplitude of the output can be controlled by varying the position of the tap on the coil. This circuit is more widely used than any other type for the generation of radio frequencies below 5,000 kilocycles. A commercial 1-kw radio-frequency generator which employs a Hartley oscillator circuit is shown in Fig. 6–3.

*Colpitts Oscillators.* The basic circuit of a Colpitts oscillator is shown in Fig. 6–4. This circuit differs from the Hartley circuit in that the cathode connection is made to the capacitive branch rather than the inductive branch of the tuned circuit. The Colpitts circuit is better suited as a variable-frequency oscillator than either the Hartley or the tuned-plate circuit, but the frequency stability is not so good.

The frequency of oscillation is determined approximately by Eq. (6–1) where $L$ is the total inductance of the tank circuit and $C$ is the equivalent capacitance of $C_1$ and $C_2$ in series $[C = C_1C_2/(C_1 + C_2)]$.

**6–2. Frequency-Controlling Oscillators.** Power oscillators, regardless of what precautions are taken, tend to drift, i.e., there is a slight change in frequency with time. Frequency drift may result from variations in load or variations in circuit parameters brought about by temperature changes.

It is necessary that the frequency of radio transmitters * be controlled within very close limits; thus power oscillators are not satisfactory. The

Fig. 6–3. Typical commercial rf generator designed for high-frequency heating. Will deliver 10-kw of 5 megacycle power. (Courtesy Westinghouse Electric Corp.)

frequency stability required for radio transmitters and many other applications, such as frequency-measuring devices, etc., can be obtained only by crystal-controlled oscillators. Although the frequency of broadcast

---

* The Federal Communications Commission requires that the frequency of commercial broadcasting stations be held within 20 cycles of the assigned frequency.

transmitters is ordinarily held constant to better than one part in $1 \times 10^5$, it is possible to obtain tolerances of as small as one part in $1 \times 10^8$ if great care is exercised to eliminate all possible causes of frequency drift.

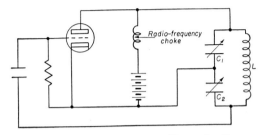

FIG. 6–4.   Colpitts oscillator circuit.

Certain crystalline substances possess a peculiar property which is referred to as the *piezoelectric effect*.*  If, when a crystal is put under mechanical stress along the mechanical axis, electrical charges are produced, and conversely, when the crystal is put under electrical stress along the electrical axis, mechanical stresses are set up, the crystal is said to possess the piezoelectric effect.  It is this effect that is utilized in the control of the frequency stability of radio-frequency oscillators.  If the frequency of the voltage applied to the electrical axis of a crystal is close to the mechanical resonant frequency of the crystal, it will vibrate with appreciable amplitude.  The resonant frequency of a crystal is determined by its dimensions and type of cut, i.e., how it is cut from the natural hexagonal quartz crystal.  The diagram of Fig. 6–5 shows how various crystal cuts suitable for use in rf oscillators are obtained from a natural quartz crystal.

The equivalent circuit for a quartz crystal is illustrated in Fig. 6–6. The series $RLC$ circuit of Fig. 6–6b represents the circuit of the crystal and the capacitance $C_1$ is the capacity of the metallic crystal holder.  The values for $L$, $C$ and $R$ for a given crystal can be calculated by use of appropriate formulae.

There are several other crystalline substances,† such as tourmaline, Rochelle salts, etc., that exhibit the piezoelectric effect; however, quartz, because of its stability and adaptability, is more widely used in this connection.  Tourmaline crystals are stronger mechanically than quartz crystals

* For a more complete discussion of the piezoelectric effect, see R. A. Heising, *Quartz Crystals for Electrical Circuits* (New York: D. Van Nostrand Co., Inc., 1946), pp. 350–410.

† Recently two synthetic crystals have been developed by the Bell Telephone Laboratories which exhibit the piezoelectric effect. They are ethylene diamine tartrate (EDT) crystals and di-potassium tartrate (DKT) crystals.  EDT crystals are now being used in crystal channel filters of long distance telephone systems.  Such crystals can also be used for frequency control of oscillators, but as yet they have not been used commercially in this connection.  For a discussion of EDT and DKT crystals, see W. P. Mason, New Low-Coefficient Synthetic Piezoelectric Crystals for Use in Filters and Oscillators, *I.R.E. Proc.* 1947, **35**, 1005–12.

and thus can be ground much thinner without the possibility of breaking. For this reason they are sometimes employed in very high-frequency oscillator circuits. However, their high cost and low sensitivity make them

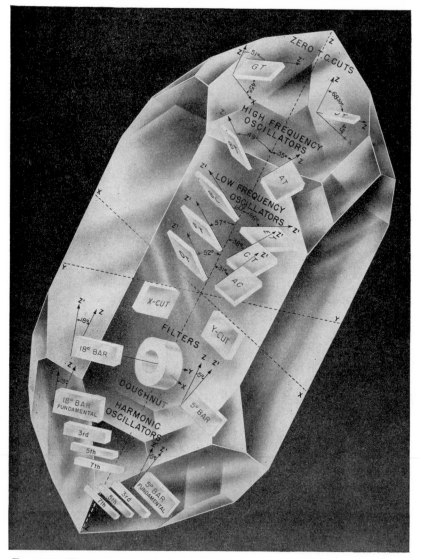

FIG. 6–5.  Illustration showing how various cuts are made from a natural quartz crystal.  (Courtesy Midland Mfg. Co., Inc.)

unsuitable for many applications.  Rochelle salts are much more sensitive than quartz crystals; that is, they will develop a much higher voltage for a given mechanical stress, but are more likely to break; this, in general, makes them less useful than quartz crystals.

The arrangement of Fig. 6–7 is the basic circuit diagram of a crystal-controlled oscillator. This circuit is essentially a tuned-grid tuned-plate oscillator, the crystal constituting the tuned-grid circuit. In the case of triodes, feedback is obtained through the grid-plate capacitance; however,

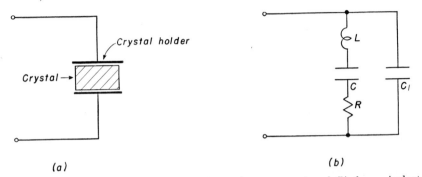

(a)                                                                         (b)

FIG. 6–6.   Diagram illustrating the (a) actual arrangement and (b) the equivalent circuit of crystal and holder.

pentodes and beam power tubes, because of their low grid-plate capacitance, often do not permit sufficient feedback through electrode capacitance to cause oscillation. In such cases a small capacitor is connected between the anode and grid in order to insure sufficient feedback.

It is possible to design crystal oscillators with as much as 100 watts output, but the fragility of crystals in general dictates much lower outputs. In practice, crystal oscillators generally develop between 5 and 15 watts.

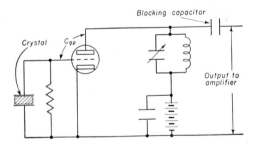

FIG. 6–7.   Crystal oscillator circuit.

The output of such an oscillator is amplified by means of high-power radio-frequency amplifiers (Class B and Class C) so that thousands of watts of radio-frequency energy can be radiated from an antenna. The frequency of a crystal is inversely proportional to the thickness and a 10-megacycle crystal * is about as thin as is practical to use; however, by use of frequency multipliers (harmonic generators), the output frequency can be of almost

* Crystals that will operate at frequencies as high as 50 megacycles have been cut, but such cuts are too fragile to be of much practical value.

any value.  If a crystal is not ground to quite the desired frequency, the frequency of oscillation can be adjusted slightly by putting a capacitor in parallel with the crystal.

**6–3. Beat-Frequency Oscillators.**  The oscillator circuits previously described are primarily radio-frequency oscillators and in general are not suitable for the generation of audio-frequencies.  There are many applications that require a variable audio frequency.  Audio oscillators are widely used in the testing of radio receivers, etc.

A convenient way of obtaining a variable source of audio frequency is to combine the output of two radio-frequency oscillators in such a way that a voltage of a frequency equal to the difference between the two frequencies is obtained at the output.  If one of the radio-frequency oscillators

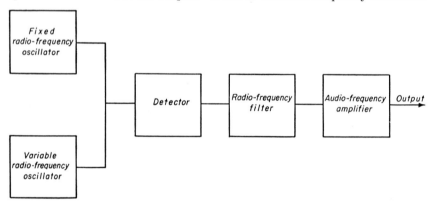

Fig. 6–8.   Block diagram of a beat-frequency oscillator.

generates a fixed frequency and the frequency of the other is variable, then a very small percentage variation in the frequency of the variable-frequency rf oscillator will result in an appreciable change in the audio-frequency output.  An oscillator making use of this principle is known as a beat-

Fig. 6–9.   Beat-frequency oscillator. (Courtesy General Radio Co.)

frequency oscillator. Referring to the block diagram of an audio oscillator, which is shown in Fig. 6–8, the outputs of the fixed and variable-frequency radio-frequency oscillators are fed into a detector circuit where they are combined to give an audio-frequency signal. The radio frequency is then filtered out and the resulting audio frequency is amplified by an appropriate audio-frequency amplifier to obtain the necessary output voltage and power. A commercial audio-frequency amplifier is shown in Fig. 6–9.

**6–4. Relaxation Oscillators.** A relaxation oscillator is characterized by a non-sinusoidal output, the frequency of which is determined by the charge and discharge time of a capacitance. Both high-vacuum and gas tubes are employed in relaxation oscillator circuits. The basic circuit of a common high-vacuum relaxation oscillator is shown in Fig. 6–10. It consists essentially of two resistance-coupled amplifiers, the output of the first being fed into the grid of the second and the output of the second being fed back into the grid of the first. Such a circuit arrangement is known as a multivibrator. The output of the multivibrator is very rich in harmonic content which makes it extremely useful in connection with frequency measurements such as the calibration of signal generators, wave meters and various types of receivers.

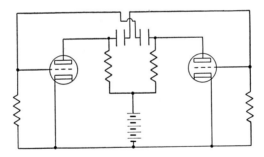

FIG. 6–10.　Relaxation oscillator circuit (multivibrator).

Gas-tube relaxation oscillators find extensive use as a means of producing a sweep voltage in cathode-ray oscillographs. Such an oscillator produces a saw-tooth wave. As this type oscillator is discussed in some detail in connection with the oscillograph (Section 8–9), it will not be discussed here.

**6–5. Miscellaneous Oscillators.** There are many miscellaneous types of oscillator circuits. A few such circuits include the dynatron oscillator, klystron oscillator, magnetostriction oscillator, magnetron oscillator and the tuning-fork oscillator. A discussion of these oscillators is beyond the scope of the text.

## Modulation

**6–6. Types of Modulation.** Although sound waves cannot be transmitted for any appreciable distance through space, audio signals produced from sound waves by microphones, etc. can be readily transmitted for long distances by utilizing radio waves. The characteristics of the radio-frequency carrier wave, which is radiated from an antenna, are altered in some way by the audio signal to be transmitted. A portion of this rf energy is picked up by a receiver and an audio signal of the same form as the original audio signal is produced from the rf wave. This signal, after being amplified, is changed by a loud speaker to a mechanical vibration which the ear interprets as sound.

The more common radio-frequency carrier waves range in frequency from 550 to 1600 kilocycles (broadcast band) and are radiated at a power level of from 250 to 50,000 watts. In general, the radio-frequency carrier wave is generated by a crystal-controlled oscillator which usually develops between 5 and 15 watts. This signal is then amplified by several stages of amplification until the desired output power level is obtained.* If the output of a radio-frequency transmitter is not altered in some way, it is essentially a pure sine wave of constant amplitude. The process of altering the characteristics of a given wave (rf signal) as a function of another wave (audio signal) is termed *modulation*. Modulation is defined as follows: "Modulation is the process of producing a wave, some characteristic of which varies as a function of the instantaneous value of another wave, called the modulating wave." † There are several different types of modulation: amplitude modulation, frequency modulation, phase modulation, and pulse modulation. At present amplitude and frequency modulation are the most common, and the only types that will be considered here.

*Amplitude Modulation.* Amplitude modulation (AM) exists when the amplitude of the radio-frequency wave is made to vary as a function of the signal to be transmitted (Fig. 6–11c).

*Frequency Modulation.* Frequency modulation (FM) exists when the frequency of the radio-frequency wave is made to vary as a function of the signal to be transmitted (Fig. 6–11d).

**6–7. Modulation Factor and Percent Modulation.** In an amplitude-modulated wave, the degree or extent of modulation is expressed as the *modulation factor* or *percent modulation*. Modulation factor and percent modulation are defined as follows: "In an amplitude-modulated wave, the modulation factor is the ratio of half the difference between the maxi-

---

* The maximum power broadcast stations in the United States are permitted to transmit is controlled by the Federal Communications Commission and is, at present, limited to 50,000 watts.

† *Standards on Transmitters and Antennas*, New York: Institute of Radio Engineers, 1938.

mum and minimum amplitudes to the average amplitude. Percent modulation is the modulation factor expressed in percent." * Referring to Fig. 6–11c, the percent modulation is expressed by Eq. (6–2).

$$\text{Percent Modulation} = 100 \left( \frac{D - d}{D + d} \right) \qquad (6\text{-}2)$$

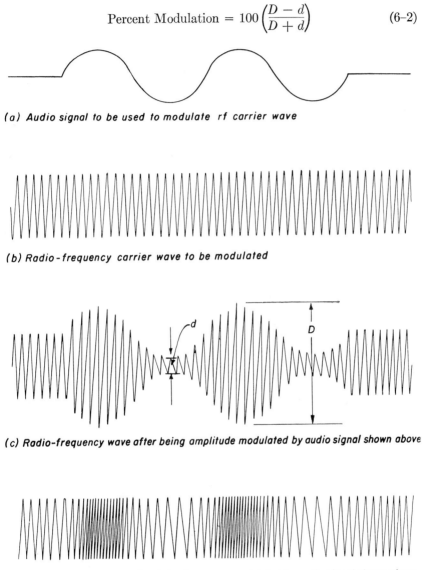

(a) Audio signal to be used to modulate rf carrier wave

(b) Radio-frequency carrier wave to be modulated

(c) Radio-frequency wave after being amplitude modulated by audio signal shown above

(d) Radio-frequency wave after being frequency modulated by audio signal shown above

FIG. 6–11.   Sketches illustrating amplitude and frequency modulation.

* Standards on Transmitters and Antennas, New York: Institute of Radio Engineers 1938.

**6–8. Methods of Producing Amplitude Modulation.** Although it is possible to amplitude modulate oscillators, such is not the general practice. As mentioned previously, crystal oscillators which are used in broadcast transmitters produce only a very small amount of power which is brought to a high level by Class C amplification and then applied to the antenna for

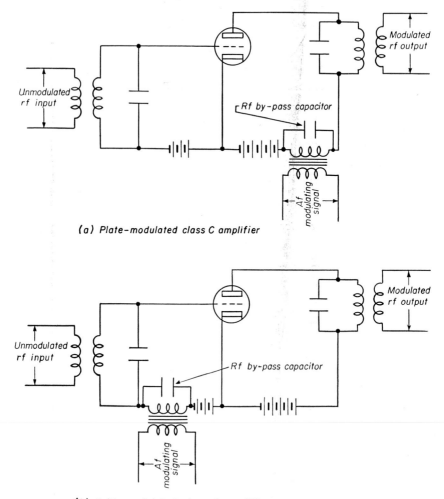

(a) Plate-modulated class C amplifier

(b) Grid-modulated class C amplifier

Fig. 6–12.   Circuit diagrams illustrating plate and grid modulation.

propagation through space. It follows then that the modulating signal would have to be applied to one of the Class C amplifiers. When modulation is applied at a point where the power level is at a maximum, high-level modulation is said to exist; and when modulation is produced at a point in the system where the power level is low compared with the power available at the antenna, the process is known as low-level modulation. Both high- and low-level modulation are used extensively in commercial broadcasting.

Regardless of whether low- or high-level modulation is employed, there are several different circuit arrangements that can be used to produce amplitude modulation. A common arrangement consists of inserting the modulating signal in the plate circuit of the amplifier to be modulated. A schematic circuit diagram of a plate-modulated Class C amplifier is shown in Fig. 6–12*a*. Another arrangement consists of varying the grid voltage in accordance with the modulating signal. This arrangement, which is illustrated in Fig. 6–12*b*, is known as grid modulation. Several other less important types of modulation are cathode modulation, screen-grid modulation and suppressor-grid modulation.

**6–9. Amplitude-Modulated Transmitters.** An amplitude-modulated broadcast transmitter consists basically of a vacuum-tube oscillator, several power amplifiers, a preamplifier, a modulator and suitable power supplies for supplying the dc for the various amplifier tubes, etc. The block diagram

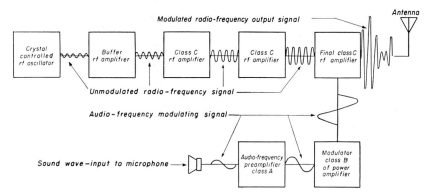

FIG. 6–13.   Block diagram of a typical amplitude-modulated transmitter.

of a typical amplitude-modulated transmitter is shown in Fig. 6–13 and a typical commercial broadcast transmitter is shown in Fig. 6–14.

The radio-frequency oscillator (Fig. 6–13), which is the frequency-controlling device, supplies only a few watts of power. This power, however, is sufficient to operate the next unit or section which is called the buffer amplifier. The function of the buffer is to isolate the power amplifying stages from the oscillator so that there will be no danger of frequency instability as a result of loading the radio-frequency oscillator. The function of the other radio-frequency amplifiers is to amplify the output of the buffer amplifier so as to obtain sufficient energy to drive the final power amplifier. The microphone converts the sound wave to be transmitted into an equivalent electrical variation which is amplified by a Class $A_1$ audio-frequency amplifier, sometimes referred to as a preamplifier. The output of the preamplifier is fed into the modulator, which is an audio-frequency power amplifier, whose function is to vary the amplitude of the radio-frequency output of the final radio-frequency power amplifier as a function of the sound picked up by the microphone. The radio-frequency energy is transmitted to the antenna by means of a suitable transmission line and then radiated into space.

Fig. 6–14. RCA Type BTA–F5, 5-kw, standard broadcast transmitter. (Courtesy Radio Corp. of America.)

**6–10. Frequency-Modulation Circuits.** To obtain a frequency-modulated wave there must be means available whereby the frequency of the carrier can be varied as a function of the intelligence or audio signal to be transmitted. The simplest circuit for producing frequency variation in an oscillator is shown in Fig. 6–15. This circuit consists of a tuned-plate oscillator with a capacitor-microphone in parallel with the tank circuit. When sound waves impinge upon the capacitor-microphone the capacitance of the tuned circuit will be changed, resulting in variation of the frequency of the oscillator. Although this scheme illustrates the principle of frequency modulation, it is not very practical.

Circuits actually employed in practice can be grouped into two main categories: direct and phase-shift modulators. Modulating circuits which

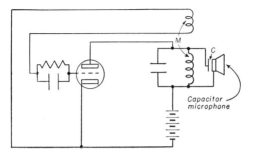

FIG. 6–15. Tuned-plate oscillator in which frequency modulation is produced by a capacitor microphone.

produce a change in the actual frequency of the oscillator are known as direct modulators. In phase-shift modulators, the frequency of the oscillator is unaffected. Phase modulation is obtained by employing a phase-shift network which acts on the output of the oscillator; the change in phase is converted into a frequency change in the rf amplifier, resulting in a frequency-modulated output.

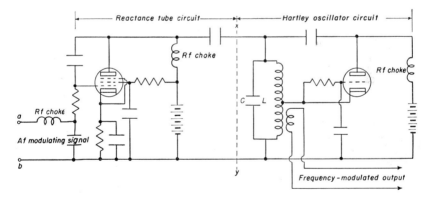
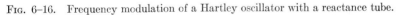

FIG. 6–16. Frequency modulation of a Hartley oscillator with a reactance tube.

The reactance-tube modulator offers one of the simplest and most direct methods of producing frequency modulation. A basic reactance-tube modulator circuit is shown in Fig. 6–16. The approximate output frequency of the oscillating circuit is defined by Eq. (6–3).

$$f = \frac{1}{2\pi L \sqrt{C + C_e}} \tag{6–3}$$

where  $L$ = inductance of the tank circuit in henrys

   $C$ = capacitance of the tank circuit in farads

   $C_e$ = equivalent capacitance to the left of points $x$ and $y$ (Fig. 6–16) in farads

The equivalent capacitance to the left of points $x$ and $y$ is a function of the audio signal applied at points $a$ and $b$. There are numerous types of reactance-tube circuits in use today; all, however, operate on the same basic principle. Other types of direct modulators include the input-capacitance modulator, the transmission-line modulator and the resistance-capacitance frequency-modulated generator.

Two methods of obtaining frequency variation from phase modulation are the Armstrong system and the phasitron system. The Armstrong system, which was developed by E. H. Armstrong, is one of the earliest methods to be employed. The phasitron system is one of the most recently developed methods of obtaining frequency modulation and has become fairly common during the last few years. This method utilizes a type of tube known as a phasitron which requires a three-phase input and an associated magnetic field. A treatment of either of these methods is beyond the scope of the text.

FM broadcasting is at present becoming increasingly popular. Because of the frequency range utilized in FM broadcasting, FM reception has several advantages over AM reception. By way of comparison, FM gives less noise and static and better reproduction, i.e., higher fidelity. There is also much less interference between stations. However, the propagation of the high frequencies employed in FM (88 to 108 megacycles) is limited to approximately the line-of-sight distance. This is the main disadvantage of FM. The height of the antenna is a major factor in determining the amount of coverage of an FM station; therefore a suitable location for the antenna is a very important consideration in FM broadcasting. FM antennas are generally located on tall buildings or high mountains if such locations are available. One large manufacturer has proposed that FM transmitters be located in planes flying high above the earth in order to obtain a large area of coverage.

## Detection

Detection is defined as "the process by which there is obtained, in response to a modulated wave, the signal imparted thereto in the modulation process." * In other words, *detection*, or *demodulation*, is the process whereby the intelligence or audio signal is obtained from the modulated carrier wave. This process is accomplished by a circuit arrangement which is termed a detector circuit. In a superheterodyne receiver this circuit is

---

* *Standards on Receivers*, New York: Institute of Radio Engineers, 1938.

known as the second detector.  After the audio-frequency wave is detected
it is amplified sufficiently to operate the speaker which in turn produces
mechanical vibrations which the ear interprets as sound.  This sound is
essentially of the same wave form as the sound picked up by the microphone in the broadcast station from which the modulated carrier wave
originated.

**6–11. AM Detection.**  There are many different circuit arrangements
for recovering the transmitted intelligence from an amplitude-modulated
radio wave.  The simplest and most widely used detector circuit consists
basically of a diode-rectifier circuit (Fig. 6–17) with a resistance and capacitance in parallel across the output terminals.  The resistance of $R$ is quite

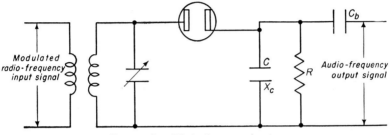

FIG.  6–17.    Diode detector circuit.

high and the capacitance of $C$ is relatively small.*  The ratio of $X_c$ to $R$
has a very important effect on the operation of the circuit; however, a discussion of detector design is beyond the scope of the text.

The operation of the diode-detector circuit is quite simple.  Let it be
assumed that the voltage applied to the detector circuit of Fig. 6–17 is the
modulated rf wave illustrated in Fig. 6–18a.  If the capacitor $C$ were not
in the circuit, the tube would conduct for half of each rf cycle and half-wave
rectification would result.  With capacitor $C$ in the circuit, however, on
each positive half-cycle of the rf wave the tube conducts only during the
period of time when the voltage across the capacitor is less than the applied
rf voltage.  This means that the tube conducts in short pulses which are
indicated in Fig. 6–18d.  During the time the tube is conducting, the
capacitor charges up to a voltage slightly less than the applied rf voltage;
however, when the applied rf voltage (Fig. 6–18b) begins to decrease, in a
very short period of time it is lower than the voltage across the capacitor,
and thus the tube ceases to conduct and the capacitor discharges through
the resistor $R$.  The capacitor continues to discharge until the applied
rf voltage again reaches a positive value greater than the voltage across the
capacitor.  When this happens the tube conducts again and the capacitor

---

* $R$ is in the order of from 50,000 to 1,000,000 ohms and $C$ is generally in the order of
$100 \times 10^{-12}$ farads.

is recharged to a value approximately equal to the applied rf voltage.   The capacitor then discharges through $R$ and the process repeats itself.

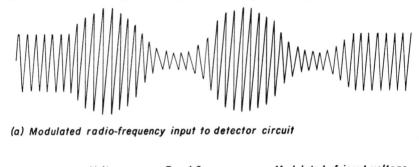

(a) Modulated radio-frequency input to detector circuit

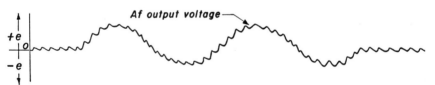

(b) Output voltage superimposed on input voltage

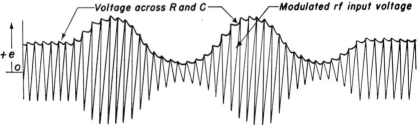

(c) Wave form of af output voltage after dc component has been removed

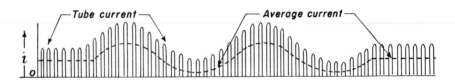

(d) Tube current and average current

FIG. 6–18.   Sketches illustrating the operation of a diode detector circuit.

The heavy line of Fig. 6–18b shows the voltage across $R$ and $C$ superimposed on the applied rf voltage.   It is seen that the voltage across the capacitor (Fig. 6–18b) is very jagged; however, in the sketch this rf ripple is greatly exaggerated compared to the magnitude of the af wave developed. The actual magnitude of this rf ripple is negligibly small.   The af wave thus derived from the modulated rf wave is of essentially the same wave form as the original af wave with which the rf wave was modulated at the transmitter.

The audio wave appearing across $R$ and $C$ contains a dc component which corresponds to the amplitude of the rf wave and it is necessary to block this dc component so that the output can be fed into an amplifier circuit. $C_b$ is the blocking capacitor in the detector circuit of Fig. 6–17 and the af voltage with the dc component removed is indicated by Fig. 6–18c. The af signal is now amplified by both voltage and power stages in order to obtain sufficient power to drive a speaker. The speaker will vibrate in essentially the same way as the audio vibration picked up by the microphone at the broadcasting station.

**6–12. Superheterodyne Radio Receivers.** Practically all broadcast radio receivers make use of what is termed *heterodyne action* * which was discovered by E. H. Armstrong. For this reason they are called super-heterodyne receivers. The block diagram of a superheterodyne receiver is shown in Fig. 6–19.

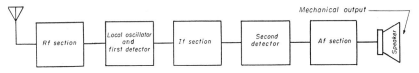

Fig. 6–19. Block diagram of a superheterodyne receiver.

The radio-frequency signal is picked up by the antenna which is coupled to the grid of the first tube. The block labeled radio-frequency section includes this coupling arrangement, and in better sets the radio-frequency section also includes a tuned radio-frequency amplifier (TRF amplifier) for amplifying the signal before it is fed into the first detector or converter-oscillator section.

The heterodyne action takes place in the first detector section. In this section an adjustable oscillator, which is usually termed the local oscillator, is made to beat with the incoming signal from the radio-frequency section so as to produce a constant difference frequency which is termed the inter-mediate frequency (IF). The intermediate frequency employed in most broadcast receivers is generally in the vicinity of 450 kilocycles. There are several circuit arrangements for producing heterodyne action. One very common arrangement consists of combining both the oscillator and mixer in the pentagrid converter tube. The intermediate-frequency signal is fed into the intermediate-frequency section which usually consists of one or two high-gain and highly selective amplifiers; these are termed IF amplifiers.

---

* For a discussion of heterodyne action, see F. E. Terman, *Radio Engineering*, 3rd ed. (New York: McGraw-Hill Book Co., Inc., 1947), pp. 525–39.

The output of the IF section is fed into the second detector which is generally a diode detector, similar to the one of Fig. 6–17. The second detector carries out the detection or demodulation process producing an audio-frequency signal. The audio signal is fed into the audio-frequency section which generally consists of one stage of voltage amplification and one stage of power amplification. The voltage amplifier develops enough voltage to drive the power amplifier and the power amplifier produces enough power to operate the speaker which changes the audio signal to a mechanical vibration which the ear interprets as sound.

In FM reception, the FM signals are detected by employing a circuit arrangement which is known as a discriminator. The discriminator

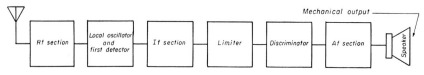

Fig. 6–20.    Block diagram of a frequency-modulation receiver.

operates on the frequency spectrum of the incoming signal in such a way as to cause the amplitude to fluctuate as a function of the intelligence being transmitted, and this signal is then demodulated by an ordinary rectifier-type detector circuit. The block diagram of a frequency-modulation receiver is shown in Fig. 6–20.

## PROBLEMS

**6–1.** If the total inductance of the tank circuit of a Hartley oscillator is $150 \times 10^{-6}$ henry and the total capacitance is $169 \times 10^{-12}$ farads, determine the frequency of oscillation.

**6–2.** Assuming that the minimum capacitance of the variable capacitor in the tank circuit of the oscillator of Prob. 6–1 is $50 \times 10^{-12}$ farads and the maximum capacitance is $365 \times 10^{-12}$ farads, determine the frequency range that the oscillator will cover.

**6–3.** A variable capacitor which has a minimum capacitance of $30 \times 10^{-12}$ farads and a maximum capacitance of $360 \times 10^{-12}$ farads is utilized in the tank circuit of a Hartley oscillator.

*a)* Determine the inductance of the coil in the tank circuit if the minimum frequency of the oscillator is to be 550 kilocycles.

*b)* What is the maximum frequency at which the circuit can be made to oscillate?

**6–4.** A 1-kw industrial radio-frequency generator which employs a Hartley circuit operates at a frequency of 10 megacycles when the variable capacitor in the tank circuit is adjusted to $60 \times 10^{-12}$ farads. Determine the inductance of the tank circuit.

**6–5.** Determine the frequency at which a Colpitts oscillator will oscillate if the inductance of the tank circuit is $150 \times 10^{-5}$ henrys and the tuning capacitor is adjusted so that each section has a capacitance of $338 \times 10^{-12}$ farads.

**6-6.** Sketch the circuit diagram of a tune-grid tuned-plate oscillator. (HINT: See the tuned-plate oscillator circuit of Fig. 6–1 and the crystal oscillator circuit of Fig. 6–7.)

**6-7.** Explain why the frequency of most radio transmitters is crystal controlled.

**6-8.** List several other applications that make use of crystals which exhibit the piezoelectric effect.

**6-9.** Determine the percent modulation of the amplitude-modulated wave of Fig. 6–11c if the maximum amplitude of the wave is six times the minimum amplitude.

**6-10.** What percentage change in the total tank circuit capacitance is produced by the reactance-tube circuit of Fig. 6–16 as a result of the audio input at points $a$ and $b$ if the frequency of the Hartley oscillator changes by 0.1 percent?

## BIBLIOGRAPHY

ALBERT, A. L. *Fundamental Electronics and Vacuum Tubes.* New York: The Macmillan Co., 1947, pp. 342–55, 377–440.

BENDZ, W. I. *Electronics for Industry.* New York: John Wiley & Sons, Inc., 1947, pp. 231–85.

CRUFT LABORATORY STAFF. *Electronic Circuits and Tubes.* New York: McGraw-Hill Book Co., Inc., 1947, pp. 482–509, 612–716, 750–73.

EASTMAN, A. V. *Fundamentals of Vacuum Tubes.* 2nd ed. New York: McGraw-Hill Book Co., Inc., 1941, pp. 403–25.

FAIR, I. E. Piezoelectric Crystals in Oscillator Circuits. *The Bell Sys. Tech. J.* 1945, **24**, 161–215.

HEISING, R. A. *Quartz Crystals for Electrical Circuits.* New York: D. Van Nostrand Co., Inc., 1946, pp. 356–410.

HENNEY, KEITH. *The Radio Engineering Handbook.* 3rd ed. New York: McGraw-Hill Book Co., Inc., 1941, pp. 283–355.

MASON, W. P. New Low-Coefficient Synthetic Piezoelectric Crystals for Use in Filters and Oscillators. *I.R.E. Proc.* 1947, **35**, 1005–12.

M.I.T. STAFF. *Applied Electronics.* New York: John Wiley & Sons, Inc., 1943, pp. 596–663.

REICH, H. J. *Theory and Applications of Electron Tubes.* 2nd ed. New York: McGraw-Hill Book Co., Inc., 1944, pp. 283–344, 387–414.

*Standards on Transmitters and Antennas.* New York: Institute of Radio Engineers. 1938, p. 3.

TERMAN, F. E. *Radio Engineering.* 3rd ed. New York: McGraw-Hill Book Co., Inc., 1947, pp. 410–39, 467–519, 732–80.

———. *Radio Engineers Handbook.* New York: McGraw-Hill Book Co., Inc., 1943, pp. 480–516, 531–60, 636–72.

VAN DER POL, B. The Nonlinear Theory of Electric Oscillations. *I.R.E. Proc.* 1934, **22**, 1051–86.

WESTINGHOUSE ELECTRIC CORPORATION. *Industrial Electronics Reference Book.* New York: John Wiley & Sons, Inc., 1948, pp. 261–77.

## CHAPTER 7

## RECTIFICATION

In the early days of the power industry, electrical power was generated and distributed in the form of dc; consequently all electrical devices were dc-operated. Although alternating current was slow in coming into its own, it was eventually proved to be more economical to generate, transmit, and distribute than was direct current. Thus, because it is not economically feasible to transmit large amounts of dc for appreciable distances, practically all of the electrical power now developed in this country is generated and distributed as ac rather than dc. There are, however, many specific applications in which dc is more suitable than ac, and a yet larger number of applications where only dc can be used. A few applications of dc include battery charging, public address systems, phonographs, radio receivers, radio transmitters, x-ray machines, transportation systems, electro-chemical industries, mining, and steel rolling mills. The statement that dc is used in radio, phonographs, etc., may at first glance seem incorrect inasmuch as such devices are plugged into an ac receptacle. However, all amplifier tubes, etc., in a radio or phonograph require dc for operation and this dc is obtained from a vacuum tube rectifier circuit contained within the radio set which converts the ac to dc.

Since electrical energy, except in rare instances,* is distributed as ac, when a particular application requires dc, auxiliary equipment for converting ac to dc is required. In the early days of conversion, rotating machinery afforded the only practical means of large-scale conversion. However, at present, electronic rectifiers are rapidly replacing machinery as a means of obtaining large blocks of dc energy. Electron tubes have been used for almost half a century for obtaining small amounts of dc, but only within the past two decades have electronic tubes been developed to such an extent that they are favorable competitors to motor-generator sets and synchronous converters in supplying the huge amounts of dc power necessary for large-scale electrochemical processes, transportation systems, driving of large rolling-mill motors, mining, etc.

Dc is obtained from ac by a process known as *rectification*. This term is defined as follows: "Rectification is the conversion of alternating cur-

---

* The dc distribution systems in use in some of the older sections of several of the larger cities in this country remain from the original dc installations dating from before ac came into common use.

rent into unidirectional current by means of electric valves." *  In order that a device can rectify, it must be a unilateral circuit element, i.e., it must offer a much greater impedance to current flow in one direction than in the other.  An ideal rectifier is one which would offer zero impedance to the flow of current in one direction and infinite impedance to the flow of current in the opposite direction.  Rectifiers may be classified as follows:

1. High-vacuum rectifiers
2. Gaseous rectifiers
3. Barrier-layer rectifiers
4. Electrolytic rectifiers
5. Mechanical rectifiers

Since gaseous and high-vacuum rectifiers are the most common of the general types of rectifiers mentioned and are the only two types that are strictly electronic in nature, the discussion which follows will be limited to rectifier circuits employed in connection with either high-vacuum or gas tubes.

## Single-Phase Rectification

**7-1. Half-Wave Rectifiers.**  The simplest type of rectifier circuit is one which is comprised of a single high-vacuum diode in series with an alternating voltage and a load resistance.  The diode may be of the heater-type as indicated by Fig. 7–1a or a filamentary-type as indicated by Fig. 7–1b.

By assuming a dynamic characteristic curve for the diode in the circuit of Fig. 7–1a or 7–1b and a sine wave input voltage, the wave form of the current through the load resistance may be determined graphically as indicated by Fig. 7–1c.  The wave form of the voltage across the load resistance is of the same form as the current through it.

A diode functions as a one-way valve (valve is actually the name employed in England for what is termed in the U. S. a tube) which allows current to flow through itself in only one direction, i.e., from anode to cathode.  When the anode is made positive with respect to the cathode, the valve opens and electrons flow from cathode to anode, which constitutes current flow from anode to cathode.  For a given filament temperature and load resistance, the number of electrons arriving per unit time— and thus the magnitude of the current—is a function of the difference of potential between cathode and anode.  When the anode is negative with respect to the cathode, there is no electron flow; therefore the current through the load resistance is zero.  If the frequency of the voltage applied to the input of the rectifier circuit under consideration is 60 cycles per second, the tube will conduct for $1/120$ second and will be nonconducting for the next $1/120$ second.  This process will repeat itself so long as the

---

* *American Standard Definitions of Electrical Terms* (New York: American Institute of Electrical Engineers, 1941), p. 196.

alternating voltage is applied to the terminals of the circuit. Since current exists during only half of each cycle, this circuit arrangement is known as a half-wave rectifier.

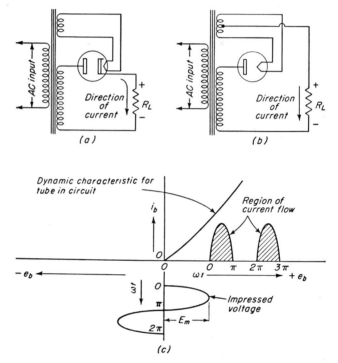

FIG. 7–1. Single-phase half-wave rectifier circuits and voltage and current wave forms.

It can be shown mathematically that current, voltage and power relationships in a single-phase half-wave rectifier circuit with a resistive load are expressed by the following equations:

$$I_m = \frac{E_m}{R_L + r_p} \tag{7-1}$$

where $E_m$ = maximum or peak value of the impressed voltage
    $I_m$ = maximum or peak value of the current through the circuit
    $R_L$ = load resistance
    $r_p$ = plate resistance of the tube

$$I_{dc} = \frac{I_m}{\pi} \tag{7-2}$$

where $I_{dc}$ = the average or direct current

$$P_{dc} = I_{dc}E_{dc} \tag{7-3a}$$

or
$$P_{dc} = \frac{E_m^2 R_L}{\pi^2 (R_L + r_p)^2}$$
(7–3b)

where $P_{dc}$ = dc power at the load

$$I_{rms} = \frac{I_m}{2}$$
(7–4)

where $I_{rms}$ = root-mean-square value of the current in circuit

$$P_{ac} = I_{rms}^2 (R_L + r_p)$$
(7–5a)

or
$$P_{ac} = \frac{E_m^2}{4(R_L + r_p)}$$
(7–5b)

where $P_{da}$ = ac power input to the rectifier

$$\text{Percent efficiency} = \frac{P_{dc}}{P_{ac}} (100)$$
(7–6a)

$$= \frac{E_m^2 R_L}{\pi^2 (R_L + r_p)^2} \cdot \frac{4(R_L + r_p)}{E_m^2} (100)$$

$$= \frac{4}{\pi^2} \cdot \frac{R_L}{R_L + r_p} (100)$$
(7–6b)

The maximum theoretical efficiency obtainable would be the value that would exist if the plate resistance were equal to zero.

$$\text{Maximum theoretical efficiency} = \frac{4}{\pi^2} (100)$$

$$= 40.6\%$$

It is obvious that the question might arise as to what happens to the other 59.4 percent of the power. If the plate resistance is assumed to be equal to zero, there is no plate loss. Because of this, all the power put into the circuit is dissipated as heat in the load resistance; however, only 40.6 percent of this power is dissipated by the dc component of the load resistance current. The term *efficiency* as used here is not the ratio of total output power to total input power but is the percent of the total power input which is converted to dc power.

In most cases, the efficiency is much lower than 40.6 percent. If $R_L$ were equal to $r_p$, the efficiency would be 20.3 percent. Aside from giving a low efficiency, the half-wave rectifier has several other disadvantages which will be considered later.

**7–2. Full-Wave Rectifiers.** The full cycle of an alternating wave may be utilized by employing a full-wave rectifier circuit such as one of those illustrated in Fig. 7–2. The schematic diagram of Fig. 7–2a is the circuit of a single-phase full-wave rectifier employing two heater-type diodes; the circuit of Fig. 7–2b is electrically identical with the exception that the two tubes are replaced with a full-wave filamentary-type diode, such as a

5Y3. The latter circuit arrangement is much more widely used than the former.

Referring to the circuit of Fig. 7–2a, when the upper terminal (terminal $a$) of the secondary of the plate transformer is positive with respect to the

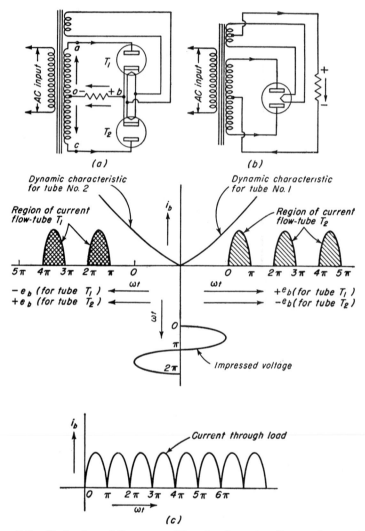

Fig. 7–2. Single-phase full-wave rectifier circuits and voltage and current wave forms.

center-tap (point $o$), the anode of tube $T_1$ is positive with respect to its cathode and conduction occurs through circuit $oabo$ in the direction from $b$ to $o$. During the time that terminal $a$ is positive with respect to point $o$ and tube $T_1$ is conducting, terminal $c$ will be negative with respect to point $o$

and tube $T_2$ will be nonconducting. On the next half-cycle, terminal $c$ will be positive with respect to point $o$. Thus the anode of tube $T_2$ will be positive with respect to its cathode and conduction will occur through circuit $ocbo$ in the direction from $b$ to $o$. On the next half-cycle, tube $T_1$ will conduct again and the process will repeat itself so long as the proper ac input voltage is applied. Regardless of the time, there will always be conduction through the load resistance $R_L$ in the direction from $b$ to $o$. The sketches of Fig. 7–2c illustrate various wave forms for a full-wave rectifier circuit.

It can be shown mathematically that current, voltage and power relationships in a single-phase full-wave rectifier circuit with a resistive load are expressed by the following equations:

$$I_{dc} = \frac{2I_m}{\pi} \tag{7–7}$$

$$P_{dc} = I_{dc}{}^2 R_L \tag{7–8a}$$

or $$P_{dc} = \frac{4I_m{}^2}{\pi^2} R_L \tag{7–8b}$$

$$I_{rms} = \frac{I_m}{\sqrt{2}} \tag{7–9}$$

$$P_{ac} = I_{rms}{}^2(R_L + r_p) \tag{7–10a}$$

or $$P_{ac} = \frac{I_m{}^2}{2}(R_L + r_p) \tag{7–10b}$$

$$\text{Percent efficiency} = \frac{P_{dc}}{P_{ac}}(100) \tag{7–11a}$$

$$= \frac{(4I_m{}^2 R_L)}{\pi^2} \cdot \frac{2}{I_m{}^2(R_L + r_p)}(100)$$

$$= \frac{8}{\pi^2}\left(\frac{R_L}{R_L + r_p}\right)(100) \tag{7–11b}$$

$$\text{Maximum theoretical efficiency} = \frac{8}{\pi^2}(100)$$

$$= 81.2\%$$

All symbols employed above have the same significance as in the case of the half-wave rectifier circuit.

It is to be noted that the maximum theoretical efficiency is twice as high as in the case of the half-wave rectifier.

Another type of full-wave rectifier circuit which is known as a full-wave bridge connection is shown in Fig. 7–3a. The operation of the circuit of Fig. 7–3a is as follows: Let it be assumed that at the instant under consideration, terminal $a$ is turning positive with respect to terminal $b$. If this be the case, the anode of tube $T_1$ is positive with respect to its cathode and the anode of tube $T_3$ is positive with respect to its cathode; thus, both tubes will conduct, current flowing through the load in the direction from $c$ to $d$ as indicated by the arrow. Tubes $T_1$ and $T_3$ will continue to conduct for the first half-cycle, during which time terminal $a$ is positive with respect to terminal $b$. At the beginning of the next half-cycle, terminal $b$ will become positive with respect to terminal $a$; when this happens, the

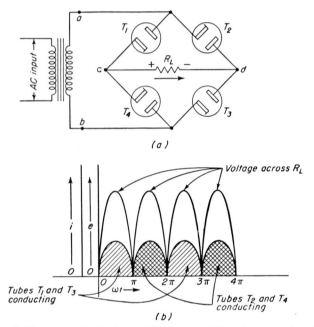

Fig. 7–3.   Bridge-type single-phase full-wave rectifier circuit and voltage and current wave forms.

anode of tube $T_4$ will become positive with respect to its cathode and at the same instant the anode of tube $T_2$ will become positive with respect to its cathode; and both tubes will conduct. This will result in current through $R_L$ in the direction from $c$ to $d$. The wave forms of the current through $R_L$ and the voltage across $R_L$ are shown in the sketch of Fig. 7–3$b$. It will be noted that the wave forms of voltage and current for the bridge circuit are the same as for the more conventional full-wave rectifier circuit of Fig. 7–2. The maximum theoretical efficiency is also equal to 81.2 percent as in the case of the circuit of Fig. 7–2.

In the bridge-circuit arrangement, the peak voltage existing across any tube which is not conducting is only half as much as in the case where a center-tapped transformer arrangement is used, i.e., assuming the dc output voltage is the same in each case. This allows the use of tubes with lower peak inverse voltage ratings. (The maximum peak inverse voltage rating of a tube is the maximum voltage which it can safely stand in the opposite direction, i.e., from anode to cathode, when it is not conducting.) In the case of the center-tapped transformer arrangement of Fig. 7–2, only one-half the secondary of the transformer is utilized at a time; but in the case of the bridge rectifier, the entire secondary winding is utilized at all times. This gives rise to what is termed a higher utilization factor, which means that the transformer cost is less per unit of output power for the bridge circuit than for the center-tapped transformer circuit.

The bridge circuit has several disadvantages. It requires four tubes; further, each tube, if of the filamentary type, must have a separate filament transformer winding which must be insulated to withstand the peak value of the applied voltage. There are always two tubes in series with the load during conduction; thus the tube drop is greater than in the center-tapped connection and the voltage regulation is correspondingly poorer.

In most applications where dc is to be obtained from single-phase ac, the center-tapped transformer arrangement is preferred to the bridge circuit. Exceptions are selenium and copper-oxide rectifier units and high-voltage light-current applications such as dc voltage for x-ray tubes. The inverse peak ratings of copper-oxide and selenium rectifiers are very low and there are no filament connections to bother with; thus the bridge circuit is ideal. In some x-ray power supplies, the bridge circuit is used in order to handle the high voltage required without using tubes with such extremely high voltage ratings.

**7–3. Comparison of Half-Wave and Full-Wave Rectifier Circuits.** The conventional full-wave rectifier circuit (Fig. 7–2), because of its several outstanding advantages over the half-wave rectifier circuit, is the most commonly used single-phase rectifier circuit. Compared to the half-wave rectifier, the full-wave rectifier exhibits the following advantages:

1. The output of the full-wave rectifier requires much less filtering to make it suitable for a given application.
2. The efficiency of the full-wave rectifier is considerably higher.
3. There is no dc saturation of the supply transformer. This means that a smaller transformer can be used for a given dc output in a full-wave rectifier than in a half-wave rectifier.
4. For the same value of peak current, the dc load current is twice as large in the full-wave rectifier. This means that the dc power for a given load will be four times as great.

The half-wave rectifier has the following advantages over the full-wave rectifier:

1. If the voltage need not be stepped up or down, the half-wave rectifier does not require a transformer.

2. The half-wave rectifier is suitable for ac-dc receivers and similar applications where it is desirable to use either ac or dc as the basic power source. The full-wave rectifier circuit can only be operated from an ac source.

Full-wave rectifiers are used as a means of obtaining dc for most ac receivers, public address systems and amplifiers in general. Half-wave rectifiers find their greatest usage in connection with ac-dc receivers.

### Smoothing Filters

Although the output of a rectifier is unidirectional, it is pulsating and contains an appreciable alternating component. This alternating component, which is known as the *ripple voltage*, is not sinusoidal but consists

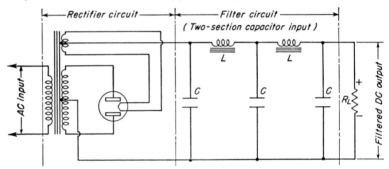

Fig. 7–4.   Single-phase full-wave rectifier with a two-section filter circuit.

of a fundamental and an infinite number of harmonic components. The ripple voltage is defined as follows: "Ripple voltage is the alternating component of the unidirectional voltage from a rectifier or generator used as a source of direct-current power." * In most applications, particularly where the dc is to be used as a source of plate potential for amplifier tubes, the unfiltered output of a rectifier cannot be tolerated because of its excessive ripple. For this reason some means must be employed for reducing the ripple voltage to a very low value. A circuit designed to smooth out or reduce the ripple is known as a *smoothing filter* or a *filter circuit*. A typical filter circuit is shown in Fig. 7–4.

**7–4. Effects of Inductance and Capacitance on Rectified Voltage.** The over-all action of a smoothing filter, such as the one of Fig. 7–4, may be best understood by considering the effects of the shunting capacitance and series inductance separately, and then considering their combined effects on the output of the rectifier circuit. First, consider a half-wave rectifier having a capacitor in parallel with the load. Such a circuit is

---

* *Standards on Transmitters and Antennas*, New York: Institute of Radio Engineers, 1938.

illustrated in Fig. 7–5a. If the impressed voltage is sinusoidal, the voltage across $R_L$ and the current through $R_L$, with the switch open, will be as indicated by the sketch of Fig. 7–5b.

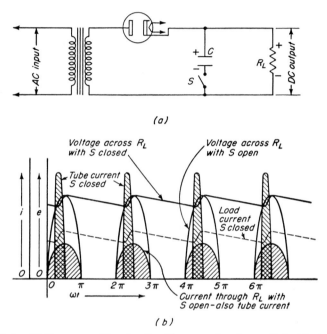

(a)

(b)

Fig. 7–5.   Half-wave rectifier circuit with a capacitor in parallel with the load.

Now if switch $S$ is closed, the wave form will change from half-sine wave pulses to approximately a saw-tooth wave as indicated. When the capacitor is applied across the output circuit, it receives charge as long as its potential is less positive with respect to the cathode of the rectifier tube than the voltage impressed across the tube by the secondary of the transformer; but as the voltage across the tube begins to decrease in magnitude, it will in a very short time become smaller than the voltage across the capacitor; thus the tube will cease to conduct and the capacitor will discharge through the load resistance. The capacitor will continue to discharge until the anode-cathode voltage of the rectifier tube again becomes larger than the capacitor voltage. When this occurs, the tube will again begin to conduct, the capacitor will be recharged and will later discharge when the anode-cathode voltage becomes less positive than the potential across the capacitor. This process repeats itself as long as an ac signal is applied across the input circuit. Since current flows through the tube only while the capacitor is charging, the tube current flows in the form of short, highly peaked pulses as indicated by the sketches of Fig. 7–5b. The current through the resistive load is of the same wave form as the voltage across it. As the capacity of the capacitor is decreased, discharge will occur more rapidly and the voltage will contain greater ripple and be of a lower dc value.

Now examine the case of a capacitor across the output of a full-wave rectifier circuit as shown in Fig. 7–6. The wave form of the voltage across the output of this filter circuit, which is illustrated in Fig. 7–6b, follows a

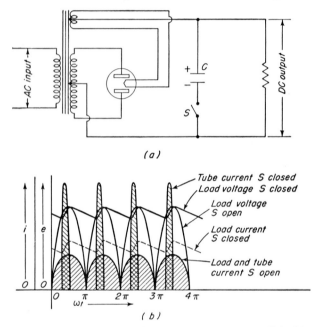

Fig. 7–6.   Full-wave rectifier circuit with a capacitor in parallel with the load.

pattern similar to that for the half-wave rectifier, the only difference being that the frequency of the charging and discharging of the capacitor is twice as great.

Now consider the smoothing action of an inductor. (In order to obtain maximum inductance with a minimum dc voltage drop, iron core inductors, which are often referred to as chokes, are used in smoothing-filter circuits.) Since an inductor opposes any change in current through itself, an inductor carrying the load current, which tends to change in magnitude, will make the current smoother and thus can be utilized to good advantage in a filter circuit. Figs. 7–7a and 7–7b illustrate half- and full-wave rectifiers, respectively, which employ chokes in series with their loads in order to produce a smoothing effect on the load current.

The wave forms for the circuits of Figs. 7–7a and 7–7b with and without switch $S$ closed are indicated by the sketches of Figs. 7–7c and 7–7d, respectively. From these wave forms it can be seen that an iron core inductor is an effective agent in smoothing out current in a rectifier circuit.

The proper combination of inductance and capacitance results in a very effective filter. A simple filter circuit is shown in Fig. 7–8. This filter is known as a single-section filter. If switch $S$ is open, $C_1$ is ineffective and the filter is said to be an inductor-input filter. When $S$ is closed, the filter becomes a capacitor-input filter.

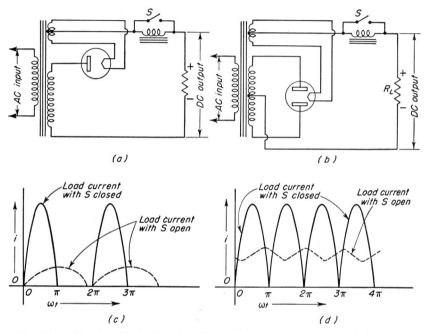

(a)          (b)

(c)          (d)

FIG. 7–7.   Sketches illustrating the effects of inductance on the rectified current in half- and full-wave rectifier circuits.

**7–5. Ripple and Smoothing Factors.** There are two important factors upon which the magnitude of the ripple voltage at the output of a filter circuit depends: *ripple factor* and *smoothing factor*. The ripple factor is the ratio of the rms value of all the alternating components of the wave to the average or dc value of the wave. *Percent ripple* is defined as follows: "Percent ripple is the ratio of the effective (root-mean-square) value of the ripple voltage to the average value of the total voltage, expressed in percent." *

$$\text{Ripple factor} = \frac{\text{rms value of ac components}}{\text{average value of voltage}} \qquad (7\text{–}12a)$$

$$\text{Percent ripple} = \text{Ripple factor} \,(100) \qquad (7\text{–}12b)$$

Referring to the diagram of Fig. 7–8, the percent ripple or ripple factor at points $a$ and $b$ (input to the filter circuits) will be much greater than at points $c$ and $d$ (output of the filter circuit). The smoothing factor is the

---

* *Standards on Radio Receivers*, New York: Institute of Radio Engineers, 1938.

ratio of the amplitude of a given frequency component at the input to the filter circuit to the amplitude of the same frequency component at the output of the filter circuit.* Eqs. (7–13a), (7–13b) and (7–13c) † are approxi-

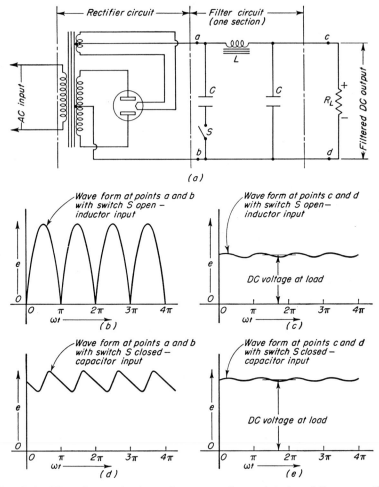

(a)

Wave form at points a and b with switch S open – inductor input

(b)

Wave form at points c and d with switch S open – inductor input

DC voltage at load

(c)

Wave form at points a and b with switch S closed – capacitor input

(d)

Wave form at points c and d with switch S closed – capacitor input

DC voltage at load

(e)

FIG. 7–8.   Wave forms of voltages between various points in a full-wave rectifier-filter circuit with both inductor and capacitor input.

mate mathematical expressions for the smoothing factors of various types of filter circuits.

$$\alpha_k = (\omega_k^2 LC - 1) \tag{7–13a}$$

---

* H. J. Reich, *Theory and Applications of Electron Tubes*, 2nd ed. (New York: McGraw-Hill Book Co., Inc., 1944), p. 565.

† For development of these equations, see H. J. Reich, *Theory and Applications of Electron Tubes*, 2nd ed. (New York: McGraw-Hill Book Co., Inc., 1944), p. 583.

where $\alpha_k$ = the smoothing factor for the $k$th harmonic for a single section
filter

$\omega_k = 2\pi f_k$

$f_k$ = frequency of the $k$th harmonic

$L$ = series inductance

$C$ = shunting capacitance. This capacitance does not include that of the capacitor directly across the output of the rectifier circuit, which is inserted in the case of a capacitor-input filter.

If there are $n$ identical sections, then

$$\alpha_k = (\omega_k^2 LC - 1)^n \qquad (7\text{--}13b)$$

If there are $n$ dissimilar sections,

$$\alpha_k = (\omega_k^2 L_1 C_1 - 1)(\omega_k^2 L_2 C_2 - 1) \cdots (\omega_k^2 L_n C_n - 1) \qquad (7\text{--}13c)$$

From examination of the above equations, it can be seen that the effectiveness of a filter circuit in reducing the magnitude of the ac components increases as the square of the frequency of the harmonic and as the power of the number of sections. In view of this fact, if a filter is designed to give proper filtering for the lowest ac component present in the output of the rectifier (fundamental), the higher order harmonics will automatically be taken care of.

**7–6. Inductor and Capacitor-Input Filters.** Filter circuits for single-phase full- and half-wave rectifiers may be classified as to inductor- or capacitor-input filter circuits.* Referring to the circuit of Fig. 7–8a, if switch $S$ is open so that the capacitor across points $a$ and $b$ is out of the circuit, the circuit is an inductor-input filter circuit. Closing the switch places the capacitor across the output of the rectifier and converts the circuit into a capacitor-input filter circuit.

For a given number of identical sections, the capacitor-input filter circuit results in a lower ripple factor at the load; however, an inductor-input filter circuit gives better regulation. For a full-wave rectifier circuit operating into an inductor-input filter circuit, the ratio of the amplitude of the fundamental ripple voltage (which is twice the power frequency) at the input to the filter circuit, to the dc can be shown to be equal to 0.6667. For capacitor input this value can be shown to be equal approximately to $1/\pi f_k RC$; where $f_k$ is the ripple frequency, $C$ the capacitance of the capacitor directly across the output of the rectifier and $R$ the load resistance. Wave forms of the voltage at the output of the rectifier (input to filter) and at the load are illustrated for both capacitor and inductor-input filter circuits by the sketches of Fig. 7–8.

The ratio of the amplitude of any frequency component at the output of the filter circuit, i.e., at the load, to the dc for either inductor or capacitor

---

* The terms choke-input and condenser-input are often used to describe such circuits.

input can be determined by dividing the ratio at the input by the smoothing factor for the filter circuit. The curves of Fig. 7–9 illustrate the differ-

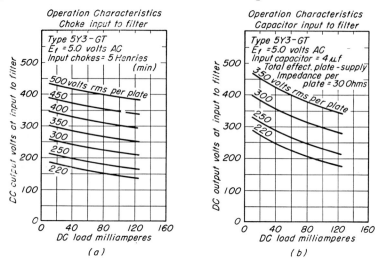

FIG. 7–9. Regulation curves for a full-wave rectifier circuit employing (a) a choke-(inductor) input filter circuit and (b) a capacitor-input filter circuit. (Courtesy Radio Corp. of America.)

FIG. 7–10. Power supply used as a source of dc in the Electronics Laboratories of the Virginia Polytechnic Institute.

ence in the regulation characteristics of inductor- and capacitor-input filter circuits.

The power supply of Fig. 7–10, which was designed and built at the Virginia Polytechnic Institute, consists of a full-wave rectifier circuit with a two-section inductor-input filter. The primary of the plate transformer is connected across the output of an auto transformer (transformer with variable output voltage) making it possible to vary the output voltage continuously from 0 to 1,000 volts. The current capacity is 300 milliamperes. This power supply is standard equipment for each laboratory work bench.

## Special Types of DC Power Supplies

**7–7. Voltage Doublers.** One very interesting and fairly common type of dc power supply is the voltage-doubler circuit. The circuit diagram of a voltage doubler which makes use of two tubes is shown in Fig. 7–11a; however, the circuit of Fig. 7–11b which employs a regular voltage-doubler tube, type 117Z6 is much more common. The 117Z6 is a high-vacuum full-wave rectifier tube with indirectly heated cathodes and a 117-volt filament. In order for a full-wave rectifier tube to be suitable for use in a voltage-doubler circuit, the two cathodes must not be connected internally.

Consider the circuit of Fig. 7–11a. When terminal $a$ is positive with respect to terminal $b$, tube $T_1$ will conduct, causing capacitor $C_1$ to become charged with the polarity indicated on the diagram. $C_1$ will, if no charge is allowed to drain off, maintain a dc difference of potential across its terminals equal in magnitude to the peak value of the ac input wave. On the next half cycle, terminal $b$ will be positive with respect to terminal $a$; thus tube $T_2$ will conduct. The conduction of tube $T_2$ will result in the charging of capacitor $C_2$ with the polarity indicated. If this charge is not allowed to leak off, $C_2$ will remain charged to a voltage equal to the peak value of the ac input wave. By noting the polarity of each of the capacitors it can be seen that the dc voltage across points $c$ and $d$ will be (if no charge is allowed to leak off) twice the peak value of the ac input wave. This means that if the rms value of the input wave is 117 volts, the dc voltage between points $c$ and $d$ will be $(117\sqrt{2})(2)$ or 331 volts. When load is applied some charge is always drained from the capacitors causing the load voltage to be somewhat less than twice the peak value of the input wave.

From the wave forms of the voltage across the individual capacitors and at the load (Fig. 7–12), it will be noted that the ripple frequency across either of the capacitors is equal to the frequency of the ac input to the rectifier, but the frequency across the load is twice as great as the frequency of the ac input to the rectifier. The circuit of Fig. 7–11b is identical in operation to the circuit of Fig. 7–11a. Voltage doublers find use in certain types of radio receivers where it is desirable to obtain fairly high plate voltages without the aid of a center-tapped step-up transformer. This type circuit is also used in some types of x-ray power supplies.

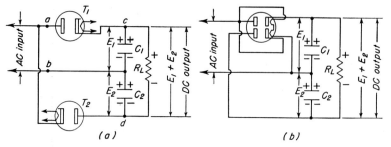

FIG. 7–11.  Typical voltage-doubler circuits.

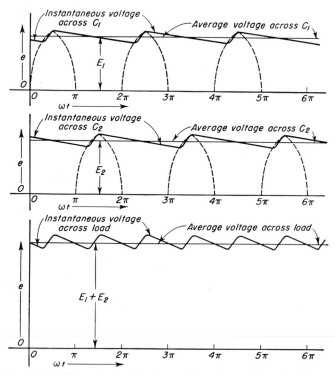

FIG. 7–12.  Wave forms of various voltages in a voltage-doubler circuit.

**7–8. Vibrators.**  When radio receivers, radio transmitters, or other types of electronic equipment employing electronic tubes are to be operated in automobiles, airplanes, etc., it is necessary to obtain the relatively high plate voltages required for the tubes by stepping it up from the relatively low voltage of the basic power source available (most often 6 or 12 volts dc). This is not always the case, however, for some planes have alternators as basic power sources; thus the dc necessary is obtained by means of rectification.

There are two general types of power supplies for "stepping up" direct voltage: the vibrator and the dynamotor. The vibrator is perhaps the most popular. The circuits of Figs. 7–13a and 7–13b are of nonsynchronous and synchronous vibrators, respectively. Consider the circuit of Fig. 7–13a.

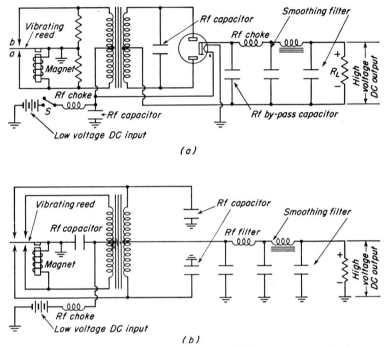

(a)

(b)

FIG. 7–13.   Typical (a) nonsynchronous and (b) synchronous vibrators.

The vibrating reed, which usually has a natural frequency of between 100 and 150 cycles per second, is the heart of the power supply. When switch $S$ is closed, dc from the battery flows through the lower half of the primary of the transformer and through the coil of the holding magnet, causing the reed to make contact at $a$. At the same time the transformer core is magnetized, which causes a high voltage to be set up in the secondary (the transformer being a step-up type). As soon as contact is made at point $a$, the holding coil is short circuited; thus the holding magnet releases and the reed makes contact at point $b$, at which time the current in the upper half of the transformer flows from center tap toward point $b$, causing the transformer core to be magnetized with reversed polarity. Almost instantly the reed swings back to position $a$ and the process repeats itself as long as switch $S$ is closed. The alternating voltage on the secondary of the transformer is rectified by means of either a high-vacuum or cold-cathode gas tube rectifier. Because of the high frequencies generated in such a piece of apparatus (due to sparking, etc.) it is necessary to employ radio-frequency inductors and radio-frequency capacitors freely in order to keep the radio frequency away from the output circuit and the battery. A regular smoothing filter is used to smooth out the ac ripple.

The synchronous vibrator, a schematic circuit diagram of which is shown in Fig. 7–13b, is in common use at present. This vibrator accomplishes rectification by employing an additional set of contacts which makes it self-rectifying. Although this type of power supply is not as expensive as the nonsynchronous type, it is more likely to give trouble due to contacts being improperly made or sticking.

**7–9. Dynamotors.** Another important type of power supply which operates on low voltage dc is the dynamotor. Fig. 7–14 is the sketch of a dynamotor. The dynamotor consists essentially of a low-voltage dc motor and

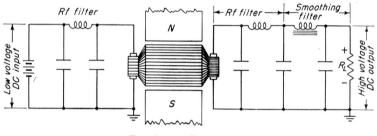

Fig. 7–14.   Dynamotor.

a much higher voltage dc generator built on the same shaft. The field may be of the permanent magnet type or the electromagnet type. The armature has two windings: a low-voltage high-current winding which is brought out to a commutator at one end, and a high-voltage low-current winding which is brought out to a commutator at the other end. The dynamotor might be termed a "dc transformer," in which the turns ratio is equal to the ratio of the armature conductors of the two windings. As in the case of the vibrator, a rather elaborate filter system is required. The dynamotor is much more expensive than the vibrator but it is more dependable and gives less radio interference; thus it is widely used in planes, police cars, etc., where dependability is of great importance.

**7–10. Electronic Voltage Regulators.** In most instances the ac line voltage is subject to some fluctuation which in turn will cause the output voltage of a dc power supply to fluctuate. The regulation of vacuum tube rectifiers is in general very poor. Therefore, any increase or decrease in current demands on such a rectifier will result in a corresponding change in voltage. In most electronic circuits a fluctuation in electrode voltages will result in erratic operation; in some circuits, even a slight change in voltage will cause the circuit to become inoperative. For this reason, regulated power supplies are often required.

There are various types of electronic regulator circuits; however, only one such circuit will be discussed here. Consider the regulated power supply of Fig. 7–15. The section of the circuit to the left of line $AA'$ is a conventional full-wave rectifier circuit; the section of the circuit between $AA'$ and $BB'$ is a conventional filter circuit and the section of the circuit to

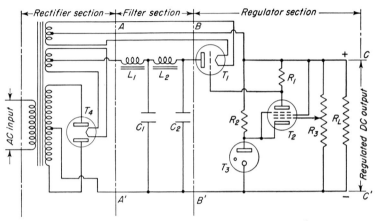

FIG. 7–15.    Circuit of a regulated power supply.

the right of $BB'$ is the electronic regulator section. Rectifier and filter circuits have been considered previously; thus, only the action of the regulator section will be discussed here.

The equivalent circuit of the electronic voltage regulator under consideration is as indicated by the sketch of Fig. 7–16. Let it be assumed

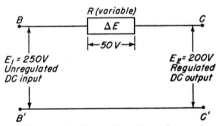

FIG. 7–16.    Diagram illustrating the action of an electronic voltage regulator.

that the voltage $E_1$ is 250 volts and at the same instant the voltage at the load $E_2$ is 200 volts. This means that $\Delta E$, the drop across $R$, is 50 volts.

$$E_2 = E_1 - \Delta E \qquad (7\text{–}14a)$$

where $E_1$ = unregulated output voltage of rectifier (voltage at $BB'$)
    $E_2$ = regulated output voltage at load (voltage at $CC'$)

If, for any reason, $E_1$ increases to 275 volts, it is possible to hold $E_2$ at its original value of 200 volts if $R$ is increased so that the voltage drop $\Delta E$ is increased to 75 volts. If, on the other hand, $E_1$ is decreased to 225 volts and $R$ is decreased enough to result in a value of 25 volts across itself, the output voltage will remain at 200 volts.

In the actual regulator circuit of Fig. 7–15, tube $T_1$, which is in series with the line, serves as the variable resistance. The voltage drop across $T_1$ is controlled by its bias which in turn is a function of the voltage across the load. The bias is adjusted automatically to the value necessary to make the difference of potential across $T_1$ enough so that the output of the rectifier minus the drop across $T_1$ will always be a constant, i.e., within certain operating limits determined by the circuit parameters.

$$E_2 = E_1 - (\text{Voltage drop across } T_1) \qquad (7\text{–}14b)$$

The automatic regulation is accomplished in the following manner. Let it be assumed that the voltage at points $CC'$ decreases slightly. This decrease may be due to a decrease in ac line voltage or it may be due to increased current demands. A decrease in voltage at points $CC'$ will result in a more negative or less positive voltage applied to the grid of tube $T_2$. This will cause the current through $T_2$ to decrease and a decrease in plate current will result in a decrease in $IR$ drop across the resistor $R_1$ which furnishes bias for $T_1$. A less negative grid bias will decrease the drop across this tube causing the voltage to increase at the load until it reaches its original value, i.e., provided the circuit constants are properly chosen. Any tendency for the voltage across the load to increase will result in a more negative bias for $T_1$ and greater voltage drop between filament and anode of this tube. The increase in voltage drop across $T_1$ will compensate approximately for the original increase in voltage causing the output voltage to remain essentially constant.

The function of the regulator tube * $T_3$ is to hold the cathode at fixed voltage relative to the negative terminal. If this voltage is equal to approximately half of the voltage to be regulated, then the grid connection of $T_2$ may be brought to near the center of the potentiometer rheostat to which it is attached. A change in voltage across the load will then result in a large change in the grid voltage of $T_2$. If the voltage regulator tube $T_3$ were not employed, the grid connection would have to be very near the ground and a change in load voltage would produce only a negligible change in grid voltage. The circuit may be adjusted for various output voltages (within a given range) by adjustment of the potentiometer rheostat $R_3$ which controls the grid bias of $T_2$.

## Polyphase Rectifiers

At present the combined ratings of the polyphase mercury-arc rectifier installations in this country run well into the millions of kilowatts and their

---

* The voltage regulator tube referred to is a cold-cathode gas diode which exhibits a constant voltage drop between cathode and anode provided the current through it is within the normal operating range.

use is steadily increasing.  The chief applications of polyphase mercury-arc rectifiers are for supplying dc for the light metal refining industries and dc transportation systems.  The popularity of mercury-arc rectifiers may be understood by comparing them to rotating machinery as a means of obtaining large blocks of dc energy.  A comparison of rectifiers and rotating machinery is given in Section 7–16.

Polyphase rectification has many advantages over single-phase rectification, particularly when the amount of power involved is large.  Among the outstanding advantages of polyphase rectifier circuits over single phase circuits are: higher efficiency, higher ratio of dc to ac voltage, greater utilization of transformers, and lower ripple factor.  Also, practically all electric energy generated in the United States is generated, transmitted and distributed as three-phase power; thus polyphase rectifiers are more suitable for operation from conventional power sources than single phase rectifiers.

Polyphase rectifier circuits utilize one multi-anode pool-type tube or several single anode pool-type tubes such as ignitrons or excitrons.  Thermionic gas diodes are often employed in three-phase rectifier circuits where the current demands are fairly light.  Supplying dc for large radio transmitters is one of the most common applications of three-phase circuits utilizing thermionic gas diodes.  Although the discussion which follows will in general apply to polyphase circuits regardless of the type tubes employed, the circuits mentioned will be those that are standard for pool-type tubes.

### 7–11.  Principles of Polyphase Rectification.  *  The circuit of Fig. 7–17a is a basic three-phase rectifier circuit employing a mercury-pool rectifier with three anodes.  The wye connected secondary of the delta-wye connected transformer supplies the necessary anode voltages and makes possible a common return to the mercury pool.  The voltages applied to the various anodes are of equal magnitude and 120 degrees apart.  The wave forms of applied anode voltages, individual anode currents and load current are sketched in Fig. 7–17b.

In this discussion it will be assumed that only one anode conducts at a time.  Such a condition could exist only if the leakage reactance of the transformer were equal to zero; thus a zero angle of overlap is not obtained in practice.  An analysis of the period of overlap in a polyphase rectifier is beyond the scope of this text.

Consider the wave form of the voltage existing between anode 1 and the neutral of the transformer (Fig. 7–17a) which is indicated in Fig. 7–17b. Since the cathode-anode drop of a mercury-arc rectifier is in the neighborhood of 15 volts, most of the voltage $V_{ao}$ will exist across the load.  This means that during conduction the mercury pool (cathode) is at essentially the same voltage as the anode that is conducting.  Referring to the sketches

---

* In the discussion of polyphase rectification, unless specifically indicated to the contrary, a half-wave delta-star rectifier circuit is to be assumed.

of Fig. 7–17, as the angle $\alpha$ is approached, the phase voltage $V_{ao}$ which exists across the circuit including anode 1 is decreasing quite rapidly and at the same time phase voltage $V_{bo}$ which exists between anode 2 and the neutral is increasing rapidly. Any time before angle $\alpha$ is reached the difference of potential between the mercury pool and the conducting anode

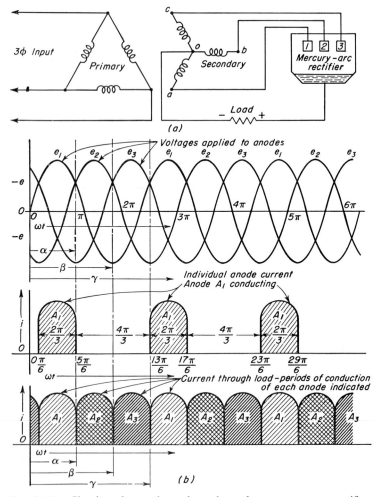

FIG. 7–17.   Circuit and wave forms for a three-phase mercury-arc rectifier.

will be around 15 volts and since the potential of the other anodes is less positive with respect to the mercury pool than anode 1, conduction cannot exist between the mercury pool and either of these anodes.   At the instant that the angle $\alpha$ is reached, anodes 1 and 2 are at the same voltage; thus anode 2 will fire.   From the sketches of Fig. 7–17 it can be seen that immediately after angle $\alpha$ is reached and anode 2 fires, the potential of anode 1 becomes less than the potential of anode 2 with respect to the cathode and since anode 2 is only positive with respect to the mercury pool by an amount equal to the tube drop, anode 1 will be less positive with respect to the mercury pool than an amount equal to the drop and thus will cease to conduct (assuming no overlap due to leakage reactance). This process repeats itself at $\beta$, $\gamma$, etc.

By referring to the same sketches it can also be seen that each anode conducts for one-third of each cycle, $2\pi/3$ radians or 120 degrees. The number of radians over which any one tube in a polyphase rectifier (or anode in the case of a multi-anode tube) conducts is expressed by Eq. (7–15).

$$\phi = \frac{2\pi}{P} \qquad (7\text{–}15)$$

where $\phi$ = number of radians over which each anode or tube conducts
$P$ = number of anodes or phases

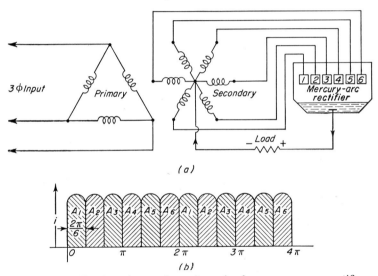

FIG. 7–18.   Circuit and wave forms for a six-phase mercury-arc rectifier.

In the case of a six-phase rectifier such as the one illustrated in Fig. 7–18a, each anode will conduct for only 60 degrees out of each 360 degrees and the arc will transfer from one anode to the next in the order of 1234561234 · · · (Fig. 7–18b). The transfer of the arc from one anode to another is known as *commutation*.

**7–12. Output Voltage as a Function of Number of Phases.** The rectified voltage in the case of a polyphase rectifier which includes the voltage drop in the arc and any other drop such as the voltage drop across a reactor in series with the load, can be obtained by integrating the voltage wave between the limits of $+\pi/P$ and $-\pi/P$ (Fig. 7–19).

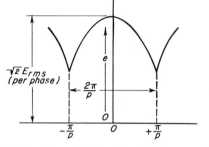

FIG. 7–19. Sketch illustrating the rectified voltage in the case of a polyphase rectifier.

$$E_d = \frac{P}{2\pi} \int_{-\pi/P}^{+\pi/P} \sqrt{2}E_{\text{rms}} \cos \omega t \, d\omega t \tag{7–16a}$$

$$= \left[ \frac{P\sqrt{2}}{2\pi} E_{\text{rms}} \sin \omega t \right]_{-\pi/P}^{+\pi/P}$$

$$= \frac{P\sqrt{2}E_{\text{rms}} \sin \dfrac{\pi}{P}}{\pi} \tag{7–16b}$$

$$\frac{E_d}{E_{\text{rms}}} = \frac{P}{\pi}\sqrt{2} \sin \frac{\pi}{P} \tag{7–16c}$$

where   $E_d$ = total rectified voltage, including the drop in the arc and any other drop such as a reactor in series

$E_{\text{rms}}$ = the root-mean-square value of the secondary voltage from neutral to anode

$P$ = number of phases or anodes

Substituting various values of $P$ in Eq. (7–16c) yields the ratios of $E_d$ to $E_{\text{rms}}$ given in Table 7–1.

TABLE  7–1

| Number of Phases | $E_d/E_{\text{rms}}$ |
|:---:|:---:|
| 3 | 1.17 |
| 6 | 1.35 |
| 12 | 1.40 |
| ∞ | 1.41 |

Eq. (7–16c) shows that as the number of phases is increased, the ratio of $E_d$ to $E_{\text{rms}}$ increases; this illustrates one advantage of having a large number of phases. It will be noted that a six-phase rectifier, which is the most common type of polyphase rectifier circuit, gives a ratio of $E_d$ to $E_{\text{rms}}$ of 1.35, which closely approaches the value obtained for an infinite number of phases.

The actual dc voltage available at the load for three and six-phase rectifiers is expressed by Eqs. (7–17a) and (7–17b), respectively.

$$E_{dc} = 1.17E_{rms} - TD - IR \qquad (7–17a)$$
$$E_{dc} = 1.35E_{rms} - TD - IR \qquad (7–17b)$$

where $E_{dc}$ = the average or dc value of the voltage across the load

$TD$ = tube drop during conduction

$IR$ = dc voltage drop across the reactor or any other series resistance

The average current per tube or per anode in the case of a multi-anode tube is expressed by Eq. (7–18) and the effective value of the current per anode is expressed by Eq. (7–19).

$$I_a = \frac{I_{dc}}{P} \qquad (7–18)$$

$$I_{rms} = \frac{I_{dc}}{\sqrt{P}} \qquad (7–19)$$

where   $I_{dc}$ = load current

$I_a$ = average current per anode

$I_{rms}$ = root-mean-square or effective value of current per anode

**7–13. Utilization Factor.**  A very important consideration in the case of any polyphase rectifier installation is the *utilization factor*.  The utilization factor of the primary of the transformer winding is the ratio of the dc or rectified power (including circuit losses) to the volt-ampere rating of the primary.  The utilization factor of the secondary is the ratio of the dc power to the volt-ampere rating of the secondary of the transformer winding.

$$\text{Primary utilization factor (PUF)} = \frac{P_{dc}}{\text{Primary volt-amperes}} \qquad (7–20a)$$

$$\text{Secondary utilization factor (SUF)} = \frac{P_{dc}}{\text{Secondary volt-amperes}} \qquad (7–20b)$$

Assuming a star-connected secondary, an expression for the secondary utilization factor may be derived as follows:

$$P_{dc} = I_{dc}E_d$$

$$P_{dc} = \frac{I_{dc}P\sqrt{2}E_{rms}\sin\frac{\pi}{P}}{\pi} \qquad (7–21)$$

$$P_{ac} = E_{rms}I_{rms}P$$

$$P_{ac} = E_{rms}I_{dc}\sqrt{P} \qquad (7–22)$$

$$\text{SUF} = \frac{P_{dc}}{P_{ac}} = \frac{\sqrt{2P}\sin\frac{\pi}{P}}{\pi} \qquad (7–23)$$

It can be shown that the secondary utilization factor is a maximum when $P = 2.69$. Since a 2.69 phase rectifier is impossible, the three-phase rectifier gives the highest obtainable secondary utilization factor. Substituting various values of $P$ in Eq. (7–23) yields the values of secondary utilization factor given in Table 7–2.

TABLE 7–2

| Number of Phases | SUF |
|---|---|
| 3 | 0.675 |
| 6 | 0.551 |
| 12 | 0.399 |
| $\infty$ | 0.000 |

A low utilization factor means that the investment in transformers is greater for a given amount of dc power. The utilization factor is in some respects similar to power factor; for the lower the power factor of a load, the greater the volt-ampere rating of the power source necessary to supply the load.

The decrease in the utilization factor with an increase in the number of phases is one of the main disadvantages of a large number of phases. There are transformer connections, which will be considered later, that give the same utilization factor as a three-phase rectifier, yet are actually six-phase rectifiers and thus exhibit the advantages of both six and three-phase rectifier circuits.

**7–14. Ripple Voltage.** Another important consideration in any polyphase rectifier circuit is the ripple voltage. The ratio of the amplitude of the $k$th harmonic in the output of an unfiltered rectifier circuit to the total rectified voltage is expressed by Eq. (7–24).

$$\frac{E_k}{E_d} = \frac{2}{k^2 - 1} \tag{7–24}$$

where $E_k$ = amplitude or peak value of $k$th harmonic

$k$ = harmonic in question; it must be a multiple of the number of phases, otherwise harmonic does not exist.

Substituting several values of $k$ in Eq. (7–24) yields the values given in Table 7–3.

TABLE 7–3

| $k$ | $E_k/E_d$ |
|---|---|
| 3 | 0.250 |
| 6 | 0.057 |
| 9 | 0.025 |
| 12 | 0.014 |
| 18 | 0.006 |

At first glance the values listed in Table 7–3 do not necessarily indicate in what way the ripple in the output is a function of the number of phases. However, values of $E_k$ cannot exist except when $k$ is equal to or greater than the number of phases $P$. This means that in the case of a three-phase rectifier, the ratio of the amplitude of the largest harmonic to the total dc voltage is 0.250 and the ratio of the next largest to the dc voltage is 0.057 and so on, the ratio decreasing rapidly with an increase in the frequency of the harmonic voltage. In the case of the twelve-phase rectifier, the highest ratio for any harmonic existing is 0.014 which means that the ripple factor at the load will be much less than in the case of the three-phase arrangement. The decrease in the ripple factor with an increase in phases is one of the main advantages of having a large number of phases.

**7–15. Arcback.** One of the obstacles in the development of high-current high-voltage mercury-arc rectifiers is a phenomenon which is known as *arcback* or *backfire.** Referring to the circuit of either Fig. 7–20a or 7–20b, it can be seen that during the nonconducting period, an anode

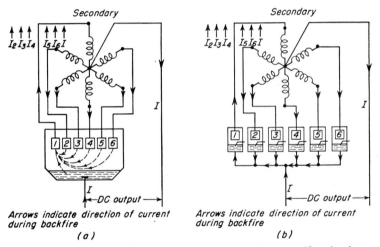

Fig. 7–20.   Diagrams illustrating arcback in six-phase rectifier circuits.

attains a peak voltage of approximately twice the peak phase voltage of the secondary of the transformer. This voltage, which is called the inverse peak voltage, is given by Eq. (7–25).

$$\text{Inverse Peak Voltage} = 2\sqrt{2}(E_{\text{rms}} \text{ per phase}) - \text{Tube Drop} \quad (7\text{–}25)$$

Due to the fact that each anode, during its nonconducting period, attains a high negative voltage with respect to its cathode (mercury pool), there is during the nonconducting period of each anode a tendency for it to act as a cathode. Under certain conditions, which are not yet fully under-

* For a more complete discussion of arcback, see O. K. Marti and Harold Winograd, *Mercury-Arc Power Rectifiers* (New York: McGraw-Hill Book Co., Inc., 1930), pp. 35–8.

stood, electrons may be emitted from some spot on the anode (usually referred to as a cathode spot) and flow to the mercury pool. This means that current will flow in the reverse direction, i.e., from the mercury pool to the anode on which the cathode spot has developed. There will also be current flow from all the other anodes to the faulty anode. The current flow during arcback is illustrated for a multi-anode six-phase arrangement in Fig. 7–20a and for a six-phase circuit employing six ignitrons in Fig. 7–20b. Arcback results in essentially a short circuit across the transformer, the current being limited only by the resistance and reactance of the transformer windings. If the rectifier in which arcback occurs is being operated in parallel with a dc generator, the generator will be shorted through the rectifier, resulting in even more current feedback through the rectifier circuit. Arcback is extremely undesirable and unless some means of automatically interrupting the circuit is available, considerable damage to the rectifier and auxiliary equipment may result. With the modern protective devices employed, when arcback occurs, the circuit is interrupted in sufficient time to prevent any appreciable damage and then closed immediately after the arcback. This results in essentially no interruption in service.

Although extensive research on arcback has been in progress for many years, as yet no fully satisfactory explanation of this phenomenon has been evolved. Backfiring has been reduced by increasing the effective distance between the mercury pool and anodes and by surrounding each anode with a shield which is held slightly negative with respect to the anode during conduction. This arrangement, however, tends to increase the voltage drop across the arc. As mentioned in Chapter 3, arcback is less likely to occur in single-anode tubes, such as ignitrons and excitrons, than in multi-anode types.

**7–16. Comparison of Mercury-Arc Rectifiers and Rotating Machinery.** In general, modern mercury-arc rectifier units are superior to rotating machinery as a means of supplying large blocks of dc energy. The maintenance cost of modern rectifier units employing single-anode tubes is reported to be considerably less than the maintenance cost of rotary converters of the same power capacity. The overload capacity of the mercury-arc rectifier is larger and the regulation is better than the typical shunt generation characteristic. The losses in the case of the rectifier unit (including the losses in all transformers and auxiliary equipment) are less; thus the efficiency is greater. The curves of Fig. 7–21 give a comparison of the ignitron units and motor-generator sets based on efficiency and losses. Other advantages include simplicity of installation, automatic operation, and no vibration. Several disadvantages of mercury-arc rectifiers are: possibility of arcback, cannot be used for power-factor improvement such as in the case of a synchronous motor-generator set, generally requires a more highly trained technician for servicing when trouble occurs, and the ripple voltage is objectional for some applications. Although the ripple voltage of a three-phase rectifier is large enough to result in overheating and in poor commutation of dc motors, the six-phase rectifier, which is the

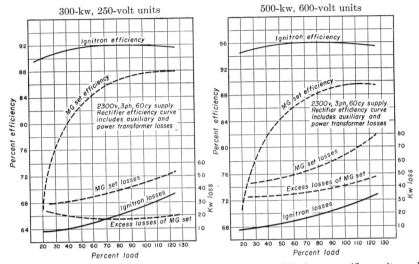

FIG. 7–21. Comparison of the efficiency and losses of ignitron rectifier units and MG sets. (Courtesy Westinghouse Electric Corp.)

most common type of polyphase rectifier circuit, gives a dc output that is sufficiently free of ripple to be suitable for most power applications. Many rectifier installations are twelve and eighteen-phase arrangements and in such cases the ripple voltage is extremely small. A typical ignitron assembly which is in chemical service is shown in Fig. 7–22.

**7–17. Common Polyphase Rectifier Circuits.** Although there are more than 40 * rectifier circuits for transforming three-phase to dc, the number of commonly used circuits is very small. A few of the more common circuits will be considered very briefly here.

*Three-Phase Delta-Wye Connection.* The three-phase delta-wye circuit, which is sometimes known as a three-phase half-wave rectifier circuit, is shown in Fig. 7–23a. This circuit has the disadvantage of giving a large ripple voltage in the output circuit, which is excessive for many dc applications. The ratio of the rectified voltage to the secondary phase voltage of the transformer is low and each leg of the transformer contains a direct component of residual magnetomotive force. Because of these disadvantages, this circuit arrangement is seldom used.

Another arrangement of the three-phase delta-wye circuit is shown in

* M.I.T. Staff, *Applied Electronics* (New York: John Wiley & Sons, Inc., 1943), p. 353.

Fig. 7–22. 5,000-ampere, 650-volt ignitron rectifier in chemical service. (Courtesy Westinghouse Electric Corp.)

Fig. 7–23b. This circuit is referred to as a three-phase full-wave rectifier circuit. Although this arrangement gives a lower value of ripple voltage than the half-wave circuit, does not result in dc saturation of the secondary of the transformer and gives a higher value of dc for a given secondary transformer voltage, it is not a very common type of connection. As will

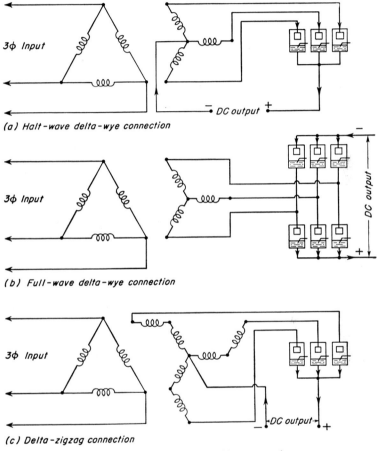

(a) Half-wave delta-wye connection

(b) Full-wave delta-wye connection

(c) Delta-zigzag connection

Fig. 7–23. Three-phase rectifier connections.

be noticed from the circuit arrangement, the cathodes are not all at the same voltage; thus only single-anode tubes such as thermionic gas diodes or ignitrons may be used. There are always two tubes conducting in series which results in poor regulation and lower efficiency than in the case of an equivalent six-phase arrangement.

*Three-Phase Delta-Zigzag Connection.* The circuit of Fig. 7–23c is known as a delta-zigzag connection. Although this circuit gives the same output wave form as the half-wave three-phase rectifier of Fig. 7–23a and thus possesses the undesirable features of a high percent ripple and low ratio of rectified to ac voltage, the secondary transformer windings are arranged so as to eliminate dc saturation. This circuit is not very widely used.

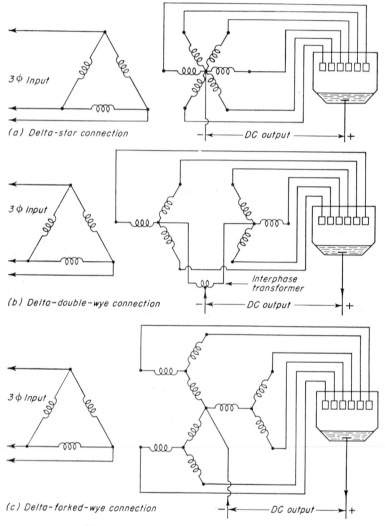

FIG. 7–24. Six-phase rectifier connections.

*Six-Phase Delta-Star Connection.* The simplest six-phase rectifier connection is shown in Fig. 7–24a. This arrangement eliminates dc saturation of the transformer and gives a much lower value of ripple voltage than the similar three-phase arrangement of Fig. 7–23a, but has the disadvantages of lower utilization factor, higher voltage regulation and lower efficiency when compared to other types of six-phase rectifier arrangements.

*Six-Phase Delta-Double-Wye or Interphase Transformer Connection.* The most common polyphase rectifier circuit in use today is the delta-double-wye connection which is shown schematically in Fig. 7–24*b*. The secondary windings which are divided into two separate wyes are connected through an interphase transformer * which acts as a voltage equalizer between them.

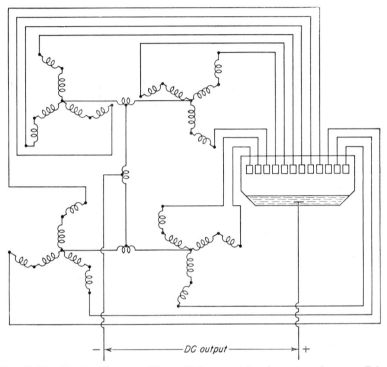

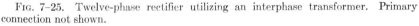

Fig. 7–25. Twelve-phase rectifier utilizing an interphase transformer. Primary connection not shown.

If the interphase transformer were not used, the two neutrals would be connected together and the circuit would operate in the same manner as the six-phase delta-star connection. The secondary voltages are displaced by 60 degrees, giving the same low ripple factor as any other six-phase arrangement; however, the secondary utilization factor is equal to that obtained with a three-phase arrangement (0.675 instead of 0.551 as in the case of the straight delta-star connected six-phase arrangement). The voltage regulation of this type circuit is also better than in the case of delta-star connected six-phase rectifiers.

*Six-Phase Forked-Wye Connection.* The forked-wye connection which is sometimes referred to as the double zigzag connection is shown in

---

* For a complete discussion of the interphase transformer, see Marti and Winograd, *Mercury-Arc Power Rectifiers* (New York: McGraw-Hill Book Co., Inc., 1930), pp. 127–46.

## TABLE 7–4

| Circuit | Diagram | Secondary Current — Wave Shape | r.m.s. | Sec. Voltage to Neut. | Total Sec. V.A. and Util. Factor | Primary Current Wave | Effective Pri. Current & Pri. Volts | Total Pri. Volt-Amps. & Utility Factor | Transformer Total V.A. & Utility Factor | Line Current Wave Form | Effective Line Current & Line Volts | Line V.A. and Utility Factor | Principal Comp. of Choke or I.P.T. Voltage |
|---|---|---|---|---|---|---|---|---|---|---|---|---|---|
| Single-Phase | | | $J/\sqrt{2}$ $0.707J$ | $\frac{\pi}{2\sqrt{2}} G$ $1.11G$ | $1.57\,JG$ U.F.=0.637 | | $t_2/t_1\,J$ $1.11\,t_1/t_2$ | $1.11\,JG$ U.F.=0.90 | $2.68\,JG$ U.F.=0.746 | Same as Primary | Same as Primary | U.F.=0.90 | $2\times$freq. $0.471\,G$ (r.m.s.) |
| Three-Phase | | | $J/\sqrt{3}$ $0.577J$ | $\frac{\sqrt{2}\,\pi}{3\sqrt{3}} G$ $0.855G$ | $1.481\,JG$ U.F.=0.675 | | $\frac{\sqrt{2}\,t_2\,J}{3\,t_1}$ $0.855\,t_1/t_2$ | $1.209\,JG$ U.F.=0.827 | $2.69\,JG$ U.F.=0.743 | | $\frac{\sqrt{2}\,t_2\,J}{\sqrt{3}\,t_1}$ $0.855\,t_1/t_2$ | $1.209\,JG$ U.F.=0.827 | $3\times$freq. $0.1167\,G$ (r.m.s.) |
| Quarter-Phase | | | $J/2$ $0.500J$ | $\frac{\pi}{4} G$ $0.785G$ | $1.57\,JG$ U.F.=0.637 | | $\frac{t_2\,J}{\sqrt{2}\,t_1}$ $0.785\,t_1/t_2$ | $1.11\,JG$ U.F.=0.90 | $2.68\,JG$ U.F.=0.746 | Same as Primary | Same as Primary | U.F.=0.90 | $4\times$freq. $0.0943\,G$ (r.m.s.) |
| Six-Phase | | | $J/\sqrt{6}$ $0.408J$ | $\frac{\pi}{3\sqrt{2}} G$ $0.741G$ | $1.814\,JG$ U.F.=0.552 | | $\frac{t_2\,J}{\sqrt{3}\,t_1}$ $0.741\,t_1/t_2$ | $1.283\,JG$ U.F.=0.780 | $3.097\,JG$ U.F.=0.646 | | $\frac{\sqrt{2}\,t_2\,J}{\sqrt{3}\,t_1}$ $0.741\,t_1/t_2$ | $1.047\,JG$ U.F.=0.955 | $6\times$freq. $0.0404\,G$ (r.m.s.) |
| Double-Y | | | $J/2\sqrt{3}$ $0.289J$ | $\frac{\sqrt{2}\,\pi}{3\sqrt{3}} G$ $0.855G$ | $1.481\,JG$ U.F.=0.675 | | $\frac{t_2\,J}{\sqrt{6}\,t_1}$ $0.855\,t_1/t_2$ | $1.047\,JG$ U.F.=0.955 | $2.528\,JG$ U.F.=0.792 | | $\frac{t_2\,J}{\sqrt{2}\,t_1}$ $0.855\,t_1/t_2$ | $1.047\,JG$ U.F.=0.955 | I.P.T. 3×f $0.1767\,G$ per section Choke 6×f $0.0404\,G$ (r.m.s.) |
| Triple Single-Phase | | | $J/3\sqrt{2}$ $0.236J$ | $\frac{\pi}{2\sqrt{2}} G$ $1.11G$ | $1.57\,JG$ U.F.=0.637 | | $\frac{t_2\,J}{3\,t_1}$ $1.11\,t_1/t_2$ | $1.11\,JG$ U.F.=0.90 | $2.68\,JG$ U.F.=0.746 | Same as Primary | $\frac{2\sqrt{2}\,t_2\,J}{3\sqrt{3}\,t_1}$ | $1.047\,JG$ U.F.=0.955 | $6\times$freq. $0.0404\,G$ (r.m.s.) |
| Y Star | | | $J/\sqrt{6}$ $0.408J$ | $\frac{\sqrt{2}\,\pi}{3\sqrt{3}} G$ $0.855G$ | $1.481\,JG$ U.F.=0.675 | | $\frac{t_2\,J}{\sqrt{6}\,t_1}$ $0.855\,t_1/t_2$ | $1.047\,JG$ U.F.=0.955 | $2.528\,JG$ U.F.=0.792 | Same as Primary | $1.11\,t_1/t_2$ | $1.047\,JG$ U.F.=0.955 | $6\times$freq. $0.0404\,G$ (r.m.s.) |
| Triple Star | | | $J/\sqrt{3}$ $0.577J$ | $0.428G$ $0.428G$ | $1.79\,JG$ U.F.=0.559 | | $\frac{t_2\,J}{3\,t_1}$ $0.428\,t_1/t_2$ | $1.047\,JG$ U.F.=0.955 | $2.837\,JG$ U.F.=0.705 | Same as Primary | $\frac{\sqrt{2}\,t_2\,J}{\sqrt{3}\,t_1}$ $0.741\,t_1/t_2$ | $1.047\,JG$ U.F.=0.955 | $6\times$freq. $0.0404\,G$ (r.m.s.) |
| Y Star Tertiary | Same as Y Star with Addition of Tertiary Winding | | $J/\sqrt{6}$ $0.408J$ | $\frac{\pi}{3\sqrt{2}} G$ $0.741G$ | $1.814\,JG$ U.F.=0.552 | | $0.741\,t_1/t_2$ | $1.047\,JG$ U.F.=0.955 | | | $1283\,t_1/t_2\,G$ | $1.047\,JG$ U.F.=0.955 | $6\times$freq. $0.0404\,G$ (r.m.s.) |

Reprinted by permission from *Principles of Mercury Arc Rectifiers and Their Circuits* by D. C. Prince and F. B. Vogdes, published by McGraw-Hill Book Co., Inc., New York, 1927.

Fig. 7–24c. This arrangement is widely used in Europe and is used to some extent in this country. The secondary utilization factor of the forked-wye connection is 0.559, which is slightly higher than the utilization factor of a straight six-phase connection but less than the value for the six-phase connection employing an interphase transformer. The regulation of this connection is also better than in the case of a straight six-phase connection.

*Twelve-Phase Interphase Transformer Connection.* The first twelve-phase connection utilizing interphase transformers was installed on the 1,500-volt system of the Midi Railway * in France in 1922. At present, this type connection, which is also known as a *delta-quadruple-zigzag* (Fig. 7–25), is the most common twelve-phase arrangement. It gives the highest utilization factor and lowest regulation of any type of twelve-phase arrangement. Table 7–4 gives several basic rectifier circuits along with fundamental data concerning each.

## PROBLEMS

**7–1.** Determine the efficiency obtainable from a single-phase half-wave rectifier if the load resistance $R_L = 500$ ohms and the plate resistance of the tube $r_p = 500$ ohms. Repeat for a full-wave rectifier with the same circuit parameters.

**7–2.** Prove that $I_{dc} = 2I_m/\pi$ for a single-phase full-wave rectifier with a pure resistive load.

**7–3.** A single-phase half-wave rectifier is comprised of a transformer which steps up 115 v to 660 v (rms value), an ideal rectifier tube (assume $r_p = 0$) and a load resistance of 10,000 ohms. Determine the dc voltage and current at the load.

**7–4.** Repeat Prob. 7–2 for a full-wave rectifier assuming that the secondary of the plate transformer gives 660 v from the center-tap to either of the outside terminals.

**7–5.** A single-phase full-wave rectifier which operates from a 115-v, 60-cycle supply feeds a resistive load of 10,000 ohms through a two section inductor-input filter circuit. Each section is comprised of a 20-henry inductor and a 16-microfarad capacitor. Assuming the resistance of the inductors to be negligible, determine the ratio of the amplitude of the fundamental ripple voltage at the load to the dc voltage at the load.

**7–6.** Repeat Prob. 7–5 assuming that the filter circuit is converted into a capacitor-input circuit by the addition of a 10-microfarad capacitor across the input terminals of the filter circuit. Compare the rectifier-filter circuits of this and the preceding problem.

**7–7.** Determine the maximum value of the dc voltage obtainable at the output of a voltage-doubler circuit if the rms value of the ac input is 117 v.

**7–8.** Explain the operation of the synchronous vibrator, the circuit of which is shown in Fig. 7–13b.

---

* Marti and Winograd, *Mercury-Arc Power Rectifiers* (New York: McGraw-Hill Book Co., Inc., 1930), p. 152.

**7-9.** Prove that theoretically the maximum value of secondary utilization factor occurs when $P = 2.69$.

**7-10.** A six-phase mercury-arc rectifier is supplied from a three-phase, 60-cycle source. The transformer primaries are connected delta and the secondaries are connected star. The secondary phase voltage is 1,000 v (rms value) and the load resistance is 10 ohms. Assuming an arc drop of 18 v determine:

    *a*) The dc voltage across the load.

    *b*) The load current.

    *c*) The average current per anode.

    *d*) The rms value of the current per anode.

    *e*) The period of time each anode fires during each cycle (assuming no overlap).

    *f*) The secondary utilization factor.

    *g*) The ratio of the amplitude of the following harmonics to the dc voltage at the load: 2, 3, 4, 6, 8, 9, 12, 18, 24 and 36.

## BIBLIOGRAPHY

BENDZ, W. I. *Electronics for Industry.* New York: John Wiley & Sons, Inc., 1947, pp. 131–65.

CRUFT LABORATORY STAFF. *Electronic Circuits and Tubes.* New York: McGraw-Hill Book Co., Inc., 1947, pp. 534–80.

EASTMAN, A. V. *Fundamentals of Vacuum Tubes.* 2nd ed. New York: McGraw-Hill Book Co., Inc., 1941, pp. 162–209.

MARTI, O. K., and WINOGRAD, HAROLD. *Mercury-Arc Power Rectifiers.* New York: McGraw-Hill Book Co., Inc., 1930, pp. 29–43, 117–209.

M.I.T. STAFF. *Applied Electronics.* New York: John Wiley & Sons, Inc., 1943, pp. 247–65, 330–75.

MILLMAN, JACOB, and SEELY, SAMUEL. *Electronics.* New York: McGraw-Hill Book Co., Inc., 1941, pp. 362–412.

PRINCE, D. C., and VOGDES, F. B. *Principles of Mercury Arc Rectifiers and Their Circuits.* New York: McGraw-Hill Book Co., Inc., 1927, pp. 83–107.

REICH, H. J. *Theory and Applications of Electron Tubes.* 2nd ed. New York: McGraw-Hill Book Co., Inc., 1944, pp. 564–95.

TERMAN, F. E. *Radio Engineering.* 3rd ed. New York: McGraw-Hill Book Co., Inc., 1947, pp. 544–76.

———. *Radio Engineers Handbook.* New York: McGraw-Hill Book Co., Inc., 1943, pp. 589–620.

WESTINGHOUSE ELECTRIC CORPORATION. *Industrial Electronics Reference Book.* New York: John Wiley & Sons, Inc., 1948, pp. 348–60.

# CHAPTER 8

## CATHODE–RAY TUBES AND APPLICATIONS

The prototype of the modern cathode-ray tube dates back to 1897 when Braun made a crude gas-filled cathode-ray tube. During the same year an exhausted glass tube, somewhat similar to Braun's tube, was employed by Thomson in the famous experiment in which he determined the ratio of the charge of an electron to its mass.

Up until about 1932 the use of the cathode-ray tube in the United States was in general limited to experimental research. In 1932 the first domestic *cathode-ray oscillograph* *—a cathode-ray tube with the associated circuits necessary for viewing electrical phenomena—was made commercially available in the United States.

At present there are a great many important applications to which the cathode-ray tube readily lends itself. Aside from their use in the study of all types of electrical phenomena, oscillographs are used in many other fields of endeavor. A few such uses include detonation studies in internal combustion engines, plotting of pressure-volume curves for engines of various types, the study of dynamic mechanical unbalance in machinery, the study of noise in all types of machinery and the production testing of musical instruments, watches, etc.

The first cathode-ray tubes made were gas filled; however, at present such tubes are obsolete. Consequently only the high-vacuum tube will be considered here. High-vacuum cathode-ray tubes fall into two general categories: tubes employing electrostatic focusing and electrostatic deflection, commonly known as EE tubes; and tubes in which the beam is focused and deflected by magnetic means, commonly known as MM tubes. Although the majority of cathode-ray tubes manufactured fall into these categories, many television sets utilize cathode-ray tubes in which focusing is accomplished by electrostatic means and the deflection by magnetic means. There are other types of tubes which employ both magnetic and electrostatic deflection. Such tubes, however, are not very common.

**8–1. EE Tubes.** Tubes employing electrostatic focusing and deflection (EE tubes) are best suited for most general applications and are the type employed in commercial oscillographs. MM tubes are employed in some

---

* *Cathode-Ray Tubes and Instruments*, Reference Manual, 1946 Ed., Passaic, N. J.: Allen B. DuMont Laboratories, Inc.

television sets and as indicators in certain types of radar sets. The sketch of a typical medium-voltage EE cathode-ray tube is shown in Fig. 8–1.

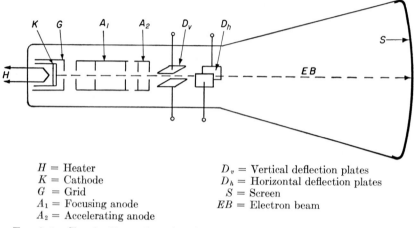

H = Heater  
K = Cathode  
G = Grid  
$A_1$ = Focusing anode  
$A_2$ = Accelerating anode  

$D_v$ = Vertical deflection plates  
$D_h$ = Horizontal deflection plates  
S = Screen  
EB = Electron beam  

FIG. 8–1. Sketch illustrating the electrode arrangement in a medium-voltage cathode-ray tube.

All electrodes are enclosed within a suitable high-vacuum glass container, the pressure being in the order of $10^{-6}$ mm of mercury. The button type oxide-coated cathode is indirectly heated by means of a 2.5- or 6.3-volt heater. The electrons are thermionically emitted from the cathode and speed toward the accelerating anode $A_2$ which is highly positive with respect to the cathode. The accelerating anode is cylindrical in shape and has a small hole in the center; thus the electrons pass through it with a velocity which is expressed approximately by Eq. (8–1), derived earlier in Section 1–7.

$$v = 5.93 \times 10^5 \sqrt{E_a} \qquad (8\text{–}1)$$

where $E_a$ = difference in potential between cathode $K$ and accelerating anode $A_2$ in volts

        $v$ = velocity with which electrons pass through the accelerating anode in meters/second

Most electrons strike the screen of the tube with approximately the same velocity, each imparting energy to the screen to the extent of $\frac{1}{2}mv^2$ joules.

If the screen is fluorescent, that is, if it is capable of giving off visible light when excited by external energy, visible rays will be produced as a result of electron bombardment. In order to see the pattern traced by the electron beam as its position on the screen is changed in accordance with some given signal, the screen material must also be phosphorescent, that is, it must be capable of emitting visible light for a short time after the external excitation ceases to exist. Screen materials are made with various degrees of phosphorescence depending upon their application. At present cathode-ray tubes employing many different types of screen materials are being manufactured; several such materials are:

*Zinc Silicate*—$Zn_2SiO_4$. This screen material, which is commonly known as willemite, gives a yellow-green trace of medium persistency; it is ideal for tubes that are to be used for visual study. Many general-purpose cathode-ray oscillographs employ tubes with willemite screens.

*Calcium Tungstate*—$CaWO_4$. This screen material gives rise to a blue-violet trace of extremely short persistency. Tubes utilizing screen materials of short persistency find their chief application in making high-frequency photographic recordings, etc.

*Zinc Sulfide*—$ZnS$. This screen material gives rise to a blue-white trace of relatively long duration. It is suitable for tubes designed to study low-speed transient phenomena, etc.

The luminous output of any cathode-ray tube screen is a function of the beam current, accelerating voltage and the physical and chemical properties of the screen. For a given cathode-ray oscillograph the chemical and physical make-up of the tube screen is fixed; thus, the only variables affecting the intensity of the beam or spot on the screen are accelerating anode voltage and grid voltage. The grid is a nickel cylinder directly in front of the cathode and its voltage can be varied by a dial on the front of the control panel of the oscillograph which is labeled INTENSITY. In most cases, the potential applied to the accelerating anode $A_2$ cannot be changed without going inside of the oscillograph, so in general it can be said that for a given oscillograph the intensity of the spot on the screen or the luminous output of the spot is a function of grid voltage only.

**8–2. Electrostatic Focusing.** To obtain best results with an oscillograph, it is necessary that the trace on the screen be sharp and well defined. Because of the irregularities of the surface of the cathode, electrostatic repulsion between individual electrons, defocusing action of the deflection plates, accelerating anode and stray electrostatic fields, the spot on the screen will not be well defined unless a special focusing mechanism is incorporated. In the EE tube, electrostatic focusing is accomplished by means of the relatively long focusing anode labeled $A_1$ which lies between the control grid and the accelerating anode. The focusing anode usually has several baffles and is operated at a positive potential with respect to the cathode. The focusing anode voltage can be changed by an adjustment labeled FOCUSING on the control panel of the oscillograph. The magnitude of the voltage applied to the focusing anode is from $\frac{1}{4}$ to $\frac{1}{3}$ of that applied to the accelerating anode. Although a rigorous mathematical analysis of electrostatic focusing is beyond the scope of this text, a physical explanation will be given.

Consider the sketches of Fig. 8–2. Assume the two parallel plates of Fig. 8–2a to be charged as indicated. Dielectric flux will exist as shown by the dotted lines. Now if a beam of electrons is shot between the parallel plates as indicated, the electrons will be attracted to the more positive plate, or stating the phenomenon differently, they will attempt to align

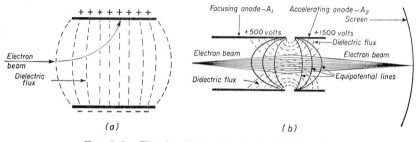

FIG. 8–2. Sketches illustrating electrostatic focusing.

their course with the dielectric lines of flux. Now consider this principle as it applies to electrostatic focusing. The focusing anode $A_1$ and the accelerating anode $A_2$ of Fig. 8–2b are both positive with respect to the cathode but the voltage of the accelerating anode $A_2$ is usually three or four times greater than the voltage of the focusing anode $A_1$. Thus $A_2$ (the accelerating anode) is positive with respect to $A_1$ (the focusing anode) and the electrostatic lines existing between the two cylinders will be as indicated. Now assume a beam of electrons entering the focusing anode with divergent velocities. The electrons that have components of velocity outward from the axis will, after they come under the influence of the focusing anode, attempt to align themselves with the dielectric flux and thus will be sent back toward the axis. The focusing system employed in a cathode-ray tube is somewhat analogous to an optical system; the focal length can be changed by varying the focusing anode voltage.

**8–3. Electrostatic Deflection.** Electrostatic deflection is accomplished by applying voltage to the deflection plates. Referring to the sketch of an EE tube (Fig. 8–1), the pair of plates labeled $D_v$ will give deflection in the vertical direction and the pair of plates labeled $D_h$ will give deflection in the horizontal direction. The sketch of Fig. 8–3 illustrates the deflection of the electron beam due to a difference in potential being applied to the vertical deflection plates. If the upper plate is positive with respect to the lower, the beam on entering the electrostatic field at point $O$ will be bent upward and follow a parabolic path between points $O$ and $A$. Assuming no fringing, the beam will follow a straight line path after leaving the electrostatic field at point $A$ and will strike the screen at point $B$. The slope of the straight line path $AB$ will be equal to the slope of curve $OA$ at point $A$. It can be shown that the deflection of the beam due to a deflecting potential $E_d$ is expressed approximately by Eq. (8–2).

$$D = \frac{lLE_d}{2dE_a} \qquad (8\text{-}2)$$

where $E_a$ = accelerating anode voltage
$E_d$ = potential applied to the deflection plates
$d$ = spacing between deflection plates in meters
$l$ = length of the deflection plates in meters
$L$ = distance from center of the deflection plates to the screen in meters
$D$ = deflection of the beam in meters

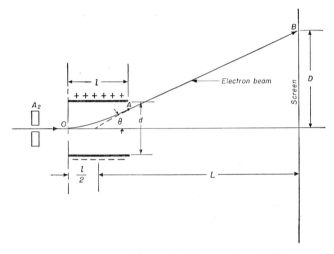

Fig. 8-3.  Sketch illustrating electrostatic deflection.

Most modern cathode-ray tubes of any appreciable size have their deflection plates bent so greater deflection can be obtained. Many of the higher voltage tubes employ an additional intensifier electrode which gives the electrons a higher velocity on striking the screen, resulting in a brighter spot. The internal structure of a modern cathode-ray tube which has an intensifier electrode and bent deflection plates is shown in Fig. 8-4. Fig. 8-5 illustrates the different steps in the manufacture of a modern three-inch EE type cathode-ray tube. At present commercial cathode-ray tubes are made with screen diameters of from one to twenty inches and operate at accelerating voltages from around 500 to as high as 80,000 volts. The size of the screen has little bearing on the accelerating voltage. Fig. 8-6 illustrates several types of commercial cathode-ray tubes.

**8-4. MM Tubes.** The sketch of Fig. 8-7 illustrates the structure of an MM tube. This tube differs from the EE tube of Fig. 8-1 in that the focusing anode has been replaced by a focusing coil labeled $FC$ and the deflection plates have been replaced by deflection coils labeled $XX$ and $YY$.

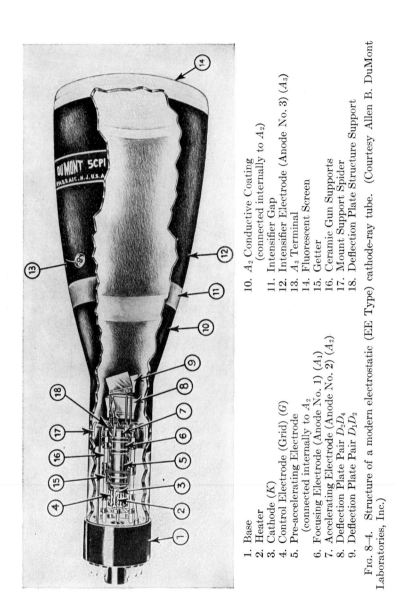

1. Base
2. Heater
3. Cathode (K)
4. Control Electrode (Grid) (G)
5. Pre-accelerating Electrode
   (connected internally to $A_2$)
6. Focusing Electrode (Anode No. 1) ($A_1$)
7. Accelerating Electrode (Anode No. 2) ($A_2$)
8. Deflection Plate Pair $D_2D_4$
9. Deflection Plate Pair $D_1D_2$
10. $A_2$ Conductive Coating
    (connected internally to $A_2$)
11. Intensifier Gap
12. Intensifier Electrode (Anode No. 3) ($A_3$)
13. $A_3$ Terminal
14. Fluorescent Screen
15. Getter
16. Ceramic Gun Supports
17. Mount Support Spider
18. Deflection Plate Structure Support

Fig. 8–4.  Structure of a modern electrostatic (EE Type) cathode-ray tube.  (Courtesy  Allen B. DuMont Laboratories, Inc.)

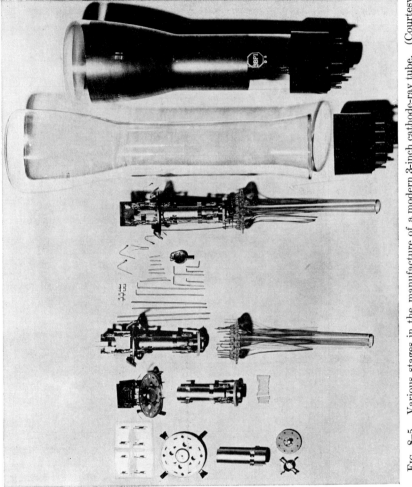

Fig. 8-5. Various stages in the manufacture of a modern 3-inch cathode-ray tube. (Courtesy Sylvania Electric Products, Inc.)

FIG. 8–6.  Typical cathode-ray tubes.  (Courtesy North American Philips Co., Inc.)

The proper focus is obtained by varying the current through the focusing coil and the deflection is controlled by the current through the deflection coils.

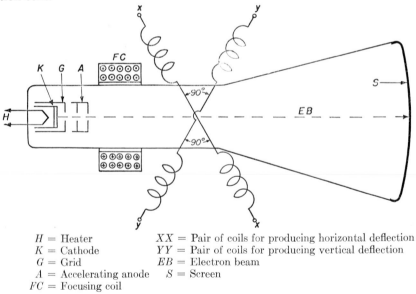

| | |
|---|---|
| $H$ = Heater | $XX$ = Pair of coils for producing horizontal deflection |
| $K$ = Cathode | $YY$ = Pair of coils for producing vertical deflection |
| $G$ = Grid | $EB$ = Electron beam |
| $A$ = Accelerating anode | $S$ = Screen |
| $FC$ = Focusing coil | |

FIG. 8–7.  Sketch illustrating the electrode and coil arrangement for an MM Tube.

**8–5. Magnetic Focusing.**  As already mentioned in Section 8–2, electrons that have outward components of velocity will, if not focused, spread over a relatively large area on the screen and instead of a well-defined spot resulting on the screen, a blurred spot will exist. Such a spot is highly undesirable.

If a magnetic field is set up which is substantially parallel to the components of velocity of the electrons in the direction toward the screen, i.e., parallel to the axis of the tube and thus perpendicular to the outward components of velocity of the electrons (assuming each electron to possess

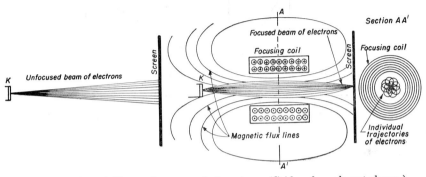

FIG. 8–8.  Sketch illustrating magnetic focusing.  (Grid and anode not shown.)

a component of velocity perpendicular to the axis), the electrons will move in helical paths as they progress toward the screen. The pattern of the magnetic field and the loci of the electrons are both illustrated in the sketch of Fig. 8–8.

It is highly probable that each individual electron will leave the cathode with a different outward component of velocity; however, as shown by Eq. (8–3), which was derived in Section 1–9,

$$T = \frac{3.57 \times 10^{-11}}{B} \qquad (8\text{--}3)$$

where $T$ = time in seconds
$B$ = flux density in webers/square meter,

the time taken for each electron to make a complete orbit and return to the axis is not a function of its outward component of velocity but is entirely dependent upon the strength of the magnetic field within which it finds itself; thus if the magnetic field is essentially uniform the electrons that have outward components of velocity will return to the axis in approximately the same time and at approximately the same distance from the cathode. The magnetic field strength can be adjusted so as to bring all electrons back to the axis at the point necessary to give best focus on the screen.

**8–6. Magnetic Deflection.**  Magnetic deflection is obtained by deflection coils located on the neck of the tube. There are usually two pairs of coils which produce fields at right angles to each other; however, in some cases, only one pair of rotating coils is employed. The sketch of Fig. 8–9 illustrates the principles of magnetic deflection. A magnetic field is set up which is normal to the motion of the beam of electrons; thus on entering the magnetic field at point $O$ the electrons will move in circular paths until

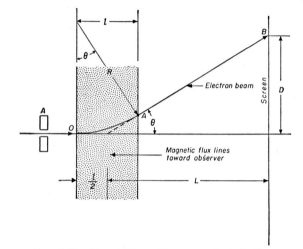

FIG. 8–9.   Sketch illustrating magnetic deflection.

they leave the field. In the case under consideration the lines of flux are considered to be toward the observer; consequently the beam will be bent up along path $OA$. On leaving the field at point $A$ the electrons will move along straight line $AB$ (assuming no fringing), striking the screen at some distance $D$ from its center.

The deflection $D$ is expressed approximately by Eq. (8–4).

$$D = \frac{2.98 \times 10^5 lLB}{\sqrt{E_a}} \qquad (8\text{–}4)$$

where  $D$ = deflection of beam in meters
$l$ = length of magnetic field normal to the axis, in meters
$L$ = distance from the center of the magnetic field to the screen, in meters
$B$ = strength of the magnetic field in webers/square meter
$E_a$ = accelerating anode voltage in volts

A typical cathode-ray tube with magnetic focusing and magnetic deflection is shown in Fig. 8–10.

## The Cathode-Ray Oscillograph

An instrument which incorporates a cathode-ray tube, suitable power supplies and the necessary circuits for indicating electrical phenomena on the screen of the tube is commonly termed a cathode-ray oscillograph or cathode-ray oscilloscope. Although oscillograph has come to be the more popular of the two terms, oscilloscope is perhaps the more proper. By definition, an oscillograph is an instrument for making a photographic recording of electrical phenomena and only highly specialized types of

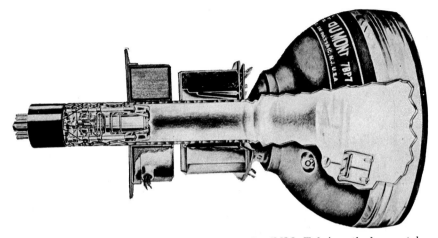

Fig. 8–10. Structure of a modern magnetic (MM Tube) cathode-ray tube. (Courtesy Allen B. DuMont Laboratories, Inc.)

cathode-ray oscillographs are designed specifically for making photographic recordings. The cathode-ray oscillograph has become one of the most versatile electronic devices ever developed.

**8–7. Components of the Cathode-Ray Oscillograph.** The accelerating voltage in the case of cathode-ray tubes is in general much higher than the plate voltages necessary for the various amplifier tubes in the oscillograph and in most applications a much greater ripple voltage can be tolerated. For these reasons it is usually common practice to have two power supplies, a low-voltage well-filtered power supply for the amplifier tubes and a high-voltage power supply, which need not be so well filtered, to furnish the high voltages required by the cathode-ray tube anodes. The cathode-ray tube itself is a relatively insensitive device. Most cathode-ray tubes require deflecting voltages of 100 volts or more to give full screen deflection. In many applications, the voltage to be analyzed is so small that it will not give a noticeable deflection if fed directly into the deflection plates; thus high-gain Class A amplifiers are required to amplify the input signals so they can be analyzed visually. There are two amplifiers, one for amplifying signals to be applied to the vertical deflection plates and the other for amplifying signals to be applied to the horizontal deflection plates. These amplifiers are referred to as vertical and horizontal amplifiers, respectively. The manufacturer of the oscillograph usually specifies in an accompanying booklet the frequency range over which each amplifier gives constant voltage amplification. In order for a signal to be shown as a

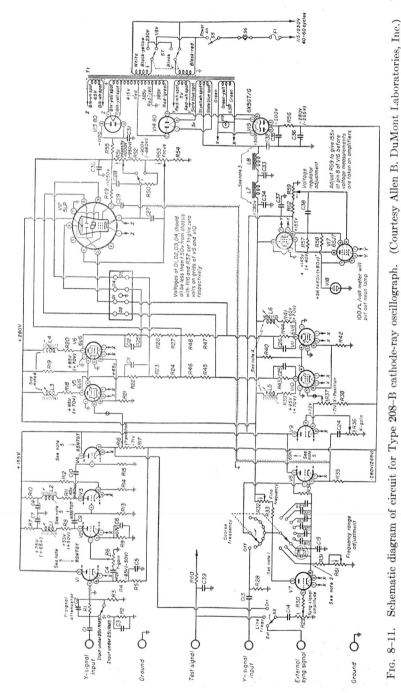

Fig. 8-11.  Schematic diagram of circuit for Type 208–B cathode-ray oscillograph.  (Courtesy Allen B. DuMont Laboratories, Inc.)

function of time, a sweep circuit, commonly termed a saw-tooth oscillator, must be incorporated. The schematic circuit diagram for the Type 208–B DuMont Oscillograph is given in Fig. 8–11 and the block diagram of a typical cathode-ray oscillograph is given in Fig. 8–12.

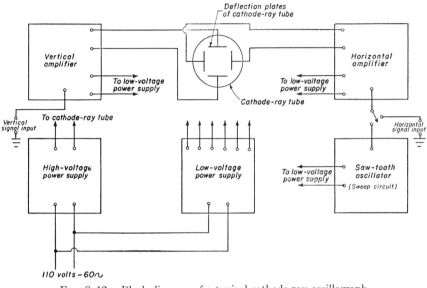

FIG. 8–12.　Block diagram of a typical cathode-ray oscillograph.

**8–8. Sweep Circuit.** One of the most common uses of an oscillograph is to show the wave form to be studied, i.e., the voltage applied to the vertical deflection plates, as a function of time. This can be accomplished by making the beam or spot sweep periodically across the screen and return instantaneously to its zero position. If the voltage applied to the horizontal deflection plates varies linearly with respect to time in the form of a saw-tooth wave and its frequency is equal to the frequency of the unknown voltage applied to the vertical deflection plates, one cycle of the unknown voltage will be shown on the screen (see the sketch of Fig. 8–13). In this sketch the return trace is shown on the screen; however, most oscillographs incorporate a blanking circuit that cuts off the beam current during the return trace, for which reason it cannot be seen. The model 208–B is such an oscillograph.

It is usually desirable that the sweep voltage be of a lower frequency than the voltage to be studied (voltage applied to the vertical deflection plates) so that several cycles of the voltage to be observed will appear on the screen. The number of cycles appearing on the screen can be determined as follows:

$$N = \frac{\text{frequency of wave to be observed}}{\text{frequency of saw-tooth wave}} \qquad (8\text{–}5)$$

where $N$ = number of cycles of the wave that will appear on the screen

If the frequency applied to the vertical deflection plates is less than the frequency of the saw-tooth oscillator, then only parts of the wave to be observed will be seen. This is quite confusing and in most instances undesirable. Fig. 8–14a shows the basic circuit of a saw-tooth oscillator which employs a gas triode and Fig. 8–14b indicates the type wave generated by this circuit. This is the basic circuit employed for obtaining the sweep voltage in most cathode-ray oscillographs.

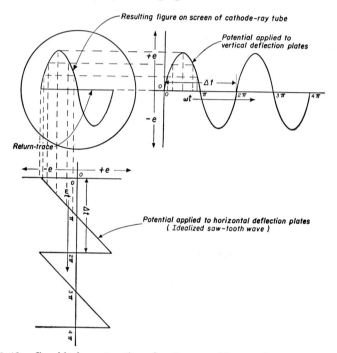

FIG. 8–13. Graphical construction of pattern resulting on the screen of a cathode-ray tube when a sine wave is applied to the vertical deflection plates and a saw-tooth wave to the horizontal deflection plates.

The principle of operation of the saw-tooth oscillator is quite simple. Before the tube fires, i.e., before the voltage across the capacitor $C$ builds up to a value necessary to fire the tube at the grid voltage employed, a simple $RC$ circuit exists. When the voltage across the capacitor reaches the firing voltage of the tube (gas triode), the tube fires and the capacitor discharges through the tube until its potential is less than the deionization potential of the tube; then the tube extinguishes itself and the cycle is repeated. In order to obtain a linear-sweep voltage the firing potential should be made small. In most practical applications the magnitude of the sweep voltage obtained from the saw-tooth oscillator is less than ten percent of $E_{bb}$. The output of the saw-tooth oscillator is amplified before being applied to the horizontal deflection plates.

Eq. (8–6) is an approximate expression for the frequency of the saw-tooth oscillator of Fig. 8–14a.

$$f = \frac{1}{\Delta t} = \frac{1}{(t_2 - t_1)} = \frac{1}{RC \ln\left(\dfrac{E_{bb} - E_d}{E_{bb} - E_f}\right)} \tag{8–6}$$

The terms in this equation are illustrated in Fig. 8–14 and defined below:

$C$ = capacitance in farads in parallel with gas triode
$R$ = resistance in ohms through which $C$ is charged
$E_{bb}$ = applied dc voltage
$E_f$ = voltage necessary for gas triode to fire at grid voltage employed
$E_d$ = voltage at which gas triode ceases to fire
$t_1$ = time in seconds at which voltage across tube begins to build up
$t_2$ = time in seconds at which tube fires
$\Delta t$ = time in seconds for one cycle of saw-tooth wave
$f$ = frequency in cycles/second

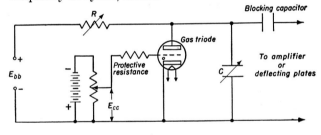

*(a)*

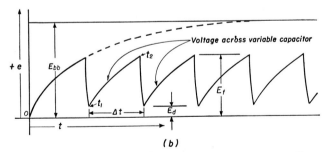

*(b)*

Fig. 8–14.   Circuit diagram and wave form of a saw-tooth oscillator.

From Eq. (8–6) it can be seen that the frequency is inversely proportional to the product of $R$ and $C$. The frequency is also a function of $E_{bb}$, $E_f$ and $E_d$ but can be controlled more conveniently by varying $R$ and $C$ than by varying these voltages.

In commercial oscillographs $R$ is continuously variable over a range of about eight to one and $C$ is variable in steps of around eight to one by a selector switch (see the oscillograph circuit of Fig. 8–11). The maximum frequency of an oscillator of this type is limited by the deionization time of the gas triode. In the case of the Type 208–B, the schematic circuit diagram of which is given in Fig. 8–11, the frequency range of the sweep circuit is from two to fifty thousand cycles per second. If a much higher sweep frequency is needed, a high-vacuum tube sweep circuit is required. Such circuits are capable of producing linear time bases with a range of from two cycles to greater than several million cycles per second.

As indicated by the block diagram of Fig. 8–12, the sweep oscillator is an integral part of the oscillograph and its frequency is controlled by varying $C$ and $R$ with dials on the panel of the oscillograph labeled COARSE FREQUENCY and FINE FREQUENCY, respectively.

## Use of the Cathode-Ray Oscillograph

It is not the object of this discussion to describe specific applications of the oscillograph but rather to acquaint the reader with the operation of an oscillograph and to indicate how it can be used for a few basic applications.

For the purpose of discussing the various controls, etc., of a typical oscillograph, the Type 208–B manufactured by the Allen B. DuMont Laboratories, Inc., will be considered. A photograph of this oscillograph is shown in Fig. 8–15.

In order for any phenomenon to be shown visually as a function of time it is necessary that it be electrical in nature. This means that before a mechanical phenomenon can be studied with an oscillograph an electrical wave or impulse must be produced which varies in exactly the same manner as the mechanical phenomenon to be studied. There are various means of interpreting mechanical changes in terms of electrical variations. A few of the more common instruments for producing electrical variations from mechanical variations are strain gages, piezoelectric crystals and microphones.

**8–9. Signal as a Function of Time.** Let it be assumed that the phenomenon to be studied, although originally mechanical in nature, has been converted to an electrical variation. If the variation in voltage is to be studied as a function of time, it will be applied to the vertical deflection plates, which means it is applied to the terminals of the Y-AXIS AMPLIFIER (Fig. 8–15). In some cases it may be that the signal available is so small that the amplifier in the oscillograph will not give enough gain to produce appreciable deflection on the screen. If such be the case, it will be necessary to amplify the signal before it is applied to the input terminals of the Y-AXIS AMPLIFIER.

The oscillograph under consideration incorporates a toggle switch directly above the gain dial for the Y-AXIS AMPLIFIER which must be in one position if the input signal is below 2.5 volts (rms) and in the opposite position if the voltage is greater than 2.5 volts.   After turning on the power and beam current (switches so labeled) and adjusting the INTENSITY, FOCUS, Y-POSITION and X-POSITION dials to obtain a well-defined spot in

FIG. 8–15.   Typical cathode-ray oscillograph.   (Courtesy Allen B. DuMont Laboratories, Inc.)

the center of the screen, the signal to be observed is applied to the Y-AXIS AMPLIFIER and the gain adjusted until the desirable vertical deflection is obtained on the screen.   The COARSE FREQUENCY selector switch is then adjusted along with the FINE FREQUENCY dial and X-AXIS AMPLIFIER until the desired number of cycles of the proper base length appears on the screen. Generally it makes little difference as to the order in which various adjustments are made. In fact, the intensity and focus, if adjusted first, often require readjustment after the pattern is obtained on the screen. The sweep voltage may be synchronized with the signal (which will result in the pattern on the screen standing still) if a part of the signal is fed into the grid of the gas triode which serves as the basis of the sweep oscillator. This may be accomplished by turning the Sync. Signal Selector to Internal position and adjusting the magnitude of the signal applied to the grid of the gas triode with the dial labeled Sync. Signal Amplitude until the pattern on the screen becomes stationary. If the synchronizing signal is made too large, the pattern on the screen will become distorted. Synchronization may also be accomplished by applying a part of the input signal between the terminal labeled External Sync. Signal and ground and turning the Sync. Signal Selector to External position. If the input signal is of the same frequency as the power frequency (source from which oscillograph gets its power) the Sync. Signal Selector should be turned to Line Frequency and then the magnitude of the synchronizing signal adjusted until the wave is "locked in" or synchronized. The Line Frequency position applies potential of power line frequency to the grid of the gas triode.

**8–10. One Signal as a Function of Another.** In many instances the oscillograph is used to show one variation as a function of another. This may be done by applying one voltage to the Y-Axis Amplifier and the other to the X-Axis Amplifier. The choice of input terminals will of course depend upon which voltage is to be plotted along the vertical axis and which along the horizontal axis. When the oscillograph is used in this way, the Coarse Frequency dial must be turned to the off position so the sweep voltage will not be applied to the horizontal deflection plates at the same time that an external voltage is applied.

**8–11. Phase Angle Determinations.** The cathode-ray oscillograph affords one of the simplest and best methods of comparing frequencies and making phase determinations. If two sinusoidal voltages are applied simultaneously to horizontal and vertical deflection plates of a cathode-ray oscillograph, the resulting pattern on the screen is known as a *Lissajous figure*. This type figure was first obtained by the French mathematician Lissajous well before the advent of the cathode-ray tube. His patterns were traced by a stream of sand falling from a compound pendulum. By proper analysis of the Lissajous figure appearing on the screen, phase and frequency relations of the two motions may be determined.

Let it be assumed that two sinusoidal voltages $E_x$ and $E_y$ which have a phase difference of $\theta$ degrees are applied to the horizontal and vertical deflection plates, respectively, of a cathode-ray tube, as illustrated by the sketch of Fig. 8–16. As shown by Eq. (8–2) the deflection of the beam along the $y$-axis will be proportional to $E_y$ and the position along the $x$-axis at

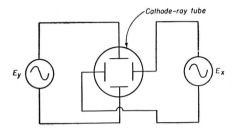

Fɪɢ. 8–16.   Arrangement for determining the phase angle between two voltages.

any instant will be proportional to the instantaneous value of $E_x$. Assuming $E_a$ fixed Eq. (8–2) can be reduced to either the form of (8–7a) or (8–7b).

$$y = K_2 E_y \qquad (8\text{–}7a)$$
$$x = K_1 E_x \qquad (8\text{–}7b)$$

where   $y =$ deflection along the $y$-axis

$x =$ deflection along the $x$-axis

$E_y =$ instantaneous voltage applied to the vertical deflection plates

$E_x =$ instantaneous voltage applied to the horizontal deflection plates

$K_1 =$ constant depending upon circuit parameters and tube sensitivity

$K_2 =$ constant depending upon circuit parameters and tube sensitivity

Since both voltages vary sinusoidally and differ by a phase angle $\theta$, the above equations may be re-written as follows:

$$y = B \sin \omega t \qquad (8\text{–}8a)$$
$$x = A \sin (\omega t - \theta) \qquad (8\text{–}8b)$$

where   $\omega t =$ angle through which sine wave has progressed

$A = K_1 E_{mx}$

$B = K_2 E_{my}$

$E_{my} =$ maximum or peak value of sinusoidal voltage applied to the vertical deflection plates

$E_{mx} =$ maximum or peak value of sinusoidal voltage applied to the horizontal deflection plates

Solving Eqs. (8–8a) and (8–8b) simultaneously and eliminating $\omega t$ gives Eq. (8–9), which is the general equation for the pattern resulting on the screen of the cathode-ray tube.

$$\frac{x^2}{A^2} - \frac{2xy \cos \theta}{AB} + \frac{y^2}{B^2} = \sin^2 \theta \qquad (8\text{–}9)$$

Eq. (8–9) is the equation of an ellipse, the position of which is a function of the phase angle $\theta$. Let it be assumed that the pattern of Fig. 8–17 appears on the screen when $E_x$ and $E_y$ are applied to the deflection plates and that

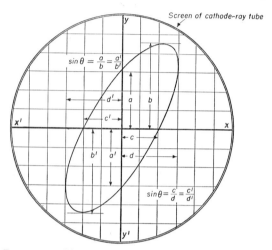

FIG. 8–17. Pattern resulting on the screen of a cathode-ray tube when two sinusoidal voltages of the same frequency which differ by phase angle $\theta$ are applied to horizontal and vertical deflection plates, respectively.

it is required to determine the phase angle between the two voltages. Returning to Eq. (8–9), let $x$ take on the value of zero ($x = 0$) which is the $y$ intercept. Eq. (8–9) then reduces the following form of (8–10a) or (8–10b).

$$\frac{y^2}{B^2} = \sin^2 \theta \qquad\qquad (8\text{–}10a)$$

or
$$\sin \theta = \frac{y}{B} \qquad\qquad (8\text{–}10b)$$

Referring to the sketch of Fig. 8–17,

when
$$x = 0$$
$$y = a = a'$$
$$B = b = b'$$

thus
$$\sin \theta = \frac{a}{b} = \frac{a'}{b'} \qquad\qquad (8\text{–}10c)$$

Similarly
$$\frac{x^2}{A^2} = \sin^2 \theta \qquad\qquad (8\text{–}10d)$$

$$\sin \theta = \frac{x}{A} \qquad\qquad (8\text{–}10e)$$

$$\sin \theta = \frac{c}{d} = \frac{c'}{d'} \qquad\qquad (8\text{–}10f)$$

Applying either Eq. (8–10c) or (8–10f) to the figure obtained on the screen of a cathode-ray tube, the phase angle between the voltages applied to the deflection plates can be readily determined.

If the phase angle between two voltages is known it is possible to predict the pattern that will result on the screen when the voltages are applied to opposite pairs of deflection plates. This can be done by substituting the value of $\theta$ in Eq. (8–9) and plotting sufficient points to determine the pattern. For angles of 0°, 90° and 180°, Eq. (8–9) reduces to forms which are readily recognized.

Consider the case where there is a phase difference of 90° between the two applied voltages.

When $$\theta = 90° \text{ or } (2n - 1) \frac{\pi}{2} \text{ rad}$$

$$\sin \theta = 1$$
and $$\cos \theta = 0$$

Then Eq. (8–9) reduces to the following form:

$$\frac{x^2}{A^2} + \frac{y^2}{B^2} = 1 \tag{8–11}$$

This is the equation of an ellipse which is symmetrical about both $x$ and $y$ axes. If $A$ and $B$ are equal, a circle results (Fig. 8–18a).

When $$\theta = 0°$$
$$\sin \theta = 0$$
$$\cos \theta = 1$$

Then Eq. (8–9) reduces to the following form:

$$\frac{x^2}{A^2} - \frac{2xy}{AB} + \frac{y^2}{B^2} = 0 \tag{8–12a}$$

Factoring $$\left(\frac{x}{A} - \frac{y}{B}\right)^2 = 0$$

$$\frac{x}{A} = \frac{y}{B}$$

$$x = \frac{A}{B} y \tag{8–12b}$$

This is the equation of a straight line which has a slope of $A/B$. If $A$ and $B$ are equal, the straight line makes a 45° angle with the axis (Fig. 8–18b).

When $$\theta = 180°$$
$$\sin \theta = 0$$
$$\cos \theta = -1$$

Then the general equation reduces to the form

$$\frac{x^2}{A^2} + \frac{2xy}{AB} + \frac{y^2}{B^2} = 0 \tag{8–13a}$$

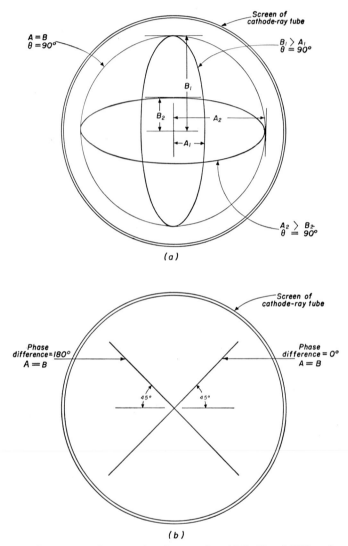

(a)

(b)

Fig. 8–18.  Patterns for phase angles of 90°, 0° and 180°.

Factoring
$$\left(\frac{x}{A} + \frac{y}{B}\right)^2 = 0$$

$$\frac{x}{A} = -\frac{y}{B}$$

$$x = -\frac{A}{B}y \tag{8-13b}$$

This is the equation of a straight line with a slope of $-A/B$. If $A$ and $B$ are equal, the straight line makes a 135° angle with the axis (Fig. 8–18b). The sketches of Fig. 8–19 illustrate patterns that will appear on the screen of the oscillograph for various phase angles between the voltages applied

Phase difference = 0°      Phase difference = 45°      Phase difference = 90°      Phase difference = 135°      Phase difference = 180°

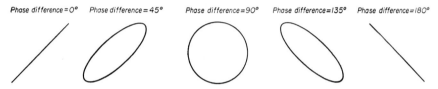

Fig. 8–19. Patterns for various phase angles when the signals applied to vertical and horizontal deflection plates are equal in magnitude.

to horizontal and vertical deflection plates. The resulting pattern on the screen may be determined graphically for any phase angle by plotting the resultant of the instantaneous values of the voltages applied to vertical and horizontal deflection plates.

**8–12. Frequency Comparison.** There are several different ways in which an oscillograph can be used to compare frequencies. As previously shown, if two voltages of the same frequency are applied to opposite pairs of deflection plates, some form of an ellipse will appear on the screen. Thus if one variable frequency oscillator is to be calibrated against another oscillator (which is to be used as a standard) of the same frequency range, it is simply necessary to apply the output of one oscillator (or generator) to one pair of deflection plates and the output of the second to the other pair (through the amplifiers). The frequency of the oscillator to be calibrated is then adjusted until an ellipse is formed on the screen for each cardinal setting on the scale of the standard signal generator and the scale of the uncalibrated oscillator marked accordingly.

If it is desired to compare a variable frequency source with a fixed frequency, the outputs of the two sources are applied to opposite pairs of deflection plates as in the case just described. The Lissajous figures formed on the screen will be different for each frequency ratio; thus by proper analysis of the pattern resulting on the screen the frequency ratio can be determined. The patterns resulting from ratios of 1:3, 2:3 and 1:4 are sketched in Fig. 8–20. Referring to these patterns, the frequency ratio in each case is the ratio of the tangencies to the line $bb'$ to the number of tangencies to line $aa'$. It is obvious that as the frequency ratio increases it becomes increasingly more difficult to interpret the pattern; thus this

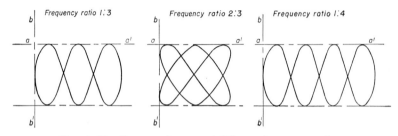

FIG. 8–20.   Patterns for several different frequency ratios.

method of comparison is quite limited. Employing this method of frequency comparison, the variable frequency can only be calibrated conveniently for frequencies that are multiples of the standard frequency and it is usually quite difficult to determine frequency ratios of greater than ten to one with this arrangement.

The pattern formed on the screen as a result of voltages of different frequencies being applied to vertical and horizontal deflection plates can be

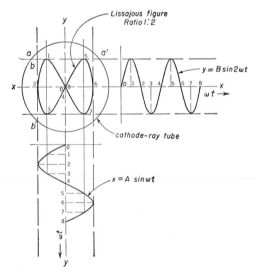

FIG. 8–21.   Graphical construction of the pattern resulting on the screen of a cathode-ray tube for a 1:2 frequency ratio.

determined graphically for any frequency ratio by plotting the resultant of the instantaneous values of the voltages applied to vertical and horizontal deflection plates. The construction of the resulting pattern for a one to two frequency ratio is illustrated in Fig. 8–21. It is a simple matter to determine the equation of such patterns. The equation for the pattern of Fig. 8–21 is derived below.

Assuming that the voltage applied to the horizontal deflection plates varies sinusoidally and that the voltage applied to the vertical deflection plates is also sinusoidal but of twice the frequency of the voltage applied to the horizontal deflection plates, the following equations can be written:

$$x = A \sin \omega t \qquad (8\text{–}14a)$$
$$y = B \sin 2\omega t \qquad (8\text{–}14b)$$
$$y = 2B \sin \omega t \cos \omega t$$
$$y = 2B \sin \omega t \sqrt{1 - \sin^2 \omega t}$$

Substituting the value of $\sin \omega t$ as defined by Eq. (8–14a)

$$y = 2B \frac{x}{A} \sqrt{1 - \left(\frac{x}{A}\right)^2}$$

$$y^2 = \frac{4B^2}{A^2} x^2 - \frac{4B^2}{A^4} x^4 \qquad (8\text{–}15)$$

There are several other methods of comparing frequencies using the cathode-ray oscillograph. The circuit of Fig. 8–22 offers a better method

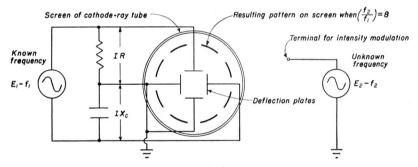

Fig. 8–22.   Circuit arrangement for comparing two frequencies.

than that already described provided the oscillograph available can be *intensity modulated*. By intensity modulation is meant varying the grid voltage of the cathode-ray tube in accordance with a given signal and thereby varying the intensity of the trace on the scope as a function of the signal. The known frequency is applied to the $RC$ circuit, as indicated by Fig. 8–22, and the circuit parameters adjusted so that the two voltages applied to the deflection plates are approximately equal in magnitude. As previously shown, if two voltages of equal magnitude and 90° phase difference are applied to opposite pairs of deflection plates, a circle will result on the screen. Now if the beam of electrons striking the screen is cut off eight times during the time it takes for the beam to sweep through the complete circle, the circle will be cut up into eight segments. The beam will be cut off and on eight times during one cycle of the voltage applied to the deflection plates, if the voltage with which the beam is modulated is of a frequency eight times as great as the voltage which gives rise to the circular pattern. By counting either the number of bright or dark spaces, the frequency ratio can be determined. Higher frequency ratios can be determined with this circuit arrangement than with the former method discussed.

A more elaborate and less common frequency comparison circuit is shown in Fig. 8–23a. It will be noted that this circuit requires that none

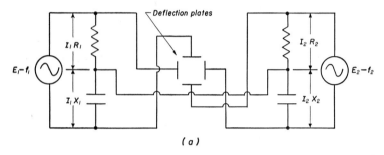

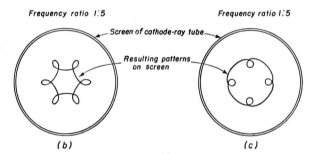

Fɪɢ. 8–23.   Circuit arrangement and oscillograph patterns for frequency comparison.

of the deflection plates be connected together. This means that the voltages to be compared cannot be applied through the amplifiers but must be applied directly to the plates, and unless the voltages are of sufficient magnitude to give appreciable deflection when applied directly to the deflection plates, this method cannot be used. Referring to the pattern resulting on the screen (Fig. 8–23b) the frequency ratio is expressed by Eq. (8–16).

$$\frac{f_2}{f_1} = (N - 1) \tag{8–16}$$

where $N$ = number of loops or cusps

Interchanging $R_1$ and $X_1$ or $X_2$ and $R_2$ but not both will result in the pattern of Fig. 8–23c. In this case the frequency ratio is defined by Eq. (8–17).

$$\frac{f_2}{f_1} = (N + 1) \qquad (8\text{--}17)$$

where $N$ = number of loops or cusps

This method of frequency comparison is interesting but not very practical.

FIG. 8–24.  Dual-beam cathode-ray oscillograph which permits two entirely independent oscillograms to be displayed simultaneously on a single cathode-ray tube screen.  (Courtesy Allen B. DuMont Laboratories, Inc.)

**8–13. Applications.** At present there are many applications of the cathode-ray oscillograph.  A few of the more common are listed below: *

1. Measurement of instantaneous current and power.
2. Frequency measurements.
3. Determination of the ratio of charge to mass of electron.
4. Measurement of phase relationships in various types of circuits.
5. Measurement of amplitude, frequency and phase modulation.
6. Study of oscillatory circuits.

---

* Beverly Dudley, Applications of Cathode Ray Tubes, *Electronics*, Oct., 1942, 49–52.

7. Study of magnetic properties of steel
8. Study of ionosphere characteristics.
9. Study of atmospheric disturbances.
10. Analysis of all types of electronic circuits, such as amplifiers, radios, transmitters, etc.
11. Studies in spectroscopy.
12. Study of the acoustic properties of gases.
13. Study of the velocity of sound through different mediums.
14. Determination of the properties of all types of acoustical devices.
15. Production of pictorial images such as in television.
16. Study of mechanical vibrations, pressure, impact, acceleration, linear and torsional oscillation, stretching, etc.
17. Illumination studies.
18. Study of gaseous reactions.
19. Radio direction and range finding (Radar).
20. Study of the rectification characteristics of various electronic tubes.

Fig. 8–25.   Cathode-ray polar-coordinate indicator designed for studying problems in mechanical engineering. Solution to such problems as the determination of peak transient pressures in fuel-injection systems, the effect of vibration and resonance on precision mechanical linkages, and angular acceleration and torsional stresses in the crankshaft of a gasoline engine when the spark plug fires, are facilitated by use of this oscillograph. (Courtesy Allen B. DuMont Laboratories, Inc.)

**8–14. Specialized Oscillographs.**  There are many specialized types of oscillographs that are much more readily adaptable to specific applications than conventional "all-round" models. Figs. 8–24 and 8–25 are specialized types of cathode-ray oscillographs.

## PROBLEMS

**8–1.** Develop Eq. (8–2). (HINT: Find the equation of curve $OA$ and then determine the slope at point $A$ (Fig. 8–3). The slope is equal to the tangent of $\theta$.)

**8–2.** If the following information is known concerning an electrostatic cathode-ray tube, determine the voltage that must be applied to the vertical deflection plates to move the beam $5 \times 10^{-2}$ m in a vertical direction.

$E_a = 200$ volts
$d = 5 \times 10^{-3}$ m
$l = 2 \times 10^{-2}$ m
$L = 2.5 \times 10^{-1}$ m

**8–3.** Develop Eq. (8–4). (HINT: Assume that straight line $AB$ (Fig. 8–9) when extended intercepts the axis of the tube at $l/2$, that angle $\theta$ is so small that arc $OA$ is approximately equal to $l$ and that $\theta$ measured in radians is equal approximately to $\tan \theta$.)

**8–4.** Assume that the dimensions and voltage given in Prob. 8–2 apply to an MM tube and determine the strength of the magnetic field necessary to give the same deflection.

**8–5.** Design a saw-tooth oscillator that will cover all frequencies from 10 to 10,000 cps. (NOTE: Characteristics of a gas triode, Type 6Q5, suitable for use in saw-tooth oscillator circuits employed as a source of sweep voltage in cathode-ray oscillographs, are given in Fig. 3–10.)

**8–6.** Sketch the pattern resulting on the screen of a cathode-ray tube if two sinusoidal voltages of the same amplitude, which differ by a phase angle of 30°, are applied to horizontal and vertical deflection plates, respectively. Repeat for angles of 60° and 120°.

**8–7.** Sketch and derive the equation of the pattern resulting on the screen of a cathode-ray tube if a 60-cycle voltage is applied to the horizontal deflection plates and a 180-cycle voltage is applied to the vertical deflection plates.

**8–8.** Sketch both possible patterns that may be obtained on the screen of a cathode-ray oscillograph for frequency ratios of 1:3, 1:6, 1:8 and 1:10, when the method of frequency comparison illustrated in Fig. 8–23 is used.

**8–9.** Explain the procedure to be followed if the current in a given circuit is to be shown as a function of time.

**8–10.** Outline and explain how the cathode-ray tube or cathode-ray oscillograph might possibly be used to solve a problem in your particular field of endeavor.

## BIBLIOGRAPHY

BLY, MERWYN. *A Guide to Cathode Ray Patterns.* New York: John Wiley & Sons, Inc., 1943.
*The Cathode-Ray Tube and Typical Applications.* Clifton, N. J.: Allen B. DuMont Laboratories. 1948.

*Cathode-Ray Tubes and Allied Types*. Harrison, N. J.: RCA Manufacturing Company. 1935.

CRUFT LABORATORY STAFF. *Electronic Circuits and Tubes*. New York: McGraw-Hill Book Co., Inc., 1947, pp. 304–24.

DOW, W. G. *Fundamentals of Engineering Electronics*. New York: John Wiley & Sons, Inc., 1937, pp. 84–93.

DUDLEY, BEVERLY. Applications of Cathode Ray Tubes. *Electronics*. October, 1942, 49–52.

FINK, D. C. *Principles of Television Engineering*. New York: McGraw-Hill Book Co., Inc., 1940, pp. 120–63.

HOAG, J. B. *Basic Radio*. New York: D. Van Nostrand Co., Inc., 1942, pp. 147–75.

MALOFF, I. G., and EPSTEIN, D. W. *Electron Optics in Television*. New York: McGraw-Hill Book Co., Inc., 1938, pp. 100–239.

MAYER, H. F. Cathode Ray Oscillograph Applications. *Electronics*. April, 1938, 14–16.

MILLMAN, JACOB, and SEELY, SAMUEL. *Electronics*. New York: McGraw-Hill Book Co., Inc., 1941, pp. 63–86.

*Reference Manual—Cathode-Ray Tubes and Instruments*. Passaic, N. J.: Allen B. DuMont Laboratories. 1946.

REICH, H. J. *Theory and Applications of Electron Tubes*. 2nd ed. New York: McGraw-Hill Book Co., Inc., 1944, pp. 628–47.

RIDER, J. F. *The Cathode-Ray Tube at Work*. New York: J. F. Rider, 1935.

RYDER, J. D. *Electronic Engineering Principles*. New York: Prentice-Hall, Inc., 1947, pp. 39–52.

SOLLER, T., STARR, M. A., and VALLEY, G. E. *Cathode Ray Tube Displays*. New York: McGraw-Hill Book Co., Inc., 1948, pp. 1–110.

TERMAN, F. E. *Radio Engineers Handbook*. New York: McGraw-Hill Book Co., Inc., 1943, pp. 322–44.

WESTINGHOUSE ELECTRIC CORPORATION. *Industrial Electronics Reference Book*. New York: John Wiley & Sons, Inc., 1948, pp. 162–70.

ZWORYKIN, V. K., and MORTON, G. A. *Television*. New York: John Wiley & Sons, Inc., 1940, pp. 329–93.

ZWORYKIN, V. K., MORTON, G. A., RAMBERG, E. G., HILLIER, J., and VANCE, A. W. *Electron Optics and the Electron Microscope*. New York: John Wiley & Sons, Inc., 1945, pp. 1–55.

## CHAPTER 9

## LIGHT–SENSITIVE DEVICES

Not long after the discovery of the photoelectric effect by H. Hertz in 1887, physicists were able to construct photoelectric tubes that were somewhat similar to those in use today. However, the potentialities of photoelectric tubes in industry did not begin to be realized until around 1930. Since that time, the use of phototubes has increased until now they are almost indispensable in many manufacturing processes. The number of applications of light-sensitive devices is quite large. Some of the more common applications are:

1. Counting objects on conveyor belts.
2. Control of automatic sheet catchers in steel mills.
3. Determining the velocity of projectiles.
4. Temperature control.
5. Humidity control.
6. Illumination control.
7. Leveling of elevators.
8. Opening and closing of doors.
9. Smoke density indicators.
10. Burglar alarms.
11. Automatic control of punch and shearing machines.
12. Control of paper cutting and paper folding machines.
13. Turbidity indicators.
14. Control of concentration of solutions.
15. Timing of various processes.
16. Traffic control.
    *a*) Lights
    *b*) Speed traps
17. Sound motion pictures.
18. Inspection of various types of manufactured products as to:
    *a*) Size
    *b*) Shape
    *c*) Variation in color
    *d*) Variation in opaqueness
    *e*) Variation in reflecting properties
    *f*) Mechanical imperfections

**9–1. Types of Light-Sensitive Devices.** Light-sensitive devices can be divided into three general categories:

1. Photoelectric tubes
2. Photovoltaic cells
3. Photoconductive cells

Photoelectric tubes constitute the most important group of light-sensitive devices and the only group that falls under the classification of electronic tubes. The other two groups are discussed briefly in order that the student may have some appreciation of the relative merits of each type, thereby aiding him in selecting the proper type of device for a given application.

*Photoelectric Effect.* Light-sensitive devices that depend upon the emission of electrons from a cathode due to the energy they receive from light rays impinging upon its surface are said to operate due to the photoelectric effect and are known as photoelectric or phototubes.

*Photovoltaic Effect.* Light-sensitive devices that generate a difference of potential in response to radiant energy are known as photovoltaic cells and are said to operate due to the photovoltaic effect. The photovoltaic cell is the only device known which will transform light energy directly into electrical energy. Photovoltaic cells are second in importance to phototubes.

*Photoconductive Effect.* If the resistance of a device is a function of illumination, the device exhibits what is termed the photoconductive effect. Photosensitive devices that operate due to this effect are known as photoconductive cells. Photoconductive cells are the least important of the three types of photosensitive devices. There are, however, a few specialized applications where other types of photosensitive devices cannot be used.

**9–2. Photoelectric Tubes.** The photoelectric effect and wavelength response of various photoelectric emitters were considered in Section 1–4 under the topic of photoelectric emission, and phototube circuits are discussed in Sections 12–1, 12–2, 12–3, 12–4 and 12–5 under the general topic of photoelectric control circuits. Therefore, the discussion here will be limited primarily to characteristics of phototubes.

Phototubes are diodes in that they have only two electrodes, a cathode and an anode, contained within an evacuated or low pressure gas-filled envelope. These electrodes, however, do not have any close resemblance to the electrodes of a high-vacuum or gas-filled thermionic diode. The cathode is of relatively large surface area in order that appreciable emission may be obtained. It usually takes the form of a half-cylinder which generally has between 0.5 and 2.5 square inches of effective emitting surface. The cathode is made of copper, nickel or some similar metal which is coated with a suitable photosensitive emitting material. The cathode-emitting surface is the most important feature of the tube since it determines the wavelength response and the sensitivity of the tubes. Commercial phototubes are available which will give maximum response at almost any desired wavelength. Wavelength-response curves for the more common commercial photosurfaces are illustrated by the curves of Fig. 9–1. Tubes

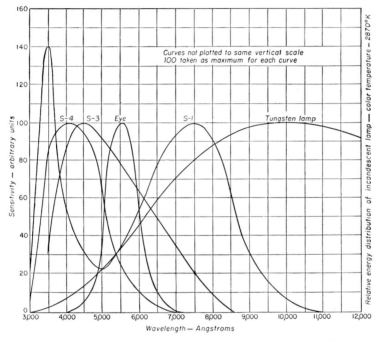

FIG. 9–1.   Relative response of the human eye and several commercial photosurfaces and the energy distribution for a tungsten lamp operated at 2,870° K. (Information courtesy Radio Corp. of America.)

utilizing surfaces S–1 and S–3 will not operate properly if the ambient temperature is greater than 100° Centigrade and the maximum temperature that can be tolerated by tubes which employ an S–4 surface is 75° Centigrade. In order for the wavelength response of these surfaces to be compared to that of the human eye and the spectral characteristics of a tungsten lamp, the spectral characteristics of a tungsten lamp and the human eye are plotted on the same curve sheet.

The anode of a phototube is extremely simple. It usually consists of a straight cylindrical wire of small cross section lying along the center line of the semicylindrical cathode. The anode is made small in order to prevent appreciable shading of the cathode. Because of the extremely low plate dissipation there is no necessity for a large anode. Sketches of the electrodes of a typical phototube are shown in Fig. 9–2.

All typical phototubes, regardless of the color response of the emitter, fall into two general categories, gas-filled phototubes and high-vacuum phototubes. Gas-filled tubes depend upon ionization as a means of handling larger currents than are possible in the case of high vacuum photo-

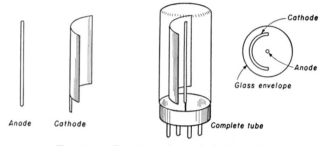

FIG. 9–2. Structure of a typical phototube.

tubes. Ionization also results in greater sensitivity than is obtainable for a high-vacuum tube with the same cathode surface. High-vacuum tubes, on the other hand, possess greater linearity, have better frequency response and more stable characteristics. Typical high-vacuum (Type 917) and

FIG. 9–3. Typical (a) high-vacuum and (b) gas-filled phototubes. (Courtesy Radio Corp. of America.)

gas-filled (Type 918) phototubes are shown in Figs. 9–3a and 9–3b, respectively. The average anode characteristics of the Type 917 and the Type 918 are shown in Figs. 9–4 and 9–5, respectively.

The *sensitivity* of a phototube is the ratio of the change in anode cur-

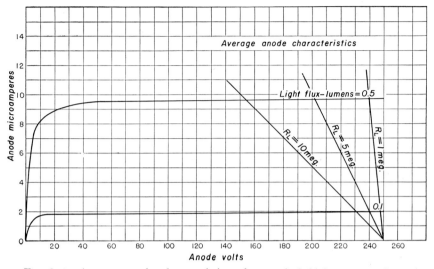

FIG. 9–4.   Average anode characteristics of a typical high-vacuum phototube Type 917.   (Courtesy Radio Corp. of America.)

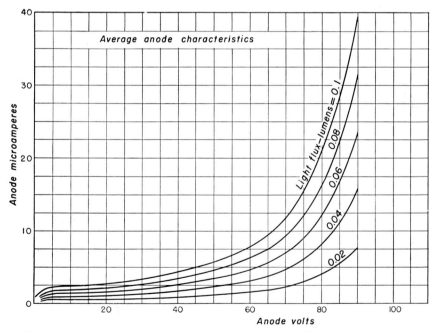

FIG. 9–5.   Average anode characteristics of a typical gas-filled phototube Type 918. (Courtesy Radio Corp. of America.)

rent to the corresponding change in light flux necessary to produce the
given change in anode current.  Sensitivity is generally expressed in microamperes per lumen.  By comparing the curves of Figs. 9–4 and 9–5 it can
be seen that the sensitivity of the gas phototube (Type 918) is much
greater than the sensitivity of the high-vacuum tube (Type 917).  It can
also be seen that the sensitivity of the gas tube changes appreciably over
the operating range of the tube while the sensitivity of the high-vacuum
tube remains essentially constant.

Before a tube is chosen for any particular application, careful consideration should be given to the frequency to be handled, the sensitivity required,
the wavelength of the light source and possible amplifying circuits to be
used in conjunction with the tube.  In general, gas tubes are used where
large sensitivity is necessary and precision or accuracy is not of utmost
importance.  One of the most common applications of gas-filled phototubes
is in connection with sound motion pictures.  High-vacuum phototubes
are used in circuits where the frequency of the light source is beyond the
satisfactory operating range of gas tubes or where greater precision than
that obtained from gas-filled phototubes is required.  Many types of instruments which operate due to a change in illumination utilize high-
vacuum phototubes.

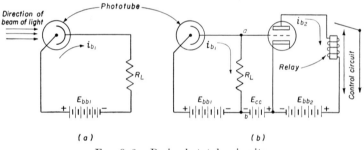

Fig. 9–6.   Basic phototube circuits.

**9–3. Basic Phototube Circuits.**  A basic phototube circuit is shown in
Fig. 9–6$a$.  Variation in the amount of luminous flux falling on the cathode
of the phototube will produce a corresponding variation in the current
through the resistance $R_L$, which in turn results in a variation in the
voltage across this resistance.  Although $R_L$ might be replaced by an indicating device which would give an indication of the change in illumination, the variation in the current obtainable, even with a large change in
light flux, is generally not sufficient for the direct operation of indicating
devices.  This means that the change in phototube current must be amplified before it is suitable for any practical application.

The arrangement of Fig. 9–6$b$ illustrates how a phototube can be used
to operate a relay, the exciting current of which is much in excess of the
current capacity of the phototube.  In this circuit the variation in photo-

tube current produced as a result of variation in illumination varies the grid potential of the amplifier tube. The resulting change in grid voltage of the amplifier tube produces a much greater change in the plate current of the amplifier tube than the original change in the phototube current. Often several stages of amplification are required before the signal is sufficiently large to operate the necessary equipment, instruments, etc. In many cases the output of the phototube is used to trigger the grid of a gas tube which in turn operates a relay, thereby energizing a control circuit. (See Section 12–1.)

The phototube current for a given set of conditions may be readily determined if the characteristics of the phototube are available.

Referring to the circuit of Fig. 9–6a or the section of the circuit of Fig. 9–6b to the left of points a and b, the following relation can be written:

$$E_{bb1} = i_{b1}R_L + e_{b1} \qquad (9\text{–}1)$$

where $E_{bb1}$ = battery voltage
$i_{b1}$ = phototube current
$R_L$ = load resistance
$e_{b1}$ = difference in potential between cathode and anode of phototube

This is the equation of the load line (see Section 5–1 for a discussion of load line) which can be constructed on the family of average anode characteristics for the phototube in question, by determining either two points or one point and the slope. Two points can be determined as follows:

When                           $i_{b1} = 0$

$e_{b1} = E_{bb1}$

and when                       $e_{b1} = 0$

$$i_{b1} = \frac{E_{bb1}}{R_L}$$

Load lines for 1, 5 and 10 megohms are constructed on the characteristics of the Type 917 high-vacuum phototube (Fig. 9–4).

The phototube current for a given light flux and load resistance is obtained by reading the value of current from the graph (Fig. 9–4) which corresponds to the intersection of the load line and the volt-ampere curve for the light flux in question. Although the load lines constructed are for a high-vacuum phototube, the same procedure would be followed for a gas phototube. The voltage across the load resistance, which is the voltage applied in series with $E_{cc}$ to the grid of the amplifier tube, is the product of the phototube current and the load resistance. The difference in potential between grid and cathode (which is the algebraic sum of the voltage developed across $R_L$ and the grid bias $E_{cc}$) having been obtained, the plate current of the amplifier tube can be determined by referring to the characteristics of the amplifier tube. If the light flux falling on the phototube varies with time, the corresponding variation in grid potential may be obtained graphically by employing essentially the same procedure outlined above. The output signal of the amplifier can then be obtained by applying the methods of amplifier analysis outlined in Chapter 5.

If the intensity of the light source used for excitation of the phototube is known, the light flux falling on the cathode of the phototube can be calculated from Eq. (9–2).

$$F = \frac{IA}{d^2} \qquad (9\text{–}2)$$

where $F$ = light flux in lumens

$I$ = luminous intensity of light source in candle power

$A$ = area of the cathode

$d$ = distance between light source and cathode of phototube

Both $A$ and $d$ must be expressed in the same system of units.

**9–4. Photovoltaic Cells.** E. Becquerel in 1839 discovered that a difference of potential exists between the terminals of two electrodes when immersed in an electrolyte, provided either one of the electrodes or the electrolyte is illuminated. This phenomenon, which is known as the photovoltaic effect, is utilized in photovoltaic cells. Photovoltaic cells are in no way similar to photoelectric tubes either in structure or characteristics. Photovoltaic cells are generators which transform light energy directly into electrical energy. The photovoltaic cell is not a very efficient generator, however, for less than one-half of one percent of the radiant energy falling on the light-sensitive surface of the cell is converted into electrical energy.

There are two basic types of photovoltaic cells, lead nitrate cells (wet cells) and barrier-layer cells (dry cells). Although the early photovoltaic cells were of the lead nitrate type, at present lead nitrate cells have been entirely superseded by barrier-layer cells and thus are no longer of commercial importance.

*Lead Nitrate Cells.* One type of lead nitrate cell, which is known as the Rayfoto cell, is comprised of a cuprous oxide-coated electrode and a lead electrode immersed in a lead nitrate solution. When light of the necessary intensity and wavelength passes through the electrolyte (lead nitrate solution) and strikes the cuprous oxide, a difference of potential will exist between the two electrodes. Another type of lead nitrate cell, which is known as the Photolytic cell, is comprised of two cuprous oxide electrodes immersed in a lead nitrate solution.

*Barrier-Layer Cells.* Barrier-layer cells were first made commercially available in the early thirties. Photronic and Photox cells are the two most common barrier-layer cells. The Photronic cell is an iron selenide cell and the Photox cell is a cuprous oxide cell.  The iron selenide cell consists basically of a thin layer of iron selenide coated on an iron disk which in turn is coated with a translucent metal and mounted firmly in a suitable

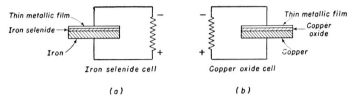

Iron selenide cell          Copper oxide cell

(a)                                    (b)

FIG. 9–7.  Basic circuits for the two most common types of photovoltaic cells.

insulated case containing a transparent window in order to allow light to fall upon the coating of translucent metal.  Copper oxide cells are quite similar to iron selenide cells.  Such cells employ a copper disk instead of an iron disk.  The copper disk is oxidized on one side and the oxidized side is coated with a translucent metal upon which light falls.  Figs. 9–7a and 9–7b illustrate the basic circuits of iron selenide and copper oxide cells and Fig. 9–8 shows a typical iron selenide cell (photronic cell).*

The photovoltaic cell when used in conjunction with the proper type filter can be made to exhibit a wavelength response almost identical to that of the human eye.  The curves of Fig. 9–9 indicate how the wavelength response of a typical photronic cell (Weston Model 594–Type 3) compares to that of the human eye when different window materials are employed.  The curves of Fig. 9–10

FIG. 9–8.  Typical iron selenide cell. (Courtesy Weston Electrical Instrument Corp.)

show how the output current of a typical photovoltaic cell is a function of the illumination and external resistance.

A study of the curves of Fig. 9–10 will indicate that in order to obtain appreciable sensitivity the external circuit resistance must be quite low. Because of the low external resistance required, the output of a photovoltaic cell is not suitable for amplification with the conventional vacuum-tube amplifier circuits.  This is the most serious disadvantage of the photovoltaic cell and renders it unsuitable for many applications.  Because of this fact, photovoltaic cells are limited in use to the operation of very

* Both copper oxide and iron selenide cells considered here are known as *front-effect* cells.  If the metallic film is omitted the cell becomes a *back-effect* cell.  Conduction is in the opposite direction in a back-effect cell and the current sensitivity is much less.

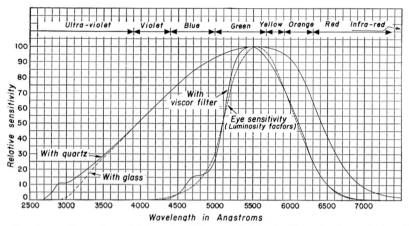

FIG. 9–9.  Spectral sensitivity of a Weston Model 594–Type 3 photovoltaic cell. (Courtesy Weston Electrical Instrument Corp.)

small relays, etc., that can be operated from the output of the cell itself without amplification.  In order to open or close a heavy relay, a chain of several relays is required, the current capacity of each increasing progressively until the required current capacity is obtained.  Such an arrangement is illustrated in Fig. 9–11.  The speed with which an arrangement of this sort can operate is limited by the speed with which the relays can open and close and therefore cannot be made to respond to very rapid fluctuations.  Relays are also quite expensive, which is one reason for the greater use of phototubes in photosensitive control circuits.

For some applications, such as light meters, etc., photovoltaic cells are superior to phototubes.  Because they do not require an external source of power and have excellent wavelength response, photovoltaic cells make ideal light measuring devices.  A light meter consists essentially of a photovoltaic cell connected across a microammeter which is calibrated in foot-candles instead of microamperes.  Different scales can be obtained by shunting the micro-

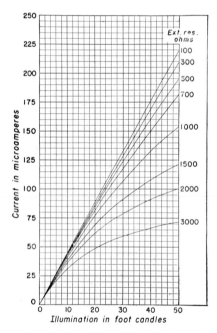

FIG. 9–10.  Effect of illumination and external resistance on current output of Type 3RR cell. (Tungsten lamp at 2,700° K.) (Courtesy Weston Electrical Instrument Corp.)

ammeter with resistances of suitable values. Fig. 9–12 shows a Weston
Model 756 illumination meter which has three different scales.

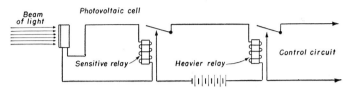

FIG. 9–11.  Arrangement for operating a relay which requires more current than
is available from a photovoltaic cell.

FIG. 9–12.  Commercial illumination meter. (Courtesy Weston Electrical Instrument Corp.)

**9–5. Photoconductive Cells.** The photoconductive effect was first reported by W. Smith in 1873.  Smith discovered that the resistance of selenium crystals varied with the light intensity falling on crystals.  The
photoconductive cell is a nonlinear circuit element, the impedance of which
is a function of the light falling on it.  Although photoconductive cells

have been made with a ratio of light to dark resistance of as high as 1 to 20 and with current capacities as high as 0.25 ampere, most commercial cells have a *light* to *dark* resistance ratio of not better than 1 to 10 and will pass only a few milliamperes. Photoconductive cells are quite sensitive to temperature changes and tend to give erratic results if exposed to the weather. They also exhibit appreciable time lag which makes them unsuitable for any application where response to rapid light fluctuations is necessary.

At present photoconductive cells are of little commercial importance. Two types of photoconductive cells are the selenium cell and the thalafide cell. Thalafide cells are sensitive to the violet end of the spectrum as well as to red and infrared radiation, while selenium cells have little sensitivity except to red and infrared radiation. Because of their few applications, photoconductive cells will not be discussed further here.

**9–6. Comparison of Phototubes, Photovoltaic Cells and Photoconductive Cells.** Phototubes, because of their greater linearity, negligible time lag and independency of ambient temperature, are superior to either photovoltaic or photoconductive cells for most applications. Although the current capacity of phototubes is small, the external circuit resistance can be made quite large; thus the output can be readily amplified by conventional vacuum-tube amplifier circuits to almost any desired power level. Photovoltaic and photoconductive cells have relatively high current capacities and are capable of carrying sufficient current to operate small relays, etc., directly; however, the low external impedance required makes amplification with conventional amplifier circuits impractical. Photovoltaic cells do not require an external source of power as do both phototubes and photoconductive cells; thus they are ideal for exposure meters and similar applications where the current demands are small and the inclusion of an external power would be quite inconvenient. Photoconductive cells require an external power source, possess a slower dynamic response and are more sensitive to changes in ambient temperature than photovoltaic cells. Because of their many disadvantages and relatively few merits, photoconductive cells have very few applications.

## PROBLEMS

**9–1.** From the curves of Fig. 9–1 determine the photosensitive surface that will give maximum response to (a) blue, (b) red and (c) violet light.

**9–2.** Assuming load resistances of 1 and 0.25 megohms and $E_{bb1} = 80$ v, plot curves of phototube current as a function of light flux for a type 918 phototube.

**9–3.** If the circuit parameters listed below are used in the circuit of Fig. 9–6a, determine the change in phototube current resulting in a change in light flux of from 0.1 to 0.5 lumen.

$$R_L = 5 \text{ megohms} \qquad E_{bb1} = 250 \text{ v} \qquad \text{Tube—Type 917}$$

**9–4.** The output signal from a phototube circuit is applied to the grid of a one-stage triode amplifier circuit. Assuming the circuit parameters listed below, determine the change in voltage produced across the load resistance of the amplifier circuit when the light flux changes from 0.02 to 0.04 lumen.

*Phototube Circuit*

Tube—Type 918
$R_L$ = 1 megohm
$E_{bb}$ = 90 v

*Amplifier Circuit*

Tube—Type 6C5
$r_p$ = 10,000 ohms
$g_m$ = 2,000 micromhos
$\mu$ = 20
$R_L$ = 50,000 ohms

**9–5.** If the following information is known concerning the circuit of Fig. 9–6b, calculate the change in the relay current when a 16 candlepower lamp is turned on at a distance of 1 ft. from the phototube. (Assume that the lamp is the only source of light.)

*Phototube Circuit*

Tube—High-vacuum type, the sensitivity
  of which can be considered to remain
  constant at 20 microamperes/lumen
Area of photoelectric emitting surface =
  1 sq. in.
$R_L$ = 0.5 megohm

*Amplifier Circuit*

Tube—Type 6J5
$r_p$ = 6,667 ohms
$g_m$ = 3,000 micromhos
$\mu$ = 20
Relay resistance = 1,000 ohms

**9–6.** Show how the circuit of Fig. 9–6b could be changed so that an increase in illumination will result in a decrease instead of an increase in relay current.

**9–7.** How may the wavelength response of a given photovoltaic cell be changed?

**9–8.** If the photovoltaic cell employed in the circuit of Fig. 9–11 is a Weston Type 3RR photovoltaic cell and the relay has a resistance of 500 ohms, determine the relay current produced by 30 foot-candles.

**9–9.** What is the most common application of photovoltaic cells?

**9–10.** List five possible applications of photosensitive devices not listed in this chapter.

## BIBLIOGRAPHY

ALBERT, A. L. *Fundamental Electronics and Vacuum Tubes.* New York: The Macmillan Co., 1947, pp. 443–63.

CAMPBELL, N. R., and RITCHIE, D. *Photoelectric Cells.* London: Sir Isaac Pitman & Sons, Ltd., 1934, pp. 23–111.

Dow, W. G. *Fundamentals of Engineering Electronics.* New York: John Wiley & Sons, Inc., 1937, pp. 339–424.

EASTMAN, A. V. *Fundamentals of Vacuum Tubes.* 2nd ed. New York: McGraw-Hill Book Co., Inc., 1941, pp. 122–37.

FIELDING, T. J. *Photo-Electric and Selenium Cells.* Pittsburgh, England: Instruments Publishing Co., 1935.

FINK, D. C. *Engineering Electronics.* New York: McGraw-Hill Book Co., Inc., 1938, pp. 160–81.

HENNEY, KEITH. *Electronic Tubes in Industry.* New York: McGraw-Hill Book Co., Inc., 1941, pp. 299–329.

HUGHES, A. L., and DUBRIDGE, L. A. *Photoelectric Phenomena.* New York: McGraw-Hill Book Co., Inc., 1932, pp. 7–37, 352–67.

JANES, R. B., and GLOVER, A. M. Recent Developments in Phototubes. *RCA Review.* 1941, **6**, 43–54.

KLOEFFLER, R. G. *Industrial Electronics and Control.* New York: John Wiley & Sons, Inc., 1949, pp. 158–78.

———. *Principles of Electronics.* New York: John Wiley & Sons, Inc., 1942, pp. 136–48.

LANGE, BRUNO. *Photoelements and Their Applications.* New York: Reinhold Publishing Corporation, 1938, pp. 22–43.

MILLMAN, JACOB, and SEELY, SAMUEL. *Electronics.* New York: McGraw-Hill Book Co., Inc., 1941, pp. 478–98.

REICH, H. J. *Theory and Applications of Electron Tubes.* 2nd ed. New York: McGraw-Hill Book Co., Inc., 1944, pp. 533–60.

RYDER, J. D. *Electronic Engineering Principles.* New York: Prentice-Hall, Inc., 1947, pp. 369–81.

WESTINGHOUSE ELECTRIC CORPORATION. *Industrial Electronics Reference Book.* New York: John Wiley & Sons, Inc., 1948, pp. 116–36.

ZWORYKIN, V. K., and RAMBERG, E. G. *Photoelectricity and Its Applications.* New York: John Wiley & Sons, Inc., 1949.

ZWORYKIN, V. K., and WILSON, E. D., *Photocells and Their Applications.* New York: John Wiley & Sons, Inc., 1932.

# CHAPTER 10

## X–RAYS

At the December, 1895, meeting of the Wurzburg Physico-Medical Society, W. K. Roentgen, Professor of Physics at the University of Wurzburg, Germany, announced his recent discovery (on November 8, 1895) of a new kind of radiation.* Roentgen found that this new type of radiation—first termed *Roentgen rays*, later *x-rays*—would penetrate, and thus photograph the internal structure of objects ordinarily considered opaque. The discovery of x-rays is considered one of the more important of scientific discoveries. During the past half-century, the number of commercial and scientific applications of x-rays has steadily increased so that use of x-rays is now routine in almost every major field of industrial and scientific endeavor. During his lifetime Roentgen had the satisfaction of seeing his discovery become a major diagnostic aid in the field of medicine; yet since his death in 1923 the use of x-rays in medicine has increased many times over. The same is true in numerous other fields, such as engineering, metallurgy, atomic physics, photo-chemistry, biology and genetics, to name but a few.

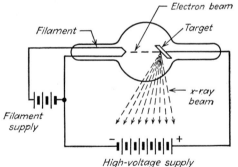

Fig. 10–1. Basic circuit arrangement for generating x-radiation.

The generation of x-radiation is associated with stoppage of high velocity electrons. Although it requires extremely high accelerating voltages to produce the more useful x-rays of appreciable penetrating power, x-rays of low penetrating power are often produced in ordinary high-voltage electronic tubes. The sketch of Fig. 10–1 illustrates the production of x-radia-

---

* G. L. Clark, *Applied X-Rays*, 3rd ed. (New York: McGraw-Hill Book Co., Inc., 1940), p. 3.

tion in a typical x-ray tube. Although in practice neither the accelerating voltage nor filament voltage is supplied by batteries, batteries are used in this illustration to avoid the necessity of showing the rather complicated power supply circuits actually used. Power supply circuits used in connection with x-ray tubes are discussed in Section 10–2.

At present there are numerous types of x-ray tubes; however, all types can be grouped into two general categories: gas or ion tubes, and high-vacuum tubes. The earlier x-ray tubes were of the ion type. In 1913 W. D. Coolidge introduced a new type of x-ray tube, one evacuated to the best vacuum obtainable at that time. The development of the *Coolidge*, or high-vacuum x-ray tube, is one of the more outstanding developments in the field of x-rays. At present, the gas tube has been almost entirely superseded by the high-vacuum type. The applications of gas tubes are restricted chiefly by their limited voltage range. In general, gas or ion tubes cannot be designed to stand voltages of greater than about 50,000 volts. The wavelengths best suited to medical diagnosis generally necessitate voltages of between 50,000 and 100,000 volts. Much higher voltages are required for most industrial radiography. Accordingly, gas tubes, because of their limited voltage range, are not suited to many present day applications. Gas tubes are, however, still used to some extent for x-ray diffraction work.

**10–1. The Coolidge X-Ray Tube.** In this text only the Coolidge (high-vacuum) x-ray tube will be considered. The Coolidge tube is essentially a high-voltage thermionic diode, evacuated to the best obtainable vacuum. The directly-heated filament usually consists of a spiral of fine tungsten wire surrounded by a thin metal cup. This type of construction tends to so focus the beam of electrons that a narrow well-defined beam of relatively high intensity will strike the anode or target. (In x-ray tubes, the anode is usually referred to as the target.) The beam current is limited by the amount of thermionic emission from the cathode. The magnitude of the emission current follows Dushman's equation, which is discussed in Section 2–4. Because of the high voltages involved, x-ray tubes are generally much longer than ordinary high-vacuum diodes. The greater the target voltage (difference in potential between the filament and target), the greater the length. Fig. 10–2 illustrates the relative lengths of one and two million volt x-ray tubes. In some x-ray units the tube is immersed in transformer oil. Use of this oil enables a tube of a given length to stand a higher voltage without breaking down around the outside of the tube. In addition, the oil serves as a cooling medium.

The material of the target may be one of several metals. The more commonly used metals are tungsten, tantalum, molybdenum, copper, and nickel. One of the major problems in designing an x-ray tube is to provide an adequate means of cooling the target. Less than one percent of the

FIG.  10–2.   Photograph illustrating relative sizes of one and two million volt x-ray tubes.  (Courtesy General Electric X-ray Corp.)

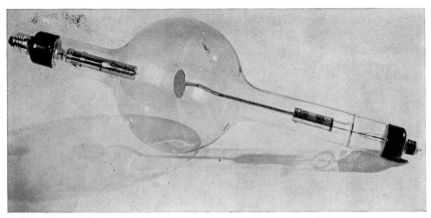

Fig. 10–3.   Universal type Coolidge x-ray tube.   (Courtesy Westinghouse Electric Corp.)

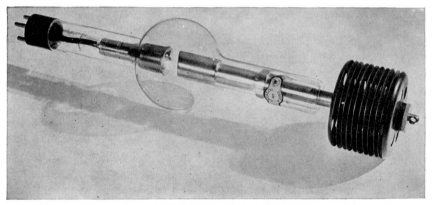

Fig. 10–4.   Non-shockproof 100-kv air-cooled radiographic x-ray tube.   (Courtesy Westinghouse Electric Corp.)

Fig. 10–5.   220-kv shockproof water-cooled x-ray tube.   (Courtesy Westinghouse Electric Corp.)

total energy imparted to the target by the electrons striking it is converted to x-radiation; the remainder is converted into heat. The lower voltage x-ray tubes do not require a special means of cooling. These tubes employ a tungsten target supported by a long rod (Fig. 10–3). Because the heat is radiated at a rate sufficient to hold the tungsten target below its melting point (3370° Centigrade), this *universal* (as it is termed) type of tube does not require an auxiliary cooling system. Another method of cooling is to mount radiating cooling fins on a rod extending from the target. Fig. 10–4 shows a tube employing this method of cooling. The most effective method of cooling is to pass a stream of water through the anode. The x-ray tube of Fig. 10–5 is a typical water-cooled tube. Although not very widely used, there is an x-ray tube on the market in which cooling is accomplished by a rotating target arrangement. The target is rotated by a two-pole induction motor at approximately 3,600 rpm. Such an arrangement does not actually carry heat away from the target; rather, it prevents the heat from becoming localized with a consequent lesser tendency for the target to melt. Obviously, construction and operation of this type of tube present many mechanical difficulties.

**10–2. Circuits for Obtaining High Voltage for X-Ray Tubes.** The fila-ment-target voltage necessary for x-ray tubes is of considerable magnitude. Although most x-ray applications do not require voltages in excess of 500,000 volts, x-ray tubes operating with filament-target voltages of greater than two million volts have been recently developed and put into use for inspection of castings up to 12 inches in thickness. It is obvious that supplying voltages of the magnitude necessary for x-ray tubes and insulating the components to which they are applied are major problems in the design of x-ray equipment.

The self-rectifying circuit for producing high voltages is about the simplest, hence is that most commonly used for relatively low voltage applications such as x-ray diffraction work, dental x-ray machines and other applications requiring a relatively low target voltage. Although both simple and inexpensive, this circuit has several disadvantages: the efficiency is low (however, since the power involved is low, efficiency is not of great importance); the ratio of peak to average dc voltage is high; it is necessary that the x-ray tube be capable of standing the peak value of the output voltage of the transformer. A self-rectifying circuit is illustrated in Fig. 10–6a. Another circuit that is in rather common use, particularly for medium voltage applications, is illustrated in Fig. 10–6b. In this circuit rectification is accomplished in the low voltage, or primary circuit, of the transformer; thus the rectifier tube may have a low voltage rating. Gas rectifier tubes are commonly used in this type circuit.

Other rectifier circuits for obtaining dc for x-ray tubes are illustrated in Figs. 10–6c, 10–6d, 10–6e and 10–6f. Fig. 10–6c is a conventional half-

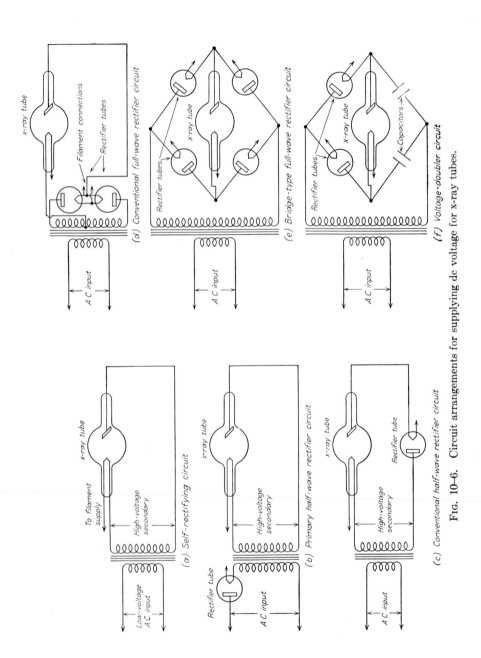

Fig. 10-6.   Circuit arrangements for supplying dc voltage for x-ray tubes.

wave rectifier circuit; Fig. 10–6d is a conventional full-wave rectifier circuit; Fig. 10–6e is a bridge-type full-wave rectifier circuit; and Fig. 10–6f is a voltage-doubler circuit. In each of these circuit diagrams the filament circuit and current and voltage controls have been omitted.

**10–3. Properties of X-Rays.** The range of possible uses of x-rays can best be appreciated by consideration of some of their more important properties:

1. Propagated in straight lines at a velocity of $3 \times 10^8$ meters per second.
2. Can be diffracted, refracted and reflected.
3. Produce fluorescence.
4. Blacken photographic plates.
5. Differentially absorbed by matter, i.e., they are absorbed at different rates by different mediums.
6. Damage or kill living cells, depending upon the time and intensity of exposure.
7. Capable of producing genetic mutations.
8. Capable of penetrating matter that can be penetrated by few other types of radiation.

The effectiveness of a beam of x-rays depends upon the intensity, the *quality* (wavelengths constituting the beam), and the exposure time. The quality of the x-ray beam obtainable from a given tube is a function of the target voltage, and the intensity of the beam is a function of both target voltage and target current.

The intensity or *dosage* of an x-ray beam can be determined by several different methods. One method * consists of causing the beam of x-rays to impinge on a metal block of sufficient size to absorb essentially all of the radiation. By determining the temperature rise of the metal block the energy of the beam can be determined. This method requires very careful measurements and is too complex to be used for general intensity determinations.

A more commonly used method of determining the intensity of an x-ray beam is to measure the extent of the ionization caused by the beam. In fact, it has been found that of the several methods available for determining the intensity of a beam of x-rays, measurement of the amount of ionization produced in a given gas traversed by the beam of x-rays enables the most accurate determination of intensity.

The ionization of air as the basis of international dosage measurement was first accepted by the International Congress of Radiology in 1928. At that time an official definition of the unit dose which was termed the

---

* For a more complete discussion of this method see G. L. Clark, *Applied X-Rays*, 3rd ed. (New York: McGraw-Hill Book Co., Inc., 1940), pp. 62–3.

roentgen unit $r$ was adopted. The original definition was slightly revised by the Fifth International Congress in 1937 to read as follows:

"The roentgen shall be that quantity of x- or gamma radiation such that the associated corpuscular emission per 0.001293 gram of air produces, in air, ions carrying 1 esu of quantity of electricity of either sign." *

There are several portable ionization chambers that are commercially available, the simplest and most common of these being the Victoreen $r$-meter, which is manufactured by the Victoreen Instrument Company.†

The penetrating power of an x-ray beam is a function of the quality of the beam and the quality of the beam is, in turn, a function of the target voltage. The minimum or shortest wavelength that can be radiated from an x-ray target is related to the target voltage by:

$$\lambda_m = \frac{12,345}{E} \text{ Å} \qquad (10\text{–}1)$$

where $\lambda_m$ is the minimum wavelength radiated

$E$ = target voltage

In general, an x-ray beam comprises a continuous band of radiation, the maximum intensity falling at about $1.3\lambda_m$. However, the beam can contain no wavelengths shorter than the value defined by Eq. (10–1).

There are several methods for measuring the quality of an x-ray beam. Clark ‡ describes four methods:

1. Diffraction by ruled gratings.
2. Diffraction by crystals.
3. Refraction in prisms.
4. Measurement of absorption by known metals.

For discussion of the methods of measuring the quality of x-rays, the reader is referred to Clark.

**10–4. Applications of X-Rays.** The major fields of use of x-rays are those of medicine, physics, and the metal industries. The use of x-rays in medicine comprises that branch of medicine now called *medical radiology*. There are two distinct divisions of x-ray usage in medicine: *diagnostic radiology* and *therapeutic radiology*. Diagnostic radiology, which is both the oldest and the most common application of x-rays, is the examination of the human body by either fluoroscopy or radiography. Typical uses of diagnostic radiology are to survey fractured bones preparatory to and after setting; locate defective teeth; locate foreign bodies such as bullets, swallowed pins, etc.; ascertain diseased conditions of internal organs such as

---

* For a more complete discussion of the roentgen, see W. T. Sproull, *X-Rays in Practice* (New York: McGraw-Hill Book Co., Inc., 1946), p. 188.
† For a discussion of the Victoreen $r$-meter, see W. T. Sproull, *X-Rays in Practice* (New York: McGraw-Hill Book Co., Inc., 1946), p. 192.
‡ G. L. Clark, *Applied X-Rays*, 3rd ed. (New York: McGraw-Hill Book Co., Inc., 1940), pp. 80–90.

occur in heart disease, cancer and tuberculosis; and so forth. Therapeutic radiology is the treatment of diseased tissues with x-radiation. Therapeutic radiology falls into two general categories: *superficial therapy*, the treatment of surface conditions such as occur in skin diseases; and *deep therapy*, the treatment of internal conditions such as cancer and tumors. As mentioned, the use of x-rays in the field of medicine is the oldest and most important application; however, inasmuch as this text is devoted primarily to the discussion of industrial applications of electronics, the reader interested in medical radiology is referred to the reference * cited below for further discussion of medical radiology.

In 1912 W. Friedich, P. Knipping and M. Laue discovered that x-rays could be diffracted with crystals. This both opened an entirely new field of usefulness of x-rays and provided the physicist with a most powerful tool for investigating the structure of matter. The study of the crystalline structure of matter by use of x-rays is known as *x-ray crystallography* and the study of the atomic and molecular structure of matter is known as *x-ray diffraction*. For excellent discussions of x-ray crystallography and diffraction, the reader is referred to the books of Clark † and Sproull.‡

The industrial uses of x-rays comprise two main divisions: *industrial radiography* and *industrial fluoroscopy*. Examining the interior of an object for flaws, etc., by passing a beam of x-rays through it and recording the relative intensities of the emerging beam on a photographic plate is termed industrial radiography. Instead of taking a photograph of the internal structure of the object, the internal structure can be observed on an x-ray sensitive fluorescent screen, placed on the side of the object opposite the x-ray source. This type of analysis is termed fluoroscopy.

Aside from their usefulness in the fields of medicine, physics and the metal industries, x-rays have numerous other applications. A few miscellaneous applications include:

1. Location of wires and pipes in walls.
2. Inspection of parcels by postal and immigration authorities.
3. Inspection of wood for internal flaws.
4. Inspection of railroad ties.
5. Inspection of rubber tires.
6. Inspection of radio tubes.
7. Inspection of reclaimed rubber for pieces of metal.
8. Inspection of cereals, boxes of candy, etc., for foreign bodies such as tacks, etc.

* W. T. Sproull, *X-Rays in Practice* (New York: McGraw-Hill Book Co., Inc., 1946), pp. 211–38.
† G. L. Clark, *Applied X-Rays*, 3rd ed. (New York: McGraw-Hill Book Co., Inc., 1940), pp. 231–592.
‡ W. T. Sproull, *X-Rays in Practice* (New York: McGraw-Hill Book Co., Inc., 1946), pp. 320–558.

9. Inspection of fruits.

10. Inspection of paintings, deeds, letters, etc., for authenticity.

11. Inspection of coal for mineral content.

12. Inspection of molded plastic objects for internal defects.

**10–5. Industrial Radiography.** During the past two decades radiography has become one of the more important inspection tools of the metal industries. Radiography makes possible the detection of any type of internal flaw in a casting, etc., provided the casting is not of such dimensions and density that it cannot be penetrated by x-rays. Although the code set up by the American Society of Mechanical Engineers recognizes 5.25 inches as the maximum thickness of a steel casting that can be radiographically inspected, castings up to 12 inches in thickness are now being successfully inspected radiographically. Table 10–1 lists the target voltages necessary for successful penetration of various steel castings.

TABLE  10–1 *

| Maximum Thickness Penetrated (inches) | Target Voltage (volts) |
| --- | --- |
| 2.25 | 200,000 |
| 4.75 | 300,000 |
| 5 | 400,000 |
| 8 | 1,000,000 |

* Adapted by permission from *Radiographic Inspection of Metals* by Otto Zmeskal, published by Harper and Brothers, New York, 1943.

An outstanding advantage of radiographic inspection over other types of inspection is that internal flaws impossible to detect by most other methods can be readily identified.† However, whether or not radiography is the most suitable method of inspection for a particular purpose depends upon several factors. If the product in question can be inspected with the same precision by a simpler and less expensive method, x-ray inspection would, of course, be undesirable. If, on the other hand, internal flaws or imperfections are of such a nature that no other method will disclose them, x-ray inspection must be employed. This is the case in many types of castings and welds. Because of the expense involved, a radiograph of every casting usually is not made unless a failure of any one casting might result in disaster. By proper methods of sampling, the average quality can be con-

† Recently a process known as *supersonic testing* has been developed for the inspection of defects in metals. This process makes use of a *supersonic reflectoscope* which sends a supersonic wave through the material to be inspected. When the wave strikes a flaw, a portion of it is reflected and gives an indication on a cathode-ray tube. Supersonic testing has the advantages of greater penetration (20 ft. of steel) and simplicity. It is displacing x-ray inspection for certain types of applications.

trolled by the inspection of one out of many castings. Radiography is also an excellent developmental tool, for it makes possible the testing of new methods of welding and casting without putting the specimen to a physical test. Radiographic inspection of castings will show, among others, the following types of defects:

1. Cracks
2. Porosity
3. Blow holes
4. Slag inclusions
5. Sand inclusions
6. Shrinkage
7. Metal segregations
8. Improper fusion of chaplets
9. Coarse structure

The following defects can be detected by radiographic inspection of welds:

1. Porosity
2. Slag inclusions
3. Imperfect fusion
4. Incomplete penetration
5. Undercuts
6. Cracks

Although it is possible to detect cavities in forgings radiographically, forgings usually contain negligible internal defects; therefore it is usually considered unnecessary to inspect them radiographically. Sproull states that although he has radiographed many forgings, he discovered only a very few with serious flaws.*

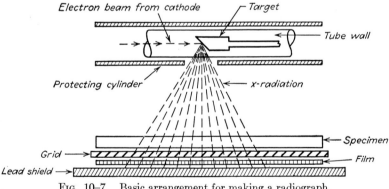

Fig. 10–7.   Basic arrangement for making a radiograph.

Fig. 10–7 illustrates the basic arrangement for making a radiograph. The object to be radiographed is placed in the direct line of the radiation

---

* W. T. Sproull, *X-Rays in Practice* (New York: McGraw-Hill Book Co., Inc., 1946), p. 266.

from the target and at such a distance from the target that the radiation
is essentially from a point source. Other conditions remaining the same,
the sharper the focal point, the sharper will be the outlines of the flaws on
the film. (For the radiographic examination of welded boiler plates, the
minimum distance between the source of radiation and the back of a plate
of certain thickness is prescribed by the A.S.M.E. Boiler Code Committee—
Table 10–2.) A suitable film is placed behind the specimen, i.e., on the
side opposite the source of radiation. The radiation, after being differentially absorbed by the object, exposes the film and gives rise to a shadow
picture. X-ray film is usually much thicker than ordinary optical film and
is generally coated on both sides.* If the target voltage exceeds 100,000

TABLE  10–2 †

| Plate Thickness in Inches | Minimum Distance from Source of Radiation to Back of Weld in Inches |
|:---:|:---:|
| 0–1 | 14 |
| 1–2 | 21 |
| 2–3 | 28 |
| 3–4 | 36 |
| 4–4.25 | 38 |

† *Mechanical Engineering*, 1933, **55**, 269.

volts, intensifier screens are usually used. These screens are placed against
both sides of the film and are held firmly in place by the metal film holder,
termed a *cassette*. The calcium tungstate screen is the most widely used
type of intensifier screen. When such screens are employed, exposure time
is reduced by a factor of from 10 to 15. In general, the film is placed as
close to the back of the specimen as possible in order to reduce blurring and
distortion. The A.S.M.E. Boiler Code Committee ‡ recommends that this
distance be not greater than one inch.

When target voltages of greater than about 200,000 volts are used, the
effects of scattered radiation often make it impossible to identify very small
imperfections. The effects of scattered radiation can be reduced materially
by placing between the film and the specimen a *Bucky grid*, that is, a grid
comprised of alternate strips of wood and lead arranged so that primary
radiation can pass while scattered radiation is absorbed. The Bucky grid
must be moved slowly across the film during exposure in order to prevent
shadows of the lead strips from appearing on the film. In some cases,
instead of a grid, a thin lead screen is placed between the film and the

* For a discussion of industrial x-ray films see W. T. Sproull, *X-Rays in Practice*
(New York: McGraw-Hill Book Co., Inc., 1946), pp. 173–86.
‡ *Mechanical Engineering*, 1933, **55**, 265.

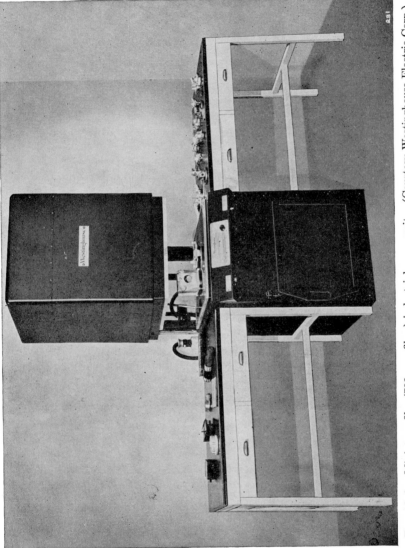

FIG. 10–8.   Miniature film (700 mm films) industrial x-ray unit.   (Courtesy Westinghouse Electric Corp.)

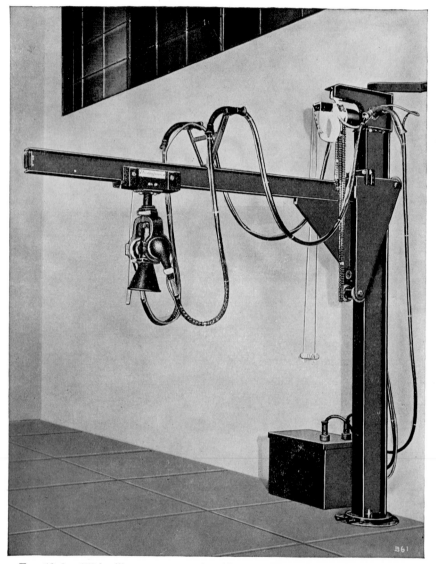

FIG. 10–9.   150-kv jib crane x-ray unit.   (Courtesy Westinghouse Electric Corp.)

object. Because of the low penetrability of scattered radiation, the lead screen will absorb most of the scattered radiation. Both grids and screens decrease the intensity of the primary radiation; but this can be compensated for by additional exposure time and higher target voltage.

Filters are often placed between the x-ray tube and the specimen to filter out the longer wavelengths. In medical deep therapy, filters are used to filter out the longer wavelengths that would be absorbed by the skin. In industrial radiography, filters are employed to filter out the longer wavelengths (softer rays) which have a greater tendency to scatter than the shorter wavelengths (hard rays). This helps to prevent fogging of the film. Aluminum and copper filters from about 0.02 inch to 0.08 inch in thickness are employed in the lower voltage ranges; if the target voltage is in excess of one million volts, lead filters are usually employed.

In general, the manufacturers of industrial radiography equipment supply all the information necessary as to grids, films, filters, intensifier screens, film distance, target voltage, exposure time, current, etc., for given applications. This enables the operator to quickly determine the best conditions for almost any common application, by reference to simple charts and tables.

The photographs of Figs. 10–8, 10–9, 10–10 and 10–11 illustrate different types of modern industrial x-ray units; typical industrial radiographs are illustrated in Fig. 10–12. Fig. 10–12a is a radiograph showing porosity in an aluminum alloy casting; Fig. 10–12b is a radiograph showing porosity in a zinc alloy casting.

**10–6. Industrial Fluoroscopy.** Had x-rays not possessed the property of producing fluorescence, Roentgen might not have discovered them. He found that a barium platinocyanide screen would fluoresce when brought near a cathode-ray tube; this led him to believe that the energy received by the screen was due to a heretofore unknown type of radiation. Fluoroscopy differs from radiography in that instead of an image of the internal structure of the specimen being photographed, the image is observed on a fluorescent screen. Various types of screens have been used in fluoroscopy. From 1895 to about 1910, barium platinocyanide was universally used. Subsequently, cadmium tungstate and zinc orthosilicate (willemite) were much used. Willemite is also widely used as a screen material for cathode-ray tubes. At present, Patterson Type B screens (zinc cadmium sulfide) are almost universally used.

An x-ray device for viewing the internal structure of an object on a fluorescing screen is known as a *fluoroscope*. Basically the fluoroscope is comprised of an x-ray tube and its associated circuits, a fluorescent screen and a protective lead-glass screen. The x-ray tube is so oriented that the radiation from the target will pass through the object to be inspected and strike the fluorescent screen. The amount of fluorescence produced on the

Fig. 10–10. Model OX–250 industrial x-ray unit mounted on mobile jib crane for x-ray inspection of castings at a voltage of 250-kv. (Courtesy General Electric X-Ray Corp.)

screen will be a function of the intensity of the radiation falling on it; consequently a shadow picture of the internal structure of the object will result on the screen. If mirrors are not used, this arrangement requires the presence of the observer directly in front of the fluorescent screen, therefore

Fig. 10–11.   Two million-volt industrial x-ray unit.  (Courtesy General Electric X-Ray Corp.)

directly in line of the x-radiation. The operator may be protected by a heavy lead-glass screen, or the image from the screen may be reflected by a mirror so that the observer does not have to stand in direct line of the x-radiation. A basic fluoroscopic arrangement is illustrated in Fig. 10–13. Best observations can be made from a fluoroscope screen if no other light

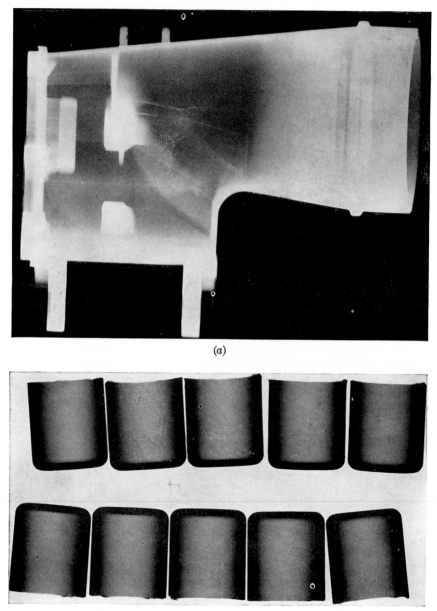

(a)

(b)

Fig. 10–12.   Radiographs of (a) aluminum alloy and (b) zinc alloy castings showing porosity.   (Courtesy Westinghouse Electric Corp.)

is allowed to fall on the screen; therefore it is general practice to view the screen in a dark room.

Because of the disadvantages mentioned below, fluoroscopy is little used in the inspection of metals; it is, however, much used for the inspection of less dense objects. Compared to radiography, fluoroscopy has the advantages of low cost, rapidity, simplicity and ready adaptability to objects moving on a conveyor belt. It has the disadvantages of low contrast, low

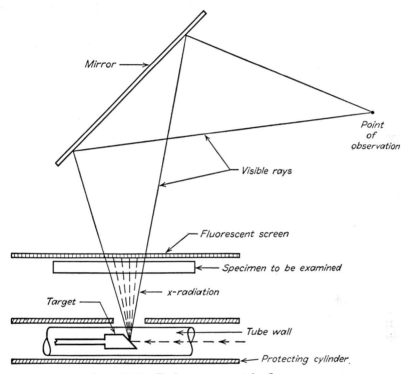

FIG. 10–13.   Basic arrangement for fluoroscopy.

resolving power and poor integrating power. No permanent record results (the image will exist so long as radiation is falling on the fluoroscopic screen), whereas in many cases a permanent record is desired. These advantages and disadvantages show that fluoroscopy is not suitable for the examination of metal castings and welds, but is well suited to inspection of low density objects moving along a conveyor belt.

For some time fluoroscopy has been widely used in the medical field; recently it has become common in industry. A few of the many industrial applications include:

1. The production line testing of packaged food for the inclusion of foreign bodies such as tacks, pieces of metal, etc.

2. Inspection of fruits such as oranges, etc. for quality, as they are moved along a conveyor belt.
3. Inspection of golf balls and rubber tires for defects.
4. Inspection of wood and plastic construction for defects.
5. Location of wires, pipes, etc., in the walls of buildings.
6. The examination of packages by the postal and immigration authorities.

Fluoroscopy has been used to a limited extent for the examination of light metal castings less than one inch in thickness; however, it is not usually possible to detect flaws which are less than ten percent of the total thickness of the specimen.

**10–7. Protection Against X-Rays.** Because of possible danger from the extremely high voltage required for x-ray tubes and because of the effects of x-rays on the human body, a discussion of x-rays would not be complete without mention of the important topic of protection.

Although the voltage employed in some industrial x-ray units may be in excess of two million volts, there is little danger of the operator being injured by the high voltage, for these units are made completely shockproof. In no case, however, should an operator unfamiliar with high voltage circuits attempt to repair x-ray equipment, for he himself is endangered in working on unfamiliar circuits which may be energized; and, in turn, he may endanger future users through faulty repair that leaves the equipment nonshockproof. Such equipment, if inoperative, should either be sent back to the factory or an experienced technician should be obtained.

The possibility of exposure is the greatest danger to the operator of x-ray equipment; however, with present methods of protection, exposure need not result if the operator will observe certain prescribed precautions. The maximum dosage of x-radiation that the average individual can safely stand during a day is $10^{-5}$ roentgen per second. Therefore the operator and others in the vicinity of the x-ray equipment should be protected by the proper amount of shielding so as to reduce the possible dosage due to stray radiation to much below this value. Commercial meters are available which an individual can carry and which will give an accurate indication of his exposure. But simpler methods can be used. Sproull suggests the following simple test for determining whether or not an x-ray operator is being exposed to radiation:

The x-ray technician may take a fresh dental-type x-ray film (not a comparatively slow film like Agfa Superay Bar Eastman Industrial Type M) and dental holder, tape a paper clip to the front side of it, then place it in his pocket with the clip side away from his body. After carrying it thus during working hours for one week or ten days, the film is developed and fixed. If there is no visible darkening of the film and no trace of an image of the paper clip, the general body exposure to x-rays is definitely safe, although it might be true that the exposure of the hands during some particular operation was dangerous. If there is only a slight darkening of the film and a faint image of the paper clip, the x-ray exposure is somewhere near the safe borderline. If the film is quite dark, a dangerous condition is indicated.*

Stationary industrial x-ray equipment is usually placed in a specially designed radiography room or in a separate radiography building. The walls of a radiography room are either made of concrete of the thickness necessary to absorb the radiation or are lined with sheet-lead of appropriate thickness. The doors must also be designed to give the same amount of protection as the walls. If windows are to be included, they are made of lead-glass of weight sufficient to reduce the dosage well below $10^{-5}$ roentgen. The control panels, etc., are located outside the radiography room. Table 10–3 gives the thickness of lead and the equivalent thickness of concrete necessary for protection from x-radiation for various target voltages when the lead or concrete barrier is 60 inches from the source of radiation.

TABLE 10–3 †

BARRIERS FOR VARIOUS WAVELENGTHS OF X-RAYS

| Voltage Generating Rays | Inches of Lead | Inches of Concrete |
|---|---|---|
| 75,000 | $\frac{1}{16}$ | $4\frac{3}{4}$ |
| 100,000 | $\frac{1}{16}$ | $4\frac{3}{4}$ |
| 200,000 | $\frac{5}{32}$ | $8\frac{3}{4}$ |
| 300,000 | $1\frac{1}{32}$ | $9\frac{1}{2}$ |
| 400,000 | $1\frac{9}{32}$ | $10\frac{1}{4}$ |
| 1,000,000 | $3\frac{13}{32}$ | 12 |

† Adapted by permission from *Radiographic Inspection of Metals*, by Otto Zmeskal, published by Harper and Brothers, New York, 1943.

In mobile x-ray equipment such as the unit shown in Fig. 10–10 a lead-lined cab is built on the back of the chassis which contains the control panel and in which the operator stands. In the x-ray unit of Fig. 10–11 the heavy metal cone localizes the radiation to a very small region; thus if the equipment is located at some appreciable distance from personnel in the plant, there is little danger from exposure if not in direct line of the primary rays.

PROBLEMS

**10–1.** Determine the shortest wavelength radiated from an x-ray tube if the filament-target voltage is (*a*) 50 kv, (*b*) 100 kv and (*c*) 1,000 kv.

**10–2.** Give the minimum filament-target voltage necessary for successfully radiographically inspecting steel castings 3 in. thick. Repeat for thicknesses of 5 and 8 in.

* By permission from *X-Rays in Practice*, by W. T. Sproull, published by McGraw-Hill Book Company., Inc., New York, 1946.

**10–3.**  Give the minimum distance a 2.25-in. boiler plate should be placed from the target of a 200-kv x-ray tube if good results are to be obtained.  Repeat for a target voltage of 300-kv and a boiler plate 4.25 in. thick.

**10–4.**  Compare the thickness and weight and if prices are available the cost of a concrete wall 10 ft by 20 ft and a sheet of lead of the same area which will give adequate protection against the x-rays generated by (a) 75-kv x-ray equipment; (b) 100-kv x-ray equipment; and (c) 200-kv x-ray equipment.

**10–5.**  Compare briefly industrial radiography and fluoroscopy.

## BIBLIOGRAPHY

CLARK, G. L.  *Applied X–Rays.*  3rd ed.  New York: McGraw-Hill Book Co., Inc., 1940, pp. 3–91, 152–84.

International Recommendations for Radiological Units.  *Brit. J. Radiology.*  June, 1937, **10,** 438–44.

*Mechanical Engineering.*  American Society of Mechanical Engineers.  April, 1933, **55,** 265–68.

SARSFIELD, L. G. H.  *Electrical Engineering in Radiology.*  Pittsburgh, Great Britain: Instruments Publishing Co., 1936, pp. 66–126.

SPROULL, W. T.  *X–Rays in Practice.*  New York: McGraw-Hill Book Co., Inc., 1946, pp. 20–35, 105–55, 168–298.

ST. JOHN, ANCEL, and ISENBURGER, H. R.  *Industrial Radiography.*  New York: John Wiley & Sons, Inc., 1943.

*Symposium on Radiography.*  American Society for Testing Materials.  1943, 13–46, 75–114.

WESTINGHOUSE ELECTRIC CORPORATION.  *Industrial Electronics Reference Book.*  New York: John Wiley & Sons, Inc., 1948, pp. 138–61.

ZMESKAL, OTTO.  *Radiographic Inspection of Metals.*  New York: Harper & Bros., 1943.

# CHAPTER 11

## HIGH–FREQUENCY HEATING

Before 1900 several patents were granted on induction-heating apparatus; however, it was not until around 1920 that induction heating began to be utilized in industry. The earliest applications were for the melting of metals in 60-cycle induction type electric furnaces. By about 1935 several manufacturers had begun to employ frequencies of from 2,000 to 10,000 cycles per second for the surface hardening of metals. During the past fifteen years, high-frequency induction heating of metals has increased in importance until it has become almost indispensable to the larger metal-working plants in this country.

High-frequency heating was first applied to nonconductors (dielectrics) on a commercial scale in 1936 when it was employed in connection with the controlled drying of tobacco. Since this time the applications of dielectric heating have become quite numerous.

All high-frequency heating falls into one of two main categories, *induction heating* and *dielectric heating*. When electrically conducting materials such as iron, brass, copper, aluminum, etc., are heated due to induced currents which are set up as a result of placing the specimen either within or adjacent to a coil carrying high-frequency alternating current, the process is termed induction heating. In the case of nonferrous materials such as brass, aluminum, etc., all heat produced results from eddy current loss ($I^2R$ loss in the materials); however, hysteresis loss contributes to some extent to the heat developed in ferrous materials. Since ferrous materials become nonmagnetic at the *Curie point,*\* which is around 1420° Fahrenheit (770° Centigrade) for most low carbon steels, hysteresis loss is not an appreciable factor in most induction-heating applications.

The process of heating electrically nonconducting materials such as wood, micarta, plastics, etc., by placing them between conducting plates forming a capacitor to which high-frequency voltage is applied, is known as dielectric heating. The heat developed results from the dielectric loss of the capacitor formed. No dielectric is perfect; thus there is some dielectric loss in all materials. The poorer the dielectric the greater the dielectric loss and the more rapidly it can be heated. Dielectric heating generally requires much higher frequencies than induction heating. The frequency

---

\* The temperature at which magnetic materials lose their magnetic properties is known as the critical temperature or *Curie point.*

range of induction heating is from 60 to 500,000 cycles per second; the range for dielectric heating is from 500,000 to 100,000,000 cycles per second.

## High-Frequency Converters

The wide range of applications to which high-frequency heating readily lends itself necessitates high-frequency generating equipment of various power ratings and frequency ranges. There are at present four basic types of high-frequency generating units, namely: spark-gap converters, motor-generator sets, vacuum-tube converters and mercury-arc converters.

**11–1. Spark-Gap Converters.** The spark-gap converter provided one of the earliest means of obtaining high-frequency energy. Such frequency converters are manufactured in sizes of around 2 to 40 kilowatts output capacity with operating frequencies of around 25,000 to 250,000 cycles per second. The spark-gap generator has the advantages of costing less per kilowatt than a vacuum-tube oscillator of similar rating and of being appreciably simpler in operation. If the gaps are properly adjusted the heating efficiency of spark-gap converters is generally around 50 percent; the power consumed during stand-by periods is almost negligible compared to the power taken by a motor-generator set of equivalent output capacity when running at no load. One rather outstanding disadvantage of the spark-gap generator is the required periodic readjustment of the gaps. A modern spark-gap converter is shown in Fig. 11–1 and the basic circuit diagram is given in Fig. 11–2.

**11–2. Motor-Generator Sets.** The motor-generator set, which is comprised of a high-speed ac-operated motor driving a high-frequency alternator, operates at fixed frequencies of around 2,000 to 12,000 cycles per second with power ratings up to around 1,500 kilowatts. Because of their limited frequency range, such converters are not suitable for case hardening, etc., but are widely used in connection with deep hardening, through heating, forging, and melting of large masses of metal. A 500-kw, 9,600 cycle motor-generator set designed to supply power for induction heating applications is shown in Fig. 11–3. The cost per kilowatt of output for the motor-generator set is much lower than for the vacuum-tube or spark-gap generator and the heating efficiency is considerably higher. Heating efficiencies of between 65 and 75 percent are realized with motor-generator sets.

**11–3. Vacuum-Tube Converters.** Although vacuum-tube converters cost more per kilowatt of output power than other types of converters and are in general less efficient, they have almost an unlimited frequency range * and thus are suitable for numerous applications for which no other

---

* Vacuum-tube oscillators that will generate frequencies in the order of $1 \times 10^{10}$ cycles per second, which is much above the maximum frequency to be utilized for any type of high-frequency heating to date, are now being made.

type of converter can be used.  Vacuum-tube converters (also commonly known as vacuum-tube oscillators and vacuum-tube generators) are available in sizes of from a fraction of a kilowatt up to 400 kilowatts, with almost any desired frequency rating.  The frequencies most commonly employed in electronic or rf induction heating lie between 100,000 and 500,000 cycles per second and the power involved is usually between 5 and

Fig. 11–1.  20-kw Ajax-Northrup spark-gap converter with 17-pound furnace. (Courtesy Ajax Electrothermic Corp.)

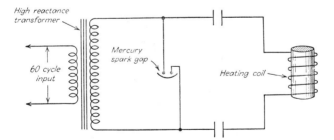

Fig. 11–2.  Basic circuit diagram of a 20-kw Ajax-Northrup spark-gap converter. (Courtesy Ajax Electrothermic Corp.)

50 kilowatts.  Since dielectric-heating applications utilize frequencies of between 0.5 and 100 megacycles, only vacuum-tube oscillators are suitable for supplying energy for dielectric heating.  Vacuum-tube generators have no moving parts, they are quiet, easily controlled and can be operated continuously up to an average of around 10,000 hours before tubes need re-

Fig. 11-3.  This 500-kw hydrogen-cooled 9,600-cycle motor-generator set is the largest rotating machine of that frequency built. (Courtesy Westinghouse Electric Corp.)

Fɪɢ. 11–4.　Views showing the internal structure of a 20-kw, 375–kc radio-frequency generator.　(Courtesy Induction Heating Corp.)

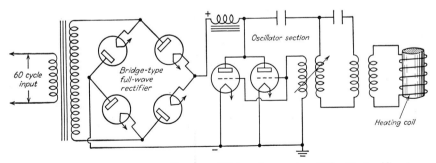

Fɪɢ. 11–5.　Schematic circuit diagram of 20-kw rf generator of Fig. 11–4.　(Courtesy Induction Heating Corp.)

Fig. 11–6.   Mercury-arc frequency converter in operation in the Alloy Steel Foundry of Michigan Products Corp.   (Courtesy Allis-Chalmers Mfg. Co.)

placing.  The heating efficiency obtainable from such converters is around 50 percent.

There are numerous types of vacuum-tube oscillator circuits, all of which depend upon amplification, storage and feedback of energy to the grid circuit.  However, there are only three basic circuits generally employed in connection with high-frequency heating, namely: Hartley, Colpitts, and tuned plate circuits.  Although each circuit exhibits certain advantages and disadvantages when compared to the others, any one of these circuits can be made to operate quite satisfactorily in connection with most high-frequency heating applications for which vacuum-tube oscillators are suitable.  Some manufacturers favor one circuit while others favor another.  Each of these circuits is discussed in Section 6–1.  A typical commercial vacuum-tube converter unit designed to be used for high-frequency heating is shown in Fig. 11–4 and a schematic circuit diagram of this converter is illustrated in Fig. 11–5.

**11–4. Mercury-Arc Converters.**  Recently, mercury-arc converters have become quite important as a means of supplying huge amounts of 500 to 3,000-cycle power (1,500 cycles per second is the most common frequency)

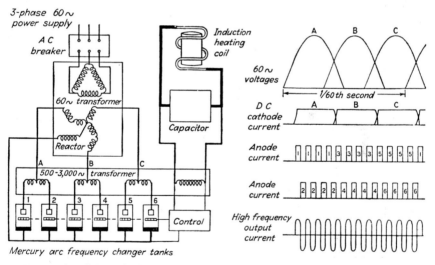

Fig. 11–7.  Schematic circuit diagram of frequency changer using six grid controlled rectifiers.  Anode current pulses are shown at right.  Converted frequency is not harmonically related to line frequency.  (Adapted by permission from Mercury Arc Converter for Induction Heating by S. R. Durand, *Electronic Industries*, June, 1945.)

for melting, forging, annealing, deep surface hardening, etc.  Because of its limited frequency range, it follows that the mercury-arc converter is very limited in its applications.  However, it affords the most efficient method known for the induction heating of large masses of metals.  Heating efficiencies as high as 90 percent may be realized at power outputs from

250 kilowatts up. The mercury-arc converter, as well as having a high efficiency, has a low maintenance cost and is very reliable. Fig. 11–6 shows a mercury-arc converter in operation in the Alloy Steel Foundry of Michigan Products Corporation and the basic circuit diagram of a mercury-arc converter is shown in Fig. 11–7.

**11–5. Frequency Spectrum and Cost per Kilowatt of Output for High-Frequency Heating Units.** Although the rate at which a given charge can be heated depends upon many factors, the frequency and power output of the frequency converter are two major considerations. In general, the frequency for a given operation is not too critical; thus, a given radio-frequency generator can be used for numerous heating operations by using different heating coils, i.e., by using a heating coil suitable for the charge or piece of stock to be heated. In some plants around 200 different types of metal parts are being processed with the same heating unit. In cases where there are many heating operations of exactly the same type, it may be advisable to have a radio-frequency generator designed for the particular job. This would, in some instances, result in a more efficient set-up than trying to adapt a standard or multipurpose generator to the job. Manufacturers of high-frequency heating equipment make standard units which are suitable for many different applications and of course are glad to recommend the unit best suited for the particular requirements of the problem

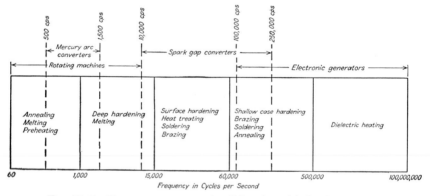

Fig. 11–8.   Frequency spectrum for dielectric and induction heating.

presented to them. If the problem is one which will result in sufficient sales of equipment to justify designing a special generator which will result in a better heat-treated product or higher efficiency, the manufacturer is usually only too glad to design such equipment.

The chart of Fig. 11–8 shows the complete high-frequency heating spectrum together with the frequency ranges and type generating equipment employed for different high-frequency heating applications. Table 11–1 gives a comparison of the cost per kilowatt of output power for several

## TABLE  11–1*

| Power Output kw | Cost per Kilowatt of Output Power | | |
|---|---|---|---|
| | Vacuum-Tube Units | Spark-Gap Units | Rotating Machines |
| 1 | $1,200–$2,200 | | |
| 2 | 500– 1,500 | | |
| 5 | 250– 1,000 | $150–$250 | |
| 10 | 250– 1,000 | | |
| 20 | 250– 700 | | |
| 50 | 150– 700 | | |
| 100 | 100– 500 | | |
| 200 | | | $50–$200 |
| 500 | | | |
| 1,000 | | | |

* B. Dudley, Induction and Dielectric Heating Equipment, *Electronics*, August, 1945, 110–12.

high-frequency units, as of 1945.  Although these costs are somewhat higher at the present time, the values given in the table indicate the relative costs of various types of generating equipment.

## Induction  Heating

As pointed out previously, when conducting materials are heated by the eddy currents generated by a high-frequency electromagnetic field, the process is known as induction heating.  The high-frequency power for induction heating can be obtained from one of four different types of frequency converters, depending upon the frequency and power requirements. Each of these four types of frequency converter has been discussed briefly; however, it is impossible in a text of this type to discuss all phases of induction heating.  Therefore only the applications for which vacuum-tube generators are utilized will be considered further.

When the energy for induction heating is supplied by a vacuum-tube oscillator the process is often termed radio-frequency induction heating. Vacuum-tube generators employed in connection with induction heating vary in output capacity from 1 to 400 kilowatts.  Although vacuum-tube generators are available in units comparable in power rating to motor-generator sets and mercury-arc converters, the vacuum-tube generator does not compete with either.  Motor-generator sets and mercury-arc rectifiers are more efficient than vacuum-tube oscillators; however, they can be designed to operate satisfactorily only in the lower frequency ranges and therefore are suitable only for melting, preheating, deep hardening, and similar low-frequency applications.  The spark-gap generator laps over to a considerable extent the lower frequency ranges of the vacuum-tube generator, but in general is not as satisfactory for most of the higher frequency applications and does not compete to any great extent with the vacuum-tube generator.

The manufacturers of vacuum tubes, as might be expected, comprised the first group of industrial concerns to utilize radio-frequency induction heating on a commercial scale. In order to produce a good vacuum in a tube it is necessary to drive out the gas in the electrodes and this must be done at the same time that the tube is being evacuated. The gas is driven

FIG. 11–9. Vacuum tubes being degassed by induction heating. After evacuation by an oil-diffusion pump, the internal metal parts in the tubes on the glass manifold are degassed by radio-frequency induction heating. (Courtesy Amperex Electronic Corp.)

out of the electrodes by heating them to a fairly high temperature. High-frequency heating was found to offer an excellent solution to this heating problem. A coil, to which high-frequency voltage is applied, is placed either around or in the vicinity of the vacuum tube to be degassed and the electromagnetic field thus produced heats up the electrodes at a very rapid rate. Fig. 11–9 shows a degassing operation in process. At the present time, radio-frequency induction heating is used to some extent in almost every major metalworking plant in this country.

The rapid increase in the use of radio-frequency induction heating during the past few years is due to its many advantages when compared to more conventional methods of heating. Some advantages are:

1. Heat is applied at a very rapid rate; the rate is many times greater than can be obtained by conventional methods. This makes possible a higher production rate.

2. Heat can be localized; thus in cases where a small section of a given object is to be heated, this method is more suitable as well as more economical.

3. Much greater uniformity can be realized both in hardening the surface of a given object and in giving objects on a production line exactly the same treatment when it is desirable to do so. This, of course, results in less rejects, decreasing the cost of production. The same temperature can be repeated automatically or returned to a specified value with absolute accuracy.

4. Many operations, such as brazing of small components and the hardening of small sections of a given piece of stock, that are impossible with any other heating methods, are made possible.

5. The heat generating equipment is usually quite flexible, can be readily adjusted to changes in production schedules and can be used for a large variety of heat treatments.

6. The control is simple; power can be turned on or off by a press button.

7. There is little or no distortion as often results due to other heating processes and there is no scaling, residue or products of combustion.

There are many other less important advantages which apply more specifically to particular applications.

**11–6. Principles of Induction Heating.** Although induction heating is one of the newest fields of electrical engineering, the principles involved were of concern to engineers shortly after the development of electric machinery. One of the chief problems that has faced the designers of transformers and rotating machines from the very beginning has been that of reducing the losses due to *eddy currents* and *hysteresis* which show up in the form of heat, thus reducing the output available from the machine. Now eddy current and hysteresis losses are being utilized in the important and fast-growing field of induction heating.

Regardless of the frequency or power involved, an induction-heating arrangement consists basically of a few turns of heavy copper wire or tubing which usually fits loosely around the piece of stock to be heat treated and which is connected to a suitable high-frequency power source. In radio-frequency heating, this source of power is a vacuum-tube oscillator. As indicated by the sketch of Fig. 11–10, a magnetic field will be set up when current flows through the coil. Although the magnetic field changes in the same way that the frequency of the power source changes, the sketch indicates the direction of magnetic flux only at the instant when the current is in the direction indicated. If the charge or piece of stock placed within the rapidly changing field is of ferrous material, both hysteresis and eddy current losses will result and if the charge is non-ferrous, only eddy current loss will exist.

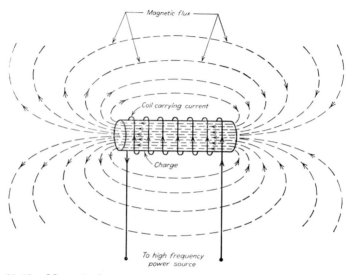

Fig. 11–10. Magnetic flux pattern set up as a result of current through the coil in the direction indicated.

**11–7. Hysteresis Loss.** Where an alternating magnetizing force is applied to an iron core, the variations in flux density produced in the iron core lag behind the magnetizing force. This phenomenon was first reported by Ewing in 1855; he referred to it as *hysteresis*.* A plot of flux density versus magnetizing force for one complete cycle of the magnetizing force is known as a *hysteresis loop*. The energy expended during one complete cycle is proportional to the area of the hysteresis loop and the volume of the iron core. The energy per unit volume is represented by Eq. (11–1a).

$$w_h = \frac{1}{4\pi} \int_{-B_{max}}^{+B_{max}} H \, dB \qquad (11\text{–}1a)$$

where the energy $w_h$, magnetizing force $H$, and flux density $B$ can be expressed in any consistent system of units.

There is no mathematical relationship between $H$ and $B$; therefore Eq. (11–1a) can only be evaluated experimentally. Steinmetz, after making hysteresis loss measurements on most of the core materials used during his time, evolved the following empirical equation for the energy loss per unit volume.

$$w_h = \eta(B_{max})^{1.6} \qquad (11\text{–}1b)$$

_____

* Greek word meaning to lag behind.

The exponent 1.6 gave fairly accurate results for core materials used during Steinmetz's time; however, it does not apply to many modern magnetic materials.

The power required to sustain the magnetic reversals in an iron core can be obtained by multiplying the energy loss per unit volume per cycle by the volume of the core and the frequency of the magnetizing force; thus:

$$P_h = \eta f V (B_{\max})^n \qquad (11\text{--}1c)$$

where $P_h$ = hysteresis loss in watts
$\quad\ f$ = magnetic cycles per second
$\quad\ n$ = constant depending on the material (ranges from 1.5 to 2.5 for modern magnetic materials)
$\quad\ V$ = volume
$\quad\ B$ = maximum flux density
$\quad\ \eta$ = constant depending on the material [1,250 (mks units) is representative for average steels]
$V$, $B$ and $\eta$ can be expressed in any consistent system of units.

As mentioned previously, magnetic materials become nonmagnetic at the Curie point (1420° F—770° C); therefore hysteresis loss does not play

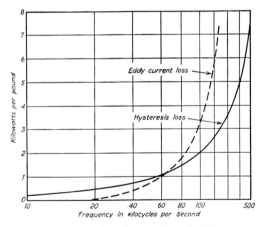

Fig. 11–11.  These curves show how hysteresis and eddy current losses in a piece of ferrous material vary with the frequency of the magnetic field. (Adapted by permission from *High-Frequency Induction Heating* by Frank W. Curtis, McGraw-Hill Book Co., Inc., New York, 1944.)

an important role in most induction-heating applications. The curves of Fig. 11–11 show how hysteresis and eddy current losses for a given piece of ferrous material compare before the Curie point is reached. The curves of Fig. 11–12 show how the rate of heating changes as the Curie point is reached and the effects of hysteresis disappear.

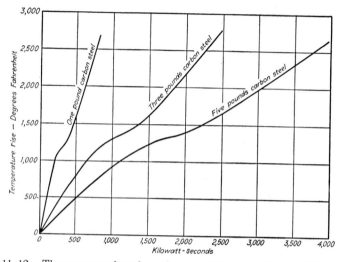

Fig. 11–12. These curves show how the rate of heating of three different masses of inductively heated carbon steel changes as the Curie temperature is reached. (Adapted by permission from *High-Frequency Induction Heating* by Frank W. Curtis, McGraw-Hill Book Co., Inc., New York, 1944.)

**11–8. Eddy Current Losses.** In ferrous materials eddy current loss is a much greater factor in producing heat than hysteresis loss, and eddy current loss is the only source of heat energy in nonferrous materials. Consider Figs. 11–13a and 11–13b. Fig. 11–13a illustrates a piece of stock to be heated with a coil of one turn, the terminals of which are connected to a high-frequency power source; Fig. 11–13b is simply another view of the

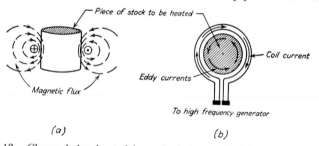

Fig. 11–13. Charge being heated by a single turn coil. (a) Magnetic flux pattern due to single turn. (b) Eddy currents resulting from current flow in the single turn.

same set-up. The discussion which follows would apply to any number of turns, but in order to simplify the problem, only a one-turn coil will be considered. Let it be assumed that the current at the instant under consideration is into the paper on the left side of the piece of stock and out of the paper on the right; the magnetic lines of force due to this current are as indicated. This flux threads through the piece of stock to be heated, which must in induction heating be made of conducting material. Any change in the flux linkage will induce currents in the charge, which will be in such a direction that the field produced as a result of these currents will be in the opposite direction from the field produced by the current in the coil surrounding the piece of stock. This means that in the case under consideration the induced currents which are popularly referred to as *eddy currents* will be in the direction indicated by the arrows of Fig. 11–13*b*. The direction of the eddy currents will change as often as the magnetizing force changes. As these eddy currents flow through the charge, they encounter resistance which results in $I^2R$ loss in the charge. The energy loss due to this phenomenon is known as *eddy current loss*.

Due to a phenomenon which is termed *skin effect*, as the applied frequency is increased, the eddy currents are crowded to the surface of the charge. Thus it is possible to concentrate practically all of the heat over a very shallow depth. This is the principle upon which surface hardening depends. Eq. (11–2) gives the depth of current penetration in the charge which is the depth in which approximately 85 percent of the heat due to eddy currents is generated.

$$\delta = 3,170 \sqrt{\frac{\rho}{\mu_r f}} \qquad (11\text{--}2)$$

where  $\delta$ = depth of current penetration in inches

$\rho$ = resistivity of charge in ohm-inches at the maximum temperature

$\mu_r$ = relative magnetic permeability

$f$ = frequency of the magnetic field in cycles/second

If the power available is sufficient and the frequency is high enough, it is possible to heat the surface to a very high temperature before the temperature of the interior has increased appreciably. Thus, if the object is quenched at this time, a hard surface will result while the interior of the piece of stock will retain its original characteristics. Table 11–2 gives the depth of current penetration for several common materials at various frequencies.

TABLE  11–2*

δ IN INCHES FOR VARIOUS MATERIALS

| Material | Frequency-Cycles | | | | |
|---|---|---|---|---|---|
| | 60 | 1,000 | 10,000 | 100,000 | 1,000,000 |
| Graphite............... | 10.1 | 2.5 | .78 | .25 | .08 |
| Iron (Molten)........... | 4.3 | 1.1 | .33 | .11 | .03 |
| Copper (Molten)........ | 1.4 | 3.5 | .11 | .03 | .011 |
| Copper................. | .42 | .10 | .03 | .01 | .003 |
| Steel.................. | .04 | .01 | .004 | .001 | .000 |

* Courtesy Ajax Electrothermic Corporation.

If the depth of penetration is small compared with the diameter and the length of the coil is large compared to the spacing between the coil and the charge, Eqs. (11–3a), (11–3b) and (11–3c) give the approximate power input to the work due to the induced eddy currents.

$$W_t = \frac{(NI)^2 \rho C}{\delta L} \tag{11-3a}$$

where $W_t$ = total power input to charge in watts
$\quad\quad N$ = number of coil turns
$\quad\quad I$ = coil current in amperes
$\quad\quad \delta$ = depth of penetration in inches
$\quad\quad \rho$ = resistivity of the charge in ohm-inches
$\quad\quad L$ = length of coil in inches
$\quad\quad C$ = average length of the current path in inches.  (If the depth of penetration is small, the average length of the current path may be assumed to be equal to the periphery of the charge.)

Substituting the value of $\delta$ as given by Eq. (11–2) in Eq. (11–3a), Eq. (11–3b) is obtained.

$$W_t = \frac{(NI)^2 C \sqrt{\rho \mu_r f}}{3170 L} \tag{11-3b}$$

Dividing Eq. (11–3b) by the area of the inductively heated surface and using the number of turns per inch instead of total number of turns, Eq. (11–2b) reduces to the form of Eq. (11–3c).

$$\Delta W = 3.16 \times 10^{-4} (N'I)^2 \sqrt{\rho \mu_r f} \tag{11-3c}$$

where $\Delta W$ = power density in watts per square inch of inductively heated surface
$\quad\quad N'$ = number of turns per inch
Other symbols have already been defined.

The amount of power required to raise a given charge through $\Delta T$ degrees in time $t$ may be determined approximately by Eq. (11–4).  This equation neglects radiation, convection and conduction losses.  In cases where high temperature gradients are involved, radiation and conduction losses must be added to the power as determined by Eq. (11–4).

$$W = \frac{17.6 M c \, \Delta T}{t} \tag{11-4}$$

where $W$ = power in watts
$\quad\quad M$ = mass of charge expressed in pounds
$\quad\quad c$ = average specific heat of charge in BTU per pound per degree Fahrenheit
$\quad\quad t$ = time in minutes
$\quad\quad \Delta T$ = temperature rise in degrees Fahrenheit

Although only a few basic equations have been considered here, rather extensive design data and sample calculations on induction heating can be found elsewhere.*

**11-9. Power Rating of RF Generators for Various Applications.** Although it is impossible to make engineering calculations as to the exact amount of rf power required for a given application, it is possible to make excellent approximations. Such calculations are generally quite involved and will not be considered here; instead, a series of graphs are given from which the power requirements for several different types of heat treatments for the more common industrial metals can be obtained. The graph of Fig. 11–14 gives the required rf power for through heating of several typical industrial metals. The power obtained from the graph includes losses for average conditions; accordingly, the values are only approximate. To obtain the required kilowatt rating of the rf generator, it is simply necessary to multiply the number of pounds of the material to be heated per minute by the required temperature rise in degrees Fahrenheit and then read from the curve for the metal under consideration the number of kilowatts corresponding to the product of pounds per minute and degrees rise. As values taken from the graph of Fig. 11–14 are only approximate, they should not be used in place of engineering calculations but only for making estimates.

By use of the graph of Fig. 11–15 the rf power required to soft solder three typical industrial metals at 370° Fahrenheit can be determined. The production rate and therefore the heating time having been decided upon, the kilowatts per square inch can be read from the curve corresponding to the metal used. To obtain the total rf power requirements the area of the metal perpendicular to the heat flow on both sides of the joint to be soldered must be multiplied by the power density as obtained from the curve. Where there are several simultaneous soldering operations utilizing the same machine, the rf power required is equal to the summation of the power required for each soldering operation. The values obtained from this graph are sufficiently accurate for engineering calculations. The graph of Fig. 11–16 is for silver soldering at 1,300° F and is utilized in the same manner as the graph of Fig. 11–15. Values obtained from this graph are within engineering accuracy.

The rf power required for the surface hardening of various types of steel tubing can be obtained by using the graph of Fig. 11–17. After the production rate and therefore the scanning time has been determined, the rf power

* R. M. Baker and C. J. Madsen, High Frequency Heating of Conductors and Nonconductors, *Electrical Engineering*, February, 1945, **64,** 55–57; G. H. Brown, C. N. Hoyler, and R. A. Bierwirth, *Theory and Applications of Radio Frequency Heating* (New York: D. Van Nostrand Co., Inc., 1947); N. R. Stansel, *Induction Heating* (New York: McGraw-Hill Book Co., Inc., 1949); Westinghouse Electric Corporation, *Industrial Electronics Reference Book* (New York: John Wiley & Sons, Inc., 1948), pp. 375–441.

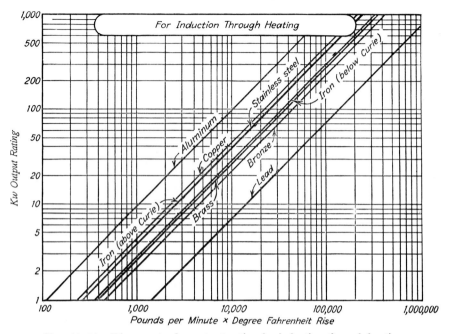

Fig. 11–14.  Rf generator kw output rating for induction through heating.

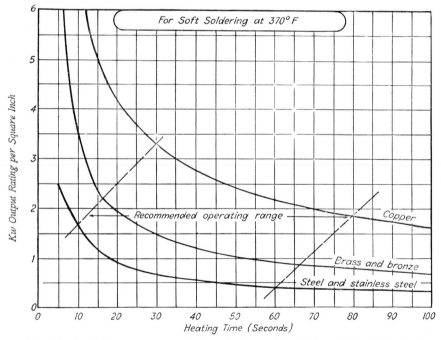

Fig. 11–15.  Rf generator kw output rating for soft soldering at 370° F. (The two charts on this page by courtesy Westinghouse Electric Corp.)

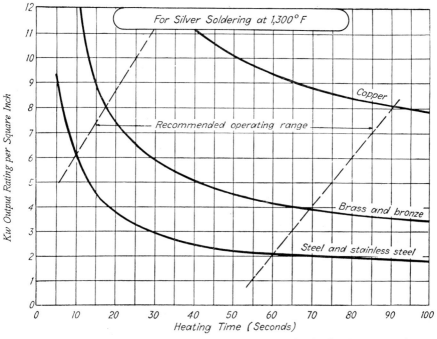

FIG. 11–16. Rf generator kw output rating for silver or hard soldering at 1,300° F.

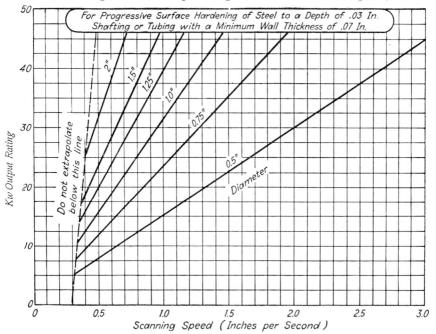

FIG. 11–17. Rf generator kw output rating for progressive hardening of steel to a depth of 0.03 inch shafting or tubing with a minimum wall thickness of 0.07 inch. (The two charts on this page by courtesy Westinghouse Electric Corp.)

329

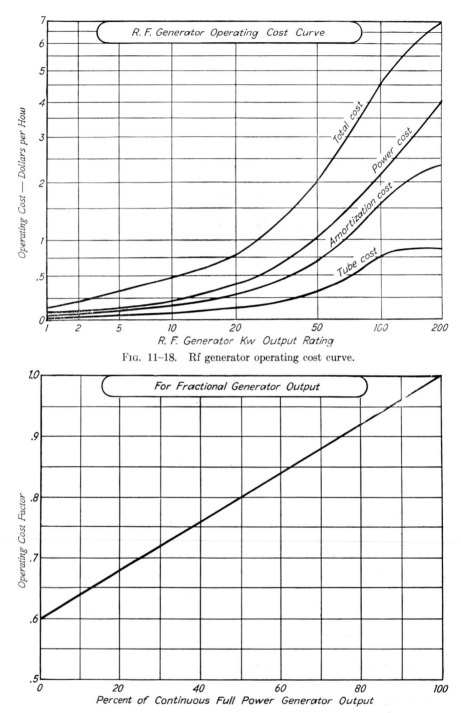

FIG. 11–18.   Rf generator operating cost curve.

FIG. 11–19.   Operating cost factor for fractional generator output. (The two charts on this page by courtesy Westinghouse Electric Corp.)

is obtained by reading from the curve corresponding to the size tubing being heat treated, the power corresponding to the scanning speed. In tubing of irregular cross-section, the value obtained by dividing the periphery by $\pi$ can be used as an equivalent diameter to obtain an approximate power rating.

It is obvious that in all of the heating operations described the size of the rf generator required increases with an increase in heating rate and, therefore, an increase in production rate. In setting up a production line which includes rf heating operations, the production rate which will give the most economical combination of generator cost and production rate should be chosen. The relative operation cost of various size rf generators can be obtained from the graph of Fig. 11–18. These costs are based on continuous full load output. For loads of less than 100 percent, the cost can be obtained by multiplying values obtained from this graph by the *operating cost factor*. The operating cost factor is a function of the percent of continuous full power output of the rf generator and can be obtained from the curve of Fig. 11–19.

**11–10. Induction-Heating Coils.*** Induction-heating coils may be of almost any conceivable size and shape. The design of the heating coil depends upon the type of heat treatment required, the characteristics of the rf generator and the size and shape of the object to be heat treated. For an rf generator of given power capacity and frequency, the rate of heat generation within the object being heat treated and the pattern of temperature distribution is a function of the characteristics of the object and the design of the heating coil. For maximum heating rate the coil should be at a distance of not greater than $\frac{3}{16}$ inch from the work; however, a high heating rate is not always of utmost importance. In many cases an even distribution of heat is the most important factor. Round copper tubing between $\frac{1}{8}$ and $\frac{1}{4}$ inch in diameter through which water can be circulated for the purpose of cooling is the most common type of coil material. However, both rectangular and flat tubing and also tubing of larger cross section is often utilized. It is best to use a good grade of copper, for a coil with low conductivity represents an appreciable power loss which decreases the over-all efficiency of the operation.

In general, coils can be classified as single or multiturn coils. Single-turn coils may take any one of many shapes. Several different types of single-turn coils are sketched in Fig. 11–20. The type of coil illustrated in Fig. 11–20a is widely used for heating small regions and the type illustrated in Fig. 11–20b is used where it is desirable to heat several objects simultaneously. For heating the inner surface of a small hole, a one-turn hair-

---

* For a more complete discussion of induction-heating coil design see F. W. Curtis, *High-Frequency Induction Heating* (New York: McGraw-Hill Book Co., Inc., 1944), pp. 43–84.

pin coil, such as the one of Fig. 11–20c, is sometimes used. (If the hole is large enough, the type coil illustrated in Fig. 11–22c is generally used.) It is necessary to continuously rotate a hairpin coil in order to obtain uniform heating over the entire surface. Several commercial single-turn heating coils and fixtures are illustrated in Fig. 11–21.

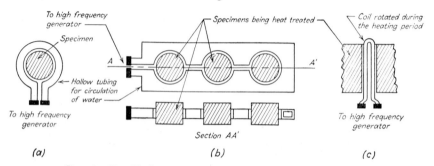

FIG. 11–20. Various types of single-turn heating coil designs.

FIG. 11–21. Table with various coils and fixtures for hardening cams, ratches, pawls and bearings of washing machine parts. (Courtesy Induction Heating Corp.)

Multiturn coils, of which there are three basic designs, are more common than single-turn coils. The basic designs are illustrated in Fig. 11–22. The external coil is more suitable for the majority of the high-frequency applications; however, there are a number of applications where only a

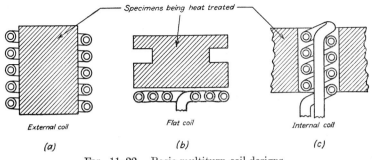

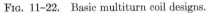

Specimens being heat treated

External coil

Flat coil

Internal coil

(a)

(b)

(c)

Fig. 11–22.  Basic multiturn coil designs.

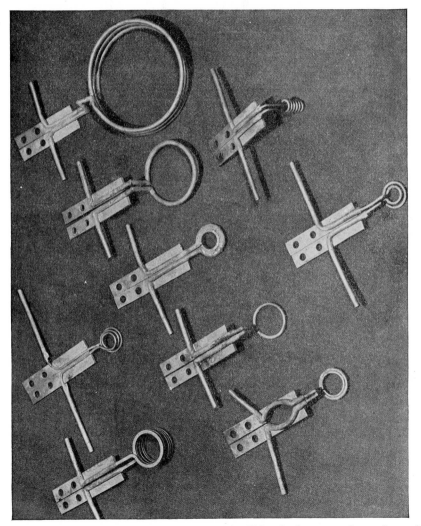

Fig. 11–23.  Samples of experimental coils utilizing both rectangular and round tubing.  (Courtesy Allis-Chalmers Mfg. Co.)

flat or internal coil is suitable. It is usually impractical to heat a hole with an internal coil if the hole is less than ⅝ inch in diameter. Typical single and multiturn coils are illustrated in Figs. 11–23 and 11–24.

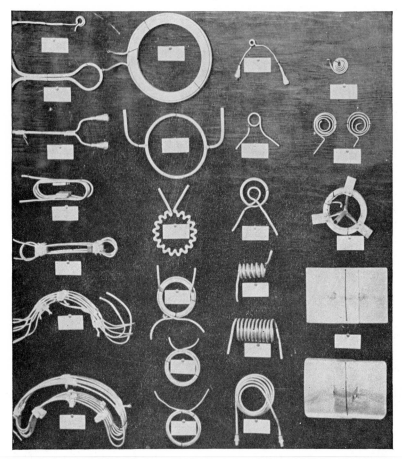

Fig. 11–24. Typical induction coils designed for various types of radio frequency heating. (Courtesy Westinghouse Electric Corp.)

In design of a multiturn coil, there are certain basic considerations that should be taken into account. It is not good practice to make the length greater than four times the diameter. In cases where the piece of stock is too long to be heated with a coil fulfilling this requirement, it is best to use a shorter coil and feed the work through it. A long coil not only results in less uniform heat distribution but it also has a much higher inductance. The pitch of the winding is another important consideration in coil design, the larger the pitch the smaller the inductance; however, the greater the pitch, the less uniform will be the heating. In general, the spacing between turns should be limited to one-half the thickness of the tubing. A wider

FIG. 11–25. Silver brazing with a 20-kw, 45-kc rf generator. Heating time is 10 seconds. (Courtesy Westinghouse Electric Corp.)

Fɪɢ. 11–26.  Soldering.  A ring of solder is placed around the brass cylinder and the brass top is placed on it.  As the assembly passes through the coil the solder melts and flows evenly and rapidly throughout the joint.  The operator can lift off the finished piece and put a new assembly in its place.  (Courtesy Westinghouse Electric Corp.)

Fɪɢ. 11–27.  Progressive hardening of a shaft as it moves down through the coil at a predetermined speed.  It is progressively heated by a coil, and is quenched by a spray of water just a fraction of an inch below the coil.  By this method the necessary high concentrations in terms of kilowatts per square inch can be obtained using low power radio-frequency generators.  (Courtesy Westinghouse Electric Corp.)

FIG. 11–28.   Annealing ends of pins used to hold a sprocket chain together.   By means of a standard Westinghouse 20-kw, 450-kc radio-frequency generator 1,200 pins per hour may be annealed with an operator only intermittently on the job.   Formerly only 250 pins per hour could be annealed by the salt bath method.   (Courtesy Westinghouse Electric Corp.)

FIG. 11–29.   Gear Hardening.   The rf heater coil is made of a single turn of rectangular coil tubing the same width as the gear being hardened.   It is connected to the generator through a current transformer.   After the gear is heated it is quenched in the water spray below the coil.   A description of typical working handling equipment for the contour hardening of gears is as follows: Gears are manually loaded on a chain conveyor, the fully loaded conveyor will hold 30 gears.   The gears are conveyed from this loading position, through the preheating, heat treating, and drawing to the unloading stations.   (Courtesy Westinghouse Electric Corp.)

spacing generally results in nonuniformity of heating. The best way to insure uniform heating is to rotate the work; however, this is not always practical. If it is necessary to heat a tapered object the coil should be made to conform to the contour of the object. If the coil pitch is made the same throughout, the small end will heat faster than the large end and therefore the spacing should be greater at the small end in order to give uniformity. A tapered coil is shown near the lower left corner of the photograph of Fig. 11–23.

Two important factors to be considered in the case of any induction-heating application is the selection of the high-frequency generating apparatus and the design of the heating coil. In many instances the generating equipment may already be available in the plant, having been purchased for another application; in such a case the problem reduces itself to that of designing suitable coils for adapting the equipment available to the particular job at hand. In the selection of equipment, it is usually best to rely on the recommendations of the manufacturer of induction heating equipment; however, it may not always be practical or convenient to consult the manufacturer when it becomes necessary to adapt the equipment already available in the plant to a slightly different heating operation which may require only a simple change in the heating coil design.

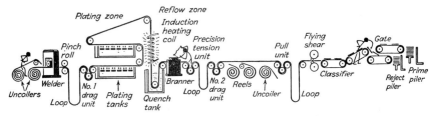

FIG. 11–30. Tin reflowing. In this tinning line, steel strip passes through horizontal plating tanks, each side being tinned separately. Speed through plating zone is reduced as fresh coil is welded onto strip. In one steel plant alone there are three 1,200-kw lines totaling 3,600-kw of electronic power. (Courtesy Westinghouse Electric Corp.)

**11–11. Typical RF Induction-Heating Applications.** As previously mentioned, rf induction heating is now being utilized in one way or another in almost every major metalworking plant in this country. Typical applications are:

1. Annealing
2. Brazing
3. Heat Treating
4. Hot Spinning
5. Melting
6. Shallow Hardening
7. Soldering
8. Spot Annealing
9. Surface Hardening
10. Tin Reflowing
11. Through Hardening
12. Welding

Time and space do not justify detailed consideration of specific induction-heating applications; however, several typical induction-heating operations are illustrated in the accompanying photographs (Figs. 11–25 through 11–30). A brief description of the type of heating operation is given under each photograph.

## Dielectric Heating

When nonconducting materials (dielectrics) are heated by use of high-frequency electric fields, the phenomenon is known as dielectric heating. The frequency range used in dielectric heating is generally from 5 to 100 megacycles and the power is supplied exclusively by vacuum-tube oscillators. While one of the main advantages of induction heating lies in the fact that the heat produced can be concentrated in a given area, dielectric heating has the advantage of giving a more uniform volume distribution of heat than any other method of heating. Dielectric heating has proved to be superior to conventional heating methods in almost every case where, during the process of fabrication of a nonconducting material, heat treatment is required. Major advantages of dielectric heating are:

1. More uniform heat distribution.
2. Heat can be applied at a more rapid rate.
3. Better quality products result.
4. Heat can be applied almost instantly; no time is lost waiting for furnace to be fired up.
5. Complete control of temperature at all times.
6. A given temperature may be repeated with exact accuracy.
7. Very simple to control; does not require a skilled operator.
8. Makes possible processes not possible with any other heating method.

**11–12. Principles of Dielectric Heating.** In dielectric heating the non-conducting material to be heated is placed between two suitable electrodes which are made of a good conducting material, commonly copper or brass.

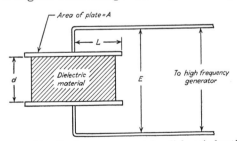

Fig. 11–31.   Basic arrangement for dielectric heating.

This combination forms a capacitor which is sometimes termed an *electrical sandwich*. Such an arrangement is illustrated in Fig. 11–31.

Although the development of heat within the dielectric material as a result of the rapidly changing electric field is not yet fully understood, it is thought to be the result of molecular action produced by the electrodynamic field. When the high-frequency field is applied to the electrodes, the molecules evidently attempt to align themselves with the field; thus they reverse their direction as the field reverses and if the frequency is several million cycles per second, the heat developed due to molecular action will be considerable.

The dielectric loss or power developed within a given nonconductor when placed within a high-frequency electric field is directly proportional to the square of the applied voltage, the first power of the frequency, dielectric constant and power factor and inversely proportional to the distance between the plates. For low-power factor materials the power developed is expressed by Eqs. (11–5a), (11–5b), (11–5c) and (11–5d).

$$W = \frac{1.41 \times 10^{-12}A\,(pf)fkE^2}{d} \tag{11–5a}$$

or

$$W = \frac{1.41 \times 10^{-12}A\,(lf)fE^2}{d} \tag{11–5b}$$

$$\Delta W = 1.41 \times 10^{-12}(pf)fk\left(\frac{E}{d}\right)^2 \tag{11–5c}$$

or

$$\Delta W = 1.41 \times 10^{-12}(lf)f\left(\frac{E}{d}\right)^2 \tag{11–5d}$$

where   $W$ = total power in watts
$\Delta W$ = watts per cubic inch of dielectric being heated
$A$ = area of one capacitor plate in square inches
$pf$ = power factor of the material
$lf$ = loss factor
$k$ = dielectric constant of material to be heated
$E$ = rms value of the voltage applied between plates
$f$ = frequency of the applied voltage in cycles/second
$d$ = plate separation in inches
All dimensions are illustrated by Fig. 11–31.

The *power factor*, which was considered in Section 4–13, is the cosine of the phase angle between the current through the dielectric and the voltage across it.

The *dielectric constant* is defined as the ratio of the capacitance between the two electrodes or capacitor plates with the dielectric material in question between them, to the capacitance that exists if the dielectric material is replaced by a vacuum, all physical dimensions remaining fixed. Since each nonconducting material has a different power factor and a different dielectric constant, it follows that each will have a different loss and will heat at a different rate even though the same voltage and frequency are applied.

The term *loss factor* is often used to indicate the relative heating rates of various dielectrics. The loss factor is equal to the product of the cotangent of the phase angle and the dielectric constant. In most cases the phase angle is very large and the cotangent of the phase angle is approximately equal to the cosine of the phase angle; thus the loss factor is expressed approximately by Eq. (11–6).

$$\text{loss factor } (lf) = (\text{power factor})(\text{dielectric constant}) = (pf)k \quad (11\text{–}6)$$

**11–13. Voltage, Frequency and Power Considerations.** The most suitable frequency and voltage for a particular dielectric-heating application depend upon the following factors: dielectric constant, power factor, mass, volume and shape of dielectric, heating rate required, difficulty and cost involved in supplying the high-frequency power, and the electrode design. It is usually necessary to hold the applied voltage within certain limits which are dictated primarily by the breakdown voltage between the plates, and insulation problems involved in the design of high-voltage generators. Eq. (11–5a) indicates that the rate at which heat is generated within a given specimen can be increased by increasing either the applied voltage or the frequency. Since there is a limit to the maximum voltage * that can be used, it is only logical that the frequency would be increased in order to obtain a higher heating rate. In most cases the frequency is usually made as high as is practical.

There are, however, factors that limit the maximum frequency that can be used. As the frequency is increased, the design of radio-frequency generators becomes more complex. However, within recent years considerable advance has been made in the design of ultra-high frequency tubes and circuits; at present, vacuum-tube generators of almost any desired frequency and power capacity are available.

If the frequency employed is sufficiently high to give rise to a wavelength which makes the distance $L$ from the connection to the farthest edge of the largest electrode less than $\frac{1}{16}$ of a wavelength, i.e., $L < \lambda/16$, standing waves will be set up which will result in nonuniform heating of the dielectric. The wavelength in the dielectric is expressed by Eq. (11–7).

$$\lambda = \frac{12,000}{f\sqrt{k}} \quad (11\text{–}7)$$

where $\lambda$ = wavelength expressed in inches
$k$ = dielectric constant of the material
$f$ = frequency in megacycles/second

Substituting $16L$ for $\lambda$ in Eq. (11–7), Eq. (11–8) is obtained.

$$f_c = \frac{750}{L\sqrt{k}} \quad (11\text{–}8)$$

---

* The maximum voltage employed in dielectric heating is around 15,000 volts.

where $f_c$ = critical frequency in megacycles/second (the highest frequency
        that can be used without danger of nonuniform heating as a
        result of standing waves)

       $L$ = distance in inches from electrode connection to farthest edge of
        the capacitor plate

The thermal power required for a given dielectric heating application
can be calculated from Eq. (11–4) in the same manner in which the thermal
power required for an induction-heating application is calculated. However, as in the case of induction heating, the power determined by use of
Eq. (11–4) does not include radiation, convection and conduction losses.

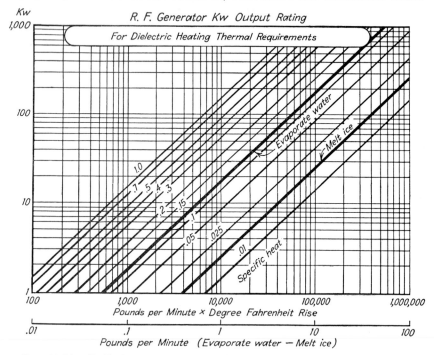

Fig. 11–32. Radio-frequency generator kw output rating for dielectric heating
thermal requirements. (Courtesy Westinghouse Electric Corp.)

Since the temperatures involved in most dielectric heating applications are
usually below 500° Fahrenheit, the losses due to radiation, convection and
conduction are not great and Eq. (11–4) gives a good approximation of the
total power required. The approximation is much better for dielectric
heating than for induction heating. The curves of Fig. 11–32, which are
based on Eq. (11–4), give the thermal power required for heating materials
of different specific heat at various rates. The curves are based on thermal
power only and do not include any losses. Values taken from these curves
should be used only for estimation purposes.

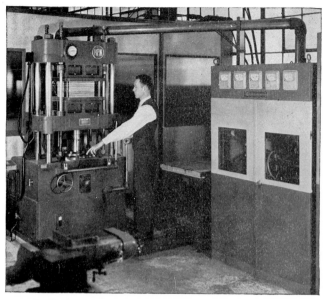

FIG. 11–33.  Radio-frequency plywood bonding.  Machine bonds blocks 12 inches square and 10 inches deep at 130° C.  Polymerization requires only 8 minutes.  (Courtesy Westinghouse Electric Corp.)

FIG. 11–34.  Rayon cakes being dried by radio-frequency energy.  The rayon cakes are carried between the electrodes by a continuous conveyor belt.  (Courtesy Westinghouse Electric Corp.)

Fig. 11–35.  Dielectric core baking unit.  The operator is feeding green sand cores onto the conveyor system which passes cores between the electrodes which are of high potential, 17 megacycles.  The cores emerge from the other end of the funnel in a cured condition in a matter of minutes rather than hours, as it would take in a conventional oven.  (Courtesy Induction Heating Corp.)

Fig. 11–36.  Radio-frequency glueing of wood.  Radio-frequency energy furnished by 20-kw unit.  (Courtesy Westinghouse Electric Corp.)

**11–14. Applications.** Since dielectric heating was first applied commercially in connection with the curing of tobacco in 1936, its applications have increased steadily. Today there are numerous industrial processes that utilize dielectric heating. A few of the present-day applications include:

1. Curing of cores for foundry use.
2. Curing of tobacco.
3. Defrosting of frozen foods.
4. Dehydration of foods.
5. Drying of ceramic ware.
6. Drying of penicillin.
7. Glueing, drying and curing of wood.
8. Glueing of shoe soles.
9. Preheating and curing of plastics.
10. Processing of chemicals during manufacture.
11. Processing of rubber.
12. Roasting and cooking processes.
13. Sterilization of foods.
14. Sterilization of medical supplies.
15. Textile processing.
16. Vulcanizing of tires.
17. Welding of glass.

Several typical dielectric heating operations are illustrated by the accompanying photographs (Figs. 11–33 through 11–36). The type of operation is described briefly under each photograph.

## PROBLEMS

**11–1.** A brass cylinder, the resistivity of which is $3.5 \times 10^{-6}$ ohm-inches at 800° F, is heated by a 450-kc generator to a temperature of 800° F. Determine the depth of current penetration.

**11–2.** If the brass cylinder of Prob. 11–1 is 1 in. in diameter and 6 in. in length, has a density of 0.305 lb/in.² and an average specific heat of 0.093 BTU/lb/deg F, determine the thermal power required to raise the temperature from 70° F to 800° F in 10 sec. All losses may be neglected. Check calculated value with value obtained from the graph of Fig. 11–14.

**11–3.** Utilizing the graph of Fig. 11–14, determine the kw output rating of the rf generator required to raise the temperature of 10 lbs of stainless steel from 70° F to 1,000° F in 30 sec.

**11–4.** Steel tubing 0.5 in. in diameter with a wall thickness of 0.07 in. is to be progressively surface hardened to a depth of 0.03 in. If the scanning speed is to be 6.5 ft/min, determine the power rating of the rf generator required. Repeat for a steel tube 1 in. in diameter with the same wall thickness.

**11–5.** *a*) A block of wood, which has the dimensions and properties listed below, is to be heated by a high-frequency electric field. The arrangement is similar to that of Fig. 11–31. If the rf voltage applied to the capacitor plates is 1,000 v (rms value) and the frequency is $3 \times 10^7$ cps, determine the power developed in the block of wood.

Dimensions of each capacitor plate $= 8$ in. $\times$ 10 in.

Dimensions of block $= 8$ in. $\times$ 10 in. $\times$ 2 in.

Power factor of block $= 0.05$

Dielectric constant of block $= 4$

*b*) Repeat for a block of bakelite of the same dimensions which has a dielectric constant of 6 and a power factor of 0.07.

*c*) Determine the highest frequency that could be used in (*a*) and (*b*) without danger of nonuniform heating.

## BIBLIOGRAPHY

BAKER, R. M., and MADSEN, C. J. High Frequency Heating of Conductors and Nonconductors. *Electrical Engineering.* February, 1945, **64**, 50–7.

BENDZ, W. I. *Electronics for Industry.* New York: John Wiley & Sons, Inc., 1947, pp. 288–352.

BROWN, G. H., HOYLER, C. N., and BIERWIRTH, R. A. *Theory and Application of Radio Frequency Heating.* New York: D. Van Nostrand Co., Inc., 1947.

CHESNUT, F. T. Heating by High-Frequency Induction. *Westinghouse Engineer.* February, 1942, **2**, pp. 11–13.

———. Induction Heating—A History of Its Development. *The Iron Age.* March, 1945, 46–51.

CURTIS, F. W. *High Frequency Induction Heating.* New York: McGraw-Hill Book Co., Inc., 1944.

DUDLEY, B. Induction and Dielectric Heating Equipment. *Electronics.* August, 1945, 110–11.

DURAND, S. R. Mercury Arc Converter for Induction Heating. *Electronic Industries.* June, 1945, 74–8, 150, 154.

JORDAN, J. P. Applications of Vacuum Tube Oscillators to Inductive and Dielectric Heating in Industry. *A.I.E.E. Tran.* 1942, **61**, 831–34.

———. Design of Electronic Heaters for Induction Heating. *I.R.E. Proc.* August, 1944, **32**, 449–52.

———. The Theory and Practice of Industrial Electronic Heating. *General Electric Rev.* December, 1943, **46**, 675–83.

LEVY, C. C., and LUNAS, L. J. Electrical Equipment for Induction Heating. *Westinghouse Engineer.* February, 1942, **2**, 20–2.

LINCOLN, E. S. *Industrial Electric Heating and Electric Furnaces.* New York: Duell, Sloan & Pearce, 1945, pp. 161–90.

MAIERS, M. J. A Survey of Dielectric Heating. *Electrical Engineering.* June, 1945, **64**, pp. 210–11.

OSBORN, H. B., BRACE, P. H., JOHNSON, W. G., CABLE, J. W., and EAGAN, T. E. *Induction Heating.* Cleveland: American Society for Metals, 1946.

STANSEL, N. R. *Induction Heating.* New York: McGraw-Hill Book Co., Inc., 1949.

STORM, H. F. Mercury Arc Converter Masters Metals in Deep Heating. *Allis-Chalmers Electrical Rev.* March, 1945, **10**, 7–13.

VENABLE, D. Dielectric Heating Fundamentals. *Electronics.* November, 1945, 120–24.

WESTINGHOUSE ELECTRIC CORPORATION. *Industrial Electronics Reference Book.* New York: John Wiley & Sons, Inc., 1948, pp. 375–441.

# CHAPTER 12

## BASIC CONTROL CIRCUITS

### Phototube Circuits

Phototube-controlled circuits constitute one of the most versatile and widely used groups of electronic control devices. The wide field of application of phototube circuits is due to the fact that they can be made to exercise almost any type of electrical control in response to a change in illumination.

The current capacity of a phototube is insufficient to operate even the smallest type of relay directly; thus in all practical applications the output must be amplified by one or more stages of vacuum-tube amplification or made to trigger the grid of a gas tube. Both ac and dc are used for the operation of phototube circuits. However, if the application requires that a linear relationship exist between light intensity and output, only dc can be used satisfactorily. For simple switching operations such as counting, etc., which constitute a large percentage of the phototube applications, ac operation is quite suitable. Although ac operation does not require a power supply, the sensitivity obtainable is much less than that obtainable from a dc circuit employing an equivalent phototube.

**12–1. DC-Operated Phototube Control Circuits.** Two basic dc phototube circuits are illustrated by Figs. 12–1a and 12–1b. In the arrangement of Fig. 12–1a an increase in illumination results in an increase in load (relay) current causing the relay to close when the illumination reaches a predetermined value. This type of circuit is referred to as a forward or positive phototube circuit. In the circuit of Fig. 12–1b, the relay current decreases with an increase in the intensity of the light falling on the phototube and is termed a reverse or negative phototube circuit. A common anode battery can be used in either of these circuits. However, for the sake of simplicity, separate anode batteries are used here. The operation of each of these circuits is quite simple.

Consider the circuit of Fig. 12–1a. Let it be assumed that the triode employed as the amplifier tube in this circuit is biased so that the plate current (which is also the current through the relay) is negligible. If such be the case, the relay will not operate. Now if radiation of the correct wavelength falls on the cathode of the phototube, it will cause current to flow through the resistor $R_g$ in the direction indicated; thus it will make the grid of the amplifier tube more positive, resulting in an increase in

347

plate current.   If the intensity of the radiation is great enough, the increase in the current through the relay will be sufficient to cause it to close.   The illumination necessary to cause the relay to close can be controlled by adjustment of the grid bias.

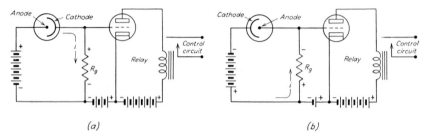

FIG. 12–1.   Dc-operated phototube relay circuits.   (a) Forward circuit.   (b) Reverse circuit.

If it is desirable to have the relay open instead of close when the phototube is illuminated, the circuit of Fig. 12–1b can be used.   In this circuit the amplifier tube is biased so that the plate current is sufficient normally to keep the relay closed.   When light strikes the phototube it will cause current to flow through $R_g$ in the direction indicated by the arrow (this is opposite to the direction of current flow through $R_g$ in the previous circuit). Current flowing in this direction will cause the grid of the triode to become more negative with respect to the cathode and if the intensity of the illumination is sufficient, the current in the plate circuit will decrease sufficiently to cause the relay to open.   The illumination necessary to cause the relay to open may be set at various values by adjustment of the grid bias.

Gas triodes are frequently used in conjunction with phototube control circuits.   Two basic gas-triode-phototube circuits are illustrated in Figs. 12–2a and 12–2b.   These circuits have the advantage over the circuits of 12–1a and 12–1b in that they "lock in" due to an instantaneous change in illumination.   This makes such circuits suitable for alarms, etc., where a continuous signal is required in response to breaking a light beam.

The circuit of Fig. 12–2a might be referred to as a forward circuit.   In this circuit the grid is biased sufficiently negative to prevent the gas triode (thyratron) from firing for the applied plate potential, and as long as the illumination is at approximately a fixed value or changes only very slightly, the relay will not operate.   Now let it be assumed that the illumination is suddenly increased to a much larger value.   If such be the case, the current through $R_1$ will increase, leaving the left side of the capacitor at a much higher potential.   This will cause it to discharge through $R_g$ resulting in a less negative grid which will allow the thyratron to fire.   The amount of change in illumination necessary to cause the gas triode to fire is determined by the circuit parameters.   As pointed out previously (Section 3–2), the characteristics of a gas triode are such that once it fires (ionizes) the only way to cause it to cease firing (deionize) is to open the plate circuit or reduce the plate potential below the ionization potential for sufficient time to permit the tube to deionize. (The deionization time for small thyratrons is usually only a few microseconds.) This means that if the illumination

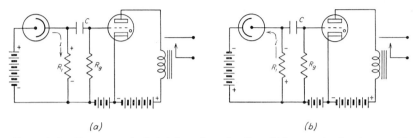

(a)                                      (b)

Fig. 12–2. Dc-operated phototube relay circuits which operate due to a sudden change in illumination. (a) Operates due to an increase in illumination. (b) Operates due to a decrease in illumination.

pulse is sufficient to cause the thyratron to fire, the relay will stay in indefinitely, regardless of the length of time the light pulse lasts. There are, of course, arrangements whereby the relay can be made to open after a predetermined time.

The circuit of Fig. 12–2b differs from the circuit of Fig. 12–2a in that both the connections to the phototube and its anode supply voltage are reversed so that a sudden decrease in illumination will result in a less negative thyratron grid potential and thus cause it to fire.

**12–2. AC-Operated Phototube Control Circuits.** For applications which do not require the high sensitivity, linearity, etc., obtainable only from dc-operated phototube control circuits, ac-operated phototube circuits are usually preferred. The elimination of the dc power supply makes the ac set-up more convenient as well as less expensive.

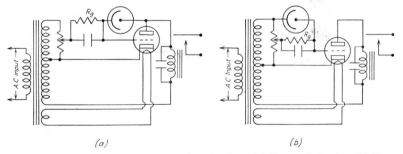

(a)                                      (b)

Fig. 12–3. Ac-operated phototube relay circuits. (a) Forward circuit. (b) Reverse circuit.

The basic circuit diagrams of forward (positive) and reverse (negative) ac-operated phototube control circuits are illustrated in Figs. 12–3a and

12–3*b*, respectively. The circuits of Figs. 12–3*a* and 12–3*b* are quite similar in operation to the dc-operated circuits of Figs. 12–1*a* and 12–1*b*. Consider the circuit of Fig. 12–3*a*. Electrons can flow through the amplifier tube and the phototube in only one direction, i.e., from cathode to anode. Therefore each tube will function as a rectifier allowing current to flow only on the half cycles when its anode is positive with respect to its cathode. From this circuit arrangement it can be seen that when the end of the transformer, which is connected through the relay to the anodes of both the amplifier and phototube, is positive with respect to the tap on the transformer to which the cathode of the amplifier tube is connected, the grid will be negative with respect to the cathode resulting in a negative grid bias. The magnitude of the negative grid bias can be adjusted by changing the

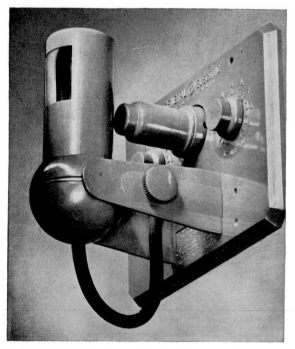

Fig. 12–4. Photoelectric lighting control unit. (Courtesy General Electric Co.)

setting on the potentiometer rheostat which in turn determines the illumination necessary to operate the relay. The current through the phototube, which will flow only during the time that the rectified current flows through the plate circuit of the amplifier tube (relay circuit), will result in a change in voltage drop across the grid resistor and consequently a change in grid bias. A change in grid bias will result in a change in the magnitude of the rectified relay current. An increase in the amount of illumination falling on the phototube will result in an increase in the phototube current which flows through the grid resistance $R_g$ in a direction so as to decrease the effective negative grid potential, increasing the relay current.  On the other hand, a decrease in light intensity will result in an increase in negative grid bias and a decrease in relay current.  The value of illumination necessary for the relay to close or open depends upon the grid bias, plate voltage, characteristics of the phototube, the amplifier and the relay.

The capacitor around the  relay prevents it from opening on negative half-cycles, and the capacitor across the grid resistor corrects for the phase difference existing between grid and plate voltages which results from interelectrode capacitances of both amplifier and phototube.

The negative or reverse ac-operated phototube circuit of Fig. 12–3b is identical to the circuit of Fig. 12–3a with the exception of the way the phototube is connected.  In this case the phototube is connected so that the phototube current flows through the grid resistor in the opposite direction from that in Fig. 12–3b, resulting in an increase in the magnitude of the negative grid bias and a decrease in the relay current with an increase in illumination.  Fig. 12–4 shows a typical ac-operated commercial photoelectric lighting control unit.

**12–3.   Phototube Light-Measuring Circuits.**  As pointed out in Section 9–4, photovoltaic cells are much more suitable for use in light meters than phototubes because they generate a voltage which is proportional to the amount of illumination.  However, phototubes are used to some extent in connection with light measurements, particularly for comparing two sources of illumination.

A simple light meter which makes use of a phototube can be made by substituting for the relay in the circuit of Fig. 12–1a a suitable indicating meter which is calibrated in foot candles instead of milliamperes.  Such an arrangement is shown in Fig. 12–5a.  This circuit has one very serious dis-

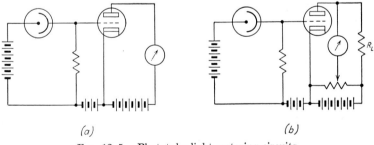

(a)                                        (b)

Fig. 12–5.   Phototube light metering circuits.

advantage in that the change in plate current produced as a result of a change in illumination is very small compared to the normal or operating current and thus would be difficult to read on a meter with sufficient range to be used in the plate circuit.  The fluctuations in line voltage (assuming the dc to be obtained from a rectifier-filter circuit) will also affect the meter indication and in some cases may give as much change in meter reading as is produced by the change in illumination. A simple circuit which eliminates the dc plate current from the meter circuit is shown in Fig. 12–5b. The operation of this circuit is as follows: With illumination on the phototube negligible, the tap on the potentiometer rheostat, which is connected in parallel with the plate supply voltage, is adjusted until the current through the meter is zero. This means that any change in plate current (which results from a change in illumination) will result in a much larger change in meter current than in current through the load resistance $R_L$. The division of current between the two branches, i.e., the meter and $R_L$, is inversely proportional to the resistances of the branches. Thus if $R_L$ is very high compared to the meter resistance, the sensitivity will be high. The operation of this circuit is also affected by line-voltage fluctuations. One way to eliminate this source of error is to employ a regulated power supply and another is to use a two-tube balanced circuit * which is not affected by supply-voltage fluctuations.

One important use of phototubes is in comparing light sources of different intensities. A very simple circuit for comparing two sources of illumination can be made by connecting the outputs of two basic phototube

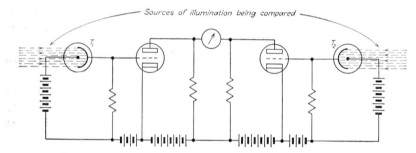

Fig. 12–6.   Circuit for comparing two sources of illumination.

circuits, such as the one illustrated in Fig. 12–1a, through a suitable indicating meter. This arrangement is illustrated in Fig. 12–6. If the two circuits have identical circuit parameters and the light falling on phototube $T_1$ is of the same wavelength and intensity as the light falling on phototube $T_2$, the indicating meter will read zero. Any change in light intensity falling on either of the phototubes will result in a proportional indication by the meter. This circuit will not function properly unless the circuit constants, tube characteristics, etc., are identical. Because of the fact that amplifier tube characteristics differ somewhat at different values of grid potential, linear readings cannot be obtained if the light intensities to be compared differ by a very large factor. The greater the difference in the two in-

---

* For such a circuit see H. J. Reich, *Theory and Applications of Electron Tubes* (New York: McGraw-Hill Book Co., Inc., 1944), p. 546.

tensities, the less the accuracy of the readings.  Although all anode potentials in the circuits of Fig. 12–6 could be obtained from the same dc supply
voltage, separate batteries are used here in order to make the circuit easier
to follow.

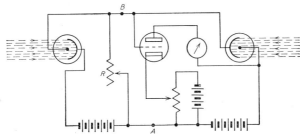

FIG. 12–7.　Circuit for comparing two sources of illumination.  This circuit is more
sensitive than the circuit of Fig. 12–6.

A more sensitive circuit which will give a comparison of illumination
over a much wider range is illustrated by Fig. 12–7.  If the illumination
falling on each of the phototubes in this circuit is the same, the voltage
across each phototube will be the same (assuming the tubes have identical
characteristics).  This means that the junction $B$ between the two phototubes will be at the same potential as point $A$.  Any change in the illumination falling on either of the phototube cathodes will result in an unbalanced
voltage and a change in grid bias which will give a corresponding change

FIG. 12–8.　Recording photoelectric spectrophotometer. (Courtesy General Electric Co.)

in the plate current of the triode.  This change in plate current will be
indicated by the meter in the plate circuit.  The sensitivity of this circuit
can be controlled by adjustment of $R$.

Fig. 12–8 shows a recording spectrophotometer which operates due to
the photoelectric principle.  This device will analyze any color which the

human eye can perceive and is used in textile, paint and chemical industries for color analysis. The phototube is also widely used in pyrometry. A typical photoelectric pyrometer is shown in Fig. 12–9. As will be noticed from the illustration, this pyrometer makes use of phototubes, high-vacuum tubes, gas-filled tubes and relays.

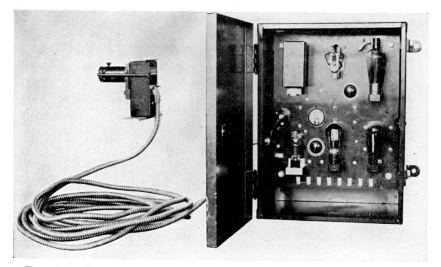

Fig. 12–9.   Photoelectric pyrometer in use in the Florence Pipe Foundry and Machine Co.   (Courtesy General Electric Co.)

**12–4. Conversion of Light to Sound.** * One of the most popular uses of the phototube is in connection with sound pictures. The sound is recorded on the film, constituting what is commonly known as a sound track and the fluctuating light which the phototube receives from the sound track must be converted into a series of electrical impulses and then amplified sufficiently to operate a loud speaker. A basic circuit for converting the light from the sound track to corresponding electrical variations is shown in Fig. 12–10. This circuit is essentially the same as phototube circuits

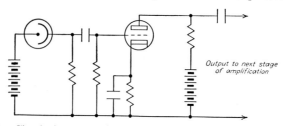

Fig. 12–10.   Circuit for converting variation in light to a varying voltage which can be converted to sound.

* For a discussion of the use of phototubes in sound reproduction see V. K. Zworykin and E. G. Ramberg, *Photoelectricity and Its Applications* (New York: John Wiley & Sons, Inc., 1949), pp. 323–47.

already discussed, the main difference being that a blocking capacitor $C$ is used to prevent the dc anode voltage from being applied to the grid of the amplifier. This capacitor must be of such a value as to offer low impedance to the audio-frequency signal so that there will be little loss in gain due to the ac drop across it. The output of the amplifier tube may be amplified by conventional amplifier circuits in order to obtain the power necessary for operation of the speakers being used.

**12–5. Phototube Counting Circuits.** A simple but very useful application of the phototube is for counting objects on a conveyor belt. The basic diagram of a counting arrangement is shown in Fig. 12–11. A beam of light is focused across the conveyor belt on to the cathode of the phototube. The light must be of the intensity necessary to produce enough current in the phototube circuit to hold the grid of the amplifier tube sufficiently

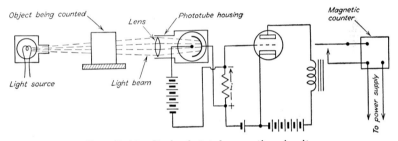

FIG 12–11.   Basic phototube counting circuit.

negative to prevent the plate current from being great enough to operate the relay. When an object on the conveyor belt passes between the light source and the phototube, it cuts off the light from the phototube causing the current in the phototube circuit to go to zero and allowing the grid of the amplifier circuit to swing sufficiently positive to allow enough current through the relay to operate it. Operation of the relay completes the circuit through the magnetic counter causing it to make one count. Most phototube counting circuits are ac-operated; however dc-operated counting circuits are considered here because dc-operation makes possible both a simpler arrangement and an easier understanding of the basic principles involved. By using two phototube circuits similar to the one of Fig. 12–11 and placing the contacts of the first relay in series with the relay of the second phototube circuit, objects moving in the direction from the first phototube to the second will be counted but objects moving in the opposite direction will not be counted. Such an arrangement is illustrated in Fig. 12–12. In this arrangement it is necessary that relay $A$ stay closed until the object passes the second phototube. The relay can be made to stay in for the necessary time in several different ways. One way is to place a capacitor of the proper size across the relay coil. The capacitor becomes charged up during

the time the triode is conducting and requires appreciable time to discharge
after the tube ceases to conduct, thus retaining voltage across the relay.

There are high-speed counting arrangements whereby the magnetic
counter may be slower than the actual number of objects moving past by
a factor $N$; thus counting rates of a much higher frequency than a magnetic
counter can operate can be handled.* Although there is a very large

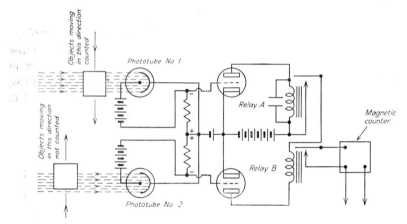

Fig. 12–12.   Directional counting circuit.

number of phototube applications (for a list of typical applications see
Chapter 9), the object of the discussion presented here is to explain a few
basic representative circuits. For a more extensive discussion of phototube applications the reader is referred elsewhere.†

## Time-Delay Circuits

There are numerous types of mechanically and magnetically operated
timing devices for the control of motors, etc. In recent years, however,
electronic timing circuits have become widely used in connection with the
opening and closing of relay contacts at fixed time intervals. There are
many different types of electronic timing circuits in use. However, only a
few basic time-delay circuits will be considered here.

**12–6. Electronic Time-Delay Circuits.** In many electronic time-delay
circuits, time delay is obtained by use of an $RC$ circuit. As pointed out in
Section 4–9, when a dc voltage is applied to the terminals of a circuit containing resistance and capacitance in series, it requires an appreciable time

---

* For such an arrangement see D. G. Fink, *Engineering Electronics* (New York:
McGraw-Hill Book Co., Inc., 1938), p. 313.

† Keith Henney, *Electron Tubes in Industry*, 2nd ed. (New York: McGraw-Hill Book
Co., Inc., 1937), pp. 331–460; Westinghouse Electric Corporation, *Industrial Electronics
Reference Book* (New York: John Wiley & Sons, Inc., 1948), pp. 628–40; V. K. Zworykin
and E. G. Ramberg, *Photoelectricity and Its Applications* (New York: John Wiley &
Sons, Inc., 1949).

for the voltage across the capacitor terminals to reach its maximum value
(the maximum value of voltage the capacitor can attain is equal to the
voltage applied to the terminals of the $RC$ circuit).  The charging time is
a function of the time constant of the circuit, which in turn depends upon
the circuit parameters.  The charging time can be made larger by increasing
either $C$ or $R$.

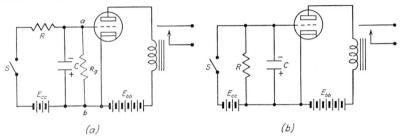

(a)                                              (b)

FIG. 12–13.  Dc-operated time-delay circuits.  (a) When switch $S$ closes there is
a delay in the opening of the relay.  (b) When switch $S$ opens there is a delay in the
closing of the relay.

Two simple dc-operated time-delay arrangements are illustrated by the
sketches of Fig. 12–13.  In the circuit of Fig. 12–13a the relay current will
be at a maximum value so long as switch $S$ is open; however, at the instant
$S$ is closed the capacitor $C$ which is connected between grid and cathode
will begin to charge up with the polarity indicated.  When the potential
across the capacitor reaches a value which makes the grid sufficiently
negative to reduce the relay current below the value necessary for the
relay to hold in, the control circuit will open.  As indicated by the sketch

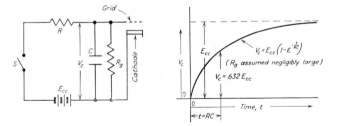

FIG. 12–14.  Grid voltage as a function of time after switch $S$ is closed.

of Fig. 12–14, the grid circuit is a simple $RC$ circuit in which the voltage
across the capacitor builds up exponentially with respect to time in accordance with Eq. (12–1).  ($R_g$ is assumed to be negligibly large.)

$$V_c = E_{cc}(1 - \epsilon^{-t/RC}) \qquad\qquad (12\text{–}1)$$

As Eq. (12–1) indicates, the time necessary for the voltage $V_c$ across
the capacitor to rise to a value equal to $E_{cc}$ is theoretically equal to infinity;
however, the voltage will rise to within a negligible amount of $E_{cc}$ in a very

short time. When the time elapsed is equal to $RC$ seconds ($t = RC$), which is known as the time constant of the circuit (for discussion of time constant see Section 4–9), the voltage $V_c$ across the capacitor will have risen to 63.2 percent of $E_{cc}$. If the circuit parameters of Fig. 12–13$a$ are chosen so that the relay current will be reduced sufficiently to cause the relay to open when the grid voltage reaches 63.2 percent of $E_{cc}$, then the delay time will be equal to $RC$ seconds. The delay time is a function of both $R$ and $C$ and can be controlled by variation in either. A change in $E_{cc}$ or $E_{bb}$ will also affect the delay time but in most cases any change in the delay time is facilitated by adjustment of either $R$ or $C$.

The circuit of Fig. 12–13$b$ operates on essentially the same principle as the circuit of Fig. 12–13$a$. In this circuit the relay closes a short time after $S$ is opened. When $S$ is closed the entire grid bias is impressed between the grid and cathode making the grid sufficiently negative to reduce the

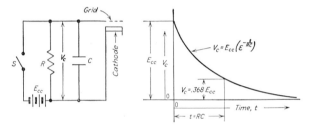

F$_{\text{IG}}$. 12–15.   Grid voltage as a function of time after switch $S$ is opened.

relay current to zero. During the time that $S$ is closed the capacitor will charge up until its voltage is essentially equal to $E_{cc}$. Now let it be assumed that $S$ is opened. At the instant that $S$ is opened the grid voltage will still be equal to $E_{cc}$ (assuming that $S$ remained closed for sufficient time to permit the capacitor to attain a voltage essentially equal to $E_{cc}$). However, at the same instant the capacitor $C$ will begin to discharge through the resistance $R$ and the grid voltage will rapidly be reduced to zero. When the negative grid voltage is reduced to such a value as to allow sufficient plate current to flow, the relay will operate. The discharge of the capacitor is in accordance with Eq. (12–2) and is illustrated by the sketch of Fig. 12–15.

$$V_c = E_{cc}(\epsilon^{-t/RC}) \qquad\qquad (12\text{–}2)$$

In the case of discharge of a capacitor, when $t = RC$ seconds (time constant) the voltage will have dropped to 36.8 percent of its initial value. The delay time can be changed by varying either $R$ or $C$.

Two ac-operated time-delay circuits are illustrated in Fig. 12–16. These circuits are similar in operation to dc time-delay circuits in that the time delay is obtained by use of an $RC$ circuit. The relays operate due to the fact that a vacuum tube will function as a rectifier, passing plate current only

when the anode is made positive with respect to the cathode.  Capacitors
are inserted in parallel with the relays in order to prevent chattering.

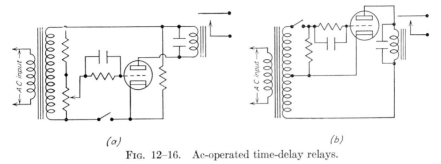

(a)                                                                    (b)

FIG. 12–16.   Ac-operated time-delay relays.

## Basic Thyratron Control Circuits

**12–7. Thyratron Switching Circuits.**  Gas triodes find wide usage as
switching or triggering devices.  When a large amount of current is to be
interrupted, it is usually desirable to use an indirect rather than a direct
means of interruption.  Relays of one type or another are often employed
in such instances, but in many cases the thyratron offers a superior means
of switching large amounts of current, particularly when the switching
must occur very rapidly or in synchronism, with a signal of fairly high frequency.  The thyratron also has the advantage that the arc is made in a
closed container (tube) and can be made as often as desired without concern for combustible fumes that may be in the vicinity of the switching
circuit.

The circuit of Fig. 12–17 is a simple switching arrangement employing
one thyratron.  Let it be assumed that the tube in the circuit of Fig. 12–17
is not conducting and that switches
$S_1$ and $S_2$ are both open.  (These are
spring switches and both will remain
open unless held closed.)  If the tube
is not conducting and the circuit is intact as indicated, then the grid potential of the thyratron is too negative
for the tube to fire.  Although the
grid circuit incorporates a series protective resistance $R_{pg}$, there is no current through this resistance before the
switch is closed; thus the grid voltage

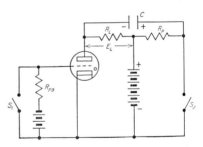

FIG. 12–17.   Basic dc switching circuit utilizing a thyratron as the switch.

is equal to the voltage of the grid battery.  Now if switch $S_1$ is closed
momentarily, the grid of the thyratron will be put at the same potential as
the cathode for a short period of time (time necessary is a function of the
type of tube under consideration but is never greater than several micro-

seconds), and if the anode is at the same time positive with respect to the cathode by an amount greater than that necessary for ionization (or firing of the tube in question at zero grid bias) the tube will fire (or conduct) and current will flow through the load resistance. The current will reach its maximum value instantly and its magnitude is given by Eq. (12–3).

$$I = \frac{V - TD}{R_L} \qquad (12\text{–}3)$$

where  $V$ = voltage of battery in series with plate circuit
$TD$ = tube drop
$R_L$ = load resistance
$I$ = load current

As soon as current begins to flow through the load resistance $R_L$, the capacitor $C$ begins to charge up with the polarity indicated. The voltage across the load will be the maximum voltage to which the capacitor will charge and is given by Eq. (12–4).

$$E_c = E_L = V - TD \qquad (12\text{–}4)$$

where  $E_c$ = maximum voltage developed across capacitor
$E_L$ = voltage across the load resistance

Now if $S_2$ is tapped, the cathode will be made positive with respect to the anode (anode negative with respect to cathode) by the value of voltage existing across the capacitor $C$. If the capacitor is large enough to store up sufficient energy to hold the anode of the tube at a negative potential with respect to its cathode long enough for the tube to deionize, the tube will cease to conduct and the grid will regain control. (The deionization time for various gas thyratrons varies from 100 to 1,000 microseconds.) So far $R_p$ has not been mentioned and the question as to its function will naturally arise. It is a protective resistance and if it were not inserted, tapping the switch $S_2$ would result in a short circuit across the battery or other source of dc that might be used. The resistance $R_p$ should be sufficiently large to prevent excessive current from being drawn from the source of dc when switch $S_2$ is closed. Tapping switch $S_1$ will cause the tube to again begin conduction. If the current capacity of a thyratron is not sufficiently great for the application at hand, the thyratron can be used to fire an ignitron which in turn will handle the heavy current to be controlled.

It is sometimes desirable to switch current between two loads. An arrangement suitable for this type of operation is shown in Fig. 12–18. In this arrangement, switch $S_2$ of Fig. 12–17 has been replaced by another thyratron similar to the first. Tapping switch $S_1$ will put tube $T_1$ in operation, thus allowing current to flow through load $R_{L1}$. The voltage $E_{L1}$ developed across $R_{L1}$ when tube $T_1$ conducts will cause the capacitor $C$ to charge up. When fully charged the right side of the capacitor will be positive with respect to the left side by voltage $E_{L1}$. Tapping $S_2$ will fire tube $T_2$ and extinguish tube $T_1$. Consider what takes place when $S_2$ is tapped. Since the anode of tube $T_2$ is highly positive with respect to its cathode, putting the grid at the same potential as the cathode will cause tube $T_2$

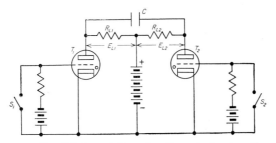

FIG. 12–18.   Parallel dc switching circuit employing two thyratrons.

to fire. At the instant tube $T_2$ fires, the positive side of the capacitor is only a few volts above the cathode potential of both tubes; thus, momentarily the cathode of tube $T_1$ will be made positive with respect to its anode (anode negative with respect to cathode) and it will cease to fire (assuming that $C$ is of sufficient capacity to store up enough energy to hold the cathode of the tube positive with respect to the anode for sufficient time to permit it to deionize). While tube $T_2$ is conducting, $C$ will charge up with opposite

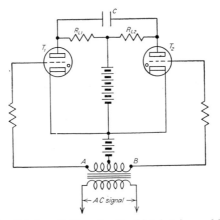

FIG. 12–19.   Parallel dc switching circuit which is triggered by an ac signal.

polarity (left side positive and right side negative); thus, tapping $S_1$ will again put tube $T_1$ in operation and extinguish tube $T_2$. The principle involved in this circuit is the basis of many more complex circuits which are utilized in various switching applications. A slightly more involved circuit which will switch current between two loads in synchronism with a small signal voltage is shown in Fig. 12–19.

Consider the circuit of Fig. 12–19. During the part of the cycle when terminal $A$ of the transformer is sufficiently positive to allow tube $T_1$ to fire, the grid of tube $T_2$ will at the same time be too negative for it to fire. On the next half cycle, terminal $B$ becomes sufficiently positive to allow tube $T_2$ to fire and as soon as tube $T_2$ fires, the capacitor discharges through tube $T_2$ causing the anode of tube $T_1$ to become negative with respect to its cathode; thus it ceases to fire. On the next half cycle, tube $T_1$ will fire and tube $T_2$ will go out. This process repeats itself each cycle so long as the signal is applied.

**12–8. Inverter Circuits.** By replacing the load in the circuit of Fig. 12–19 with a suitable center-tapped transformer and placing an iron core inductor in series with the dc supply, a circuit capable of converting dc to ac results. Such an arrangement, termed a parallel inverter circuit, is shown in Fig. 12–20$a$. As will be noted from the circuit diagram, an exciting signal of the same frequency as the desired output is required for operation.

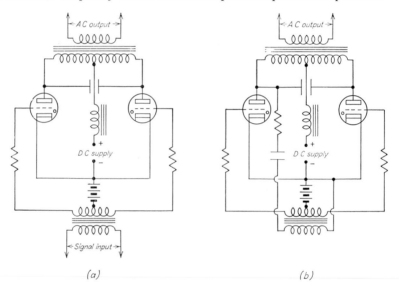

FIG. 12–20.   Parallel inverter circuits. ($a$) Separately excited. ($b$) Self-excited.

By inserting a tuned $RLC$ circuit, it is possible to convert the separately excited inverter circuit of Fig. 12–20$a$ to the self-excited inverter circuit of Fig. 12–20$b$. The output frequency of the self-excited inverter is equal to the resonant frequency of the tuned circuit from which the input signal is obtained. Although the necessity of an external signal is eliminated, the frequency stability of the self-excited circuit is not so good as that of the separately-excited circuit.

There are many more complex types of electronic inverter circuits. High-power inverter circuits employ ignitrons, excitrons and multi-anode pool-type tubes and generally operate in conjunction with three-phase power systems. In such cases, it is, of course, necessary to use thyratrons or some other means of controlling the firing of the mercury-pool tubes.

One very important application of inversion is in the interconnection of two ac power systems of different frequencies, such as a 25- and a 60-cycle system. An electronic frequency changer for interconnecting two ac power systems consists, first, of a mercury-arc rectifier unit for converting ac to dc and second, of an inverter unit for changing the dc to ac of the desired frequency. Electronic frequency conversion is ideal in that the amount of power interchanged between the two power systems may be controlled in any manner whatsoever.

Another important use of inversion is in connection with regenerative braking. When the train which uses regenerative braking is going down a heavy grade, the railway motor acts as a dc generator, braking the train and at the same time generating dc power. This dc power can be converted to ac by an appropriate electronic inverter and then returned to the ac line.

**12–9. Grid-Controlled Rectifier Circuits.** The thyratron (gas triode) is widely used as a grid-controlled rectifier. In all of the rectifier circuits considered in Chapter 7, the only means of changing the magnitude of the rectified current is to change the magnitude of the ac input voltage or the load resistance. With both the load resistance and the applied alternating voltage held constant, it is possible with a thyratron rectifier circuit to exercise very fine control over the rectified current. This makes the thyratron extremely useful in many types of industrial control circuits.

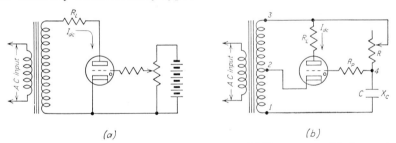

(a)                                    (b)

Fig. 12–21. Grid-controlled rectifier circuits. (a) Dc or amplitude control. (b) Phase control.

The dc current in a thyratron rectifier circuit can be controlled by varying the magnitude of the dc grid bias, as illustrated by the circuit of Fig. 12–21a, or by applying ac to the grid and controlling the phase relation between the grid and plate voltages as indicated by the circuit of Fig. 12–21b.

**12–10. Amplitude Control.** The dc current through the load resistance $R_L$ in the circuit of Fig. 12–21a is controlled by varying the magnitude of the grid bias and is termed amplitude control. If the grid bias is zero, the thyratron will begin conduction as soon as the anode is made only slightly positive with respect to the cathode (this value depends upon the type tube and is as low as 20 volts for some tubes) and will continue to conduct until the anode-cathode potential falls below the tube drop which is in the neighborhood of 12 volts for the average thyratron. This means that the tube will conduct for essentially a half-cycle and the wave form of the load current will be the same as that of a half-wave rectifier employing a mercury-vapor diode. If the grid is made negative with respect to the cathode, a much higher anode voltage will be required to cause the tube to fire. This means that the tube will fire later in the cycle and the average value of the rectified current will be decreased as indicated by Fig. 12–22. There is a limit to how negative the grid can be made. If it is made too negative the tube will not conduct during any part of the cycle.

The rectified current for any given set of conditions can be determined either graphically or analytically; however, regardless of whether a graphical or analytical solution is employed, the control characteristic for the thyratron being used must be available. The control characteristic for a gas triode, which is discussed in Section 3–2, represents a plot of grid voltage against corresponding values of anode voltage necessary for firing.

The graphical analysis of the grid-controlled rectifier circuit of Fig. 12–21a is illustrated in Fig. 12–22. The control characteristic of the tube being

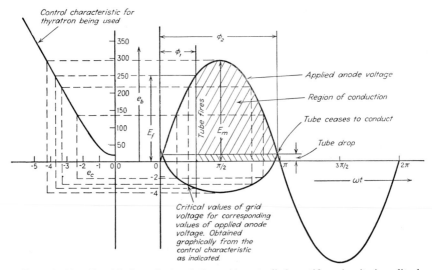

Fig. 12–22. Graphical analysis of the grid-controlled rectifier circuit (amplitude control) of Fig. 12–21a.

used is plotted to the same scale as the sinusoidal impressed voltage. From the control characteristic a critical grid-voltage curve can be plotted. The construction of this curve is indicated on the diagram. By projecting any value of grid voltage from the critical grid-voltage curve vertically until the impressed anode-voltage curve is intersected, the value of anode voltage that must be reached before the tube fires is obtained. This value which will be designated as $E_f$ (firing voltage) can also be obtained directly from the control characteristic by projecting the value of grid voltage being used, up to the control characteristic and determining the corresponding value of anode voltage. Although plotting the critical grid-voltage curve is not necessary for a solution, it does give a better picture of what is happening.

The shaded area in the diagram represents the region of current flow; thus by determining the shaded area graphically * (excluding the area representing the tube drop) and dividing by the base, which is $2\pi$ radians for one complete cycle, the average or dc voltage drop across $R_L$ can be determined. The average or direct current can be obtained by dividing the dc voltage drop by the load resistance.

The analytical approach offers the best solution to this type of problem. The rectified current can be determined by integrating under the anode-voltage curve between the firing angle $\phi_1$ and the extinction angle $\phi_2$, excluding the tube drop, and then dividing the area thus obtained by $2\pi R_L$.

Before the area in question can be determined the limits of the integral, $\phi_1$ and $\phi_2$, must be determined. The firing voltage $E_f$ can be determined from the control characteristic for the grid-bias being used. After the firing voltage $E_f$ has been determined the firing angle $\phi_1$ can be determined analytically as follows:

$$\text{Equation of applied anode voltage} = E_m \sin \omega t$$

When the magnitude of the applied potential is equal to $E_f$, then

$$\omega t = \phi_1$$

Therefore

$$E_f = E_m \sin \phi_1$$

and

$$\sin \phi_1 = \frac{E_f}{E_m} \tag{12–5}$$

where $E_f$ = firing voltage for the grid bias used
   $E_m$ = maximum value of the applied anode voltage

The angle $\phi_2$ at which the tube is extinguished can be determined by equating the deionizing potential or tube drop (tube drop is equal approximately to the deionization potential) to the equation for the impressed voltage.

$$TD = E_m \sin \phi_2$$

$$\sin \phi_2 = \frac{TD}{E_m}$$

where $TD$ = voltage drop across tube during conduction

---

* If curve is plotted on fine cross-section paper, the area can be determined fairly accurately by counting blocks. The area can also be determined by a mechanical integrating device such as a planimeter, if such an instrument is available.

The average or dc voltage existing across the load resistance can be found by integrating the sine wave between the limits of $\phi_2$ and $\phi_1$ and subtracting the voltage that is consumed by the tube drop.

$$E_{av} = E_{dc} = \frac{1}{2\pi} \int_{\phi_1}^{\phi_2} (E_m \sin \omega t - TD) \, d(\omega t) \qquad (12\text{--}6a)$$

$$I_{dc} = \frac{E_{dc}}{R_L} = \frac{1}{2\pi R_L} \int_{\phi_1}^{\phi_2} (E_m \sin \omega t - TD) \, d(\omega t) \qquad (12\text{--}6b)$$

EXAMPLE. Assume that the tube, the control characteristic of which is given in Fig. 12–22, is employed in the grid-controlled rectifier circuit of Fig. 12–21a with the circuit parameters listed below. Determine the reading of a dc ammeter placed in the plate circuit.

$R_L = 100$ ohms

$E_c = -3.75$ v

Secondary transformer voltage $= 212$ v (rms value)

*Solution:* From the graph of Fig. 12–22 it can be seen that with a grid potential of $-3.75$ v the thyratron requires an anode potential of 250 v for firing; therefore $E_f = 250$ v

$$E_m = 212\sqrt{2} = 300 \text{ v}$$

$$\sin \phi_1 = \frac{E_f}{E_m}$$

$$= \tfrac{250}{300} = 0.834$$

$$\phi_1 = 56.5° \text{ or } 0.987 \text{ rad}$$

$$\sin \phi_2 = \frac{TD}{E_m}$$

Assuming a tube drop of 20 v,

$$\sin \phi_2 = \tfrac{20}{300} = 0.0666$$

$$\phi_2 = 176.2° \text{ or } 3.08 \text{ rad}$$

Substituting in Eq. (12–6b),

$$I_{dc} = \frac{1}{2\pi 100} \int_{56.5° \text{ or } 0.987 \text{ rad}}^{176.2° \text{ or } 3.08 \text{ rad}} (300 \sin \omega t - 20) \, d(\omega t)$$

$$= \frac{1}{200\pi} [-300 \cos \omega t - 20\omega t]_{56.5° \text{ or } 0.987 \text{ rad}}^{176.2° \text{ or } 3.08 \text{ rad}}$$

$$= \frac{1}{200\pi} [299 - 61.5 + 165.5 + 19.75]$$

$$= 0.672 \text{ amp}$$

Employing amplitude control it is only possible to vary the firing angle from approximately zero up to 90°. If the plate potential does not reach a value great enough to cause the tube to fire before it passes its maximum value which occurs at 90° it is obvious that the tube will never fire. This means that it is only possible to vary the rectified current from its maximum or half-wave value to approximately half of this value.

**12–11. Phase Control.** The magnitude of the load current in a controlled-grid rectifier circuit can be varied from its maximum value to approximately zero by applying ac to the grid and shifting the phase angle between grid and plate voltages. Since this method allows a wider range of control over the rectified current than amplitude control and does not necessitate a dc supply for grid bias, it is generally preferred to amplitude control.

Although there are many different circuit arrangements for controlling the phase angle between grid and plate voltages, discussion of one phase-shift network will make clear the fundamental principles of operation. Utilizing the phase-shift circuit of Fig. 12–21b, the phase angle $\theta$ between grid and plate potentials can be varied over a range of approximately 180° by variation in either $R$ or $C$. (By replacing $R$ with a phototube the rectified current can be made to be a function of the light falling on the phototube.) An expression for the phase angle $\theta$ in terms of circuit parameters can be readily determined. Applying Kirchhoff's voltage law to the phase-shift circuit of Fig. 12–21b, the following equations can be written.

$$\mathbf{V}_{12} + \mathbf{V}_{23} + \mathbf{V}_{34} + \mathbf{V}_{41} = 0$$
$$\mathbf{V}_{12} + \mathbf{V}_{23} = \mathbf{V}_{43} + \mathbf{V}_{14}$$
$$\mathbf{V}_{12} + \mathbf{V}_{23} = \mathbf{V}_{13}$$
$$\mathbf{V}_{12} = \mathbf{V}_{23} \text{ (center-tapped transformer)}$$
$$\mathbf{V}_{23} = \mathbf{V}_{kp} \text{ (voltage between cathode and plate)}$$
$$\mathbf{V}_{24} = \mathbf{V}_{kg} \text{ (voltage between cathode and grid)}$$
$$\mathbf{V}_{24} + \mathbf{V}_{43} + \mathbf{V}_{32} = 0$$
$$\mathbf{V}_{24} = \mathbf{V}_{34} + \mathbf{V}_{23}$$
$$\mathbf{V}_{24} + \mathbf{V}_{41} + \mathbf{V}_{12} = 0$$
$$\mathbf{V}_{24} = \mathbf{V}_{14} + \mathbf{V}_{21}$$

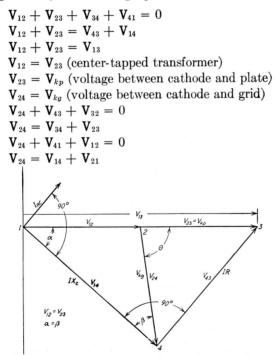

Fig. 12–23.  Vector diagram of phase-shift network of Fig. 12–21b.

From these equations the vector diagram of Fig. 12–23 can be constructed. Referring to the vector diagram the following relationships will be seen to exist.

$$\tan \alpha = \frac{IR}{IX_C}$$

or
$$\tan \alpha = \frac{R}{X_C}$$

but
$$\alpha + \beta = \theta$$

Since the triangle under consideration is an isosceles triangle ($\mathbf{V}_{12} = \mathbf{V}_{24}$),

then
$$\alpha = \beta$$

and
$$\theta = 2\alpha$$

and
$$\theta = 2 \tan^{-1} \frac{R}{X_C} \tag{12-7}$$

By use of Eq. (12–7) the phase angle between grid and plate voltages can be determined.

The rectified load current in the case of phase control can be determined either graphically or analytically in essentially the same manner as in the case of amplitude control. The only difference is in determining the firing

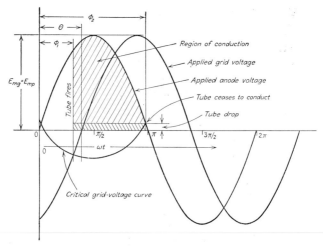

Fig. 12–24. Graphical analysis of grid-controlled rectifier circuit (phase control) of Fig. 12–21b.

angle $\phi_1$. Referring to the graphical analysis of the circuit of Fig. 12–21b which is given in Fig. 12–24 it can be seen that the expression for the rectified current is the same as in the case of amplitude control; therefore

$$I_{av} = I_{dc} = \frac{1}{2\pi R_L} \int_{\phi_1}^{\phi_2} (E_m \sin \omega t - TD)\, d(\omega t)$$

The symbols used here have the same significance as in the case of amplitude control and $\phi_2$, the angle at which the tube ceases to fire, is found in the same way as in the case of amplitude control. The firing angle $\phi_1$, however, is found differently. Before the value of $\phi_1$ can be determined the phase angle $\theta$ must be determined by applying Eq. (12–7). Although $\theta_1$ is approximately equal to $\theta$ and the two angles can generally be considered as being equal without any appreciable error, if a better approximation of $\phi_1$ is required the following procedure can be used.

Let $K$ * = ratio of plate voltage $E_p$ to grid voltage $E_g$ necessary for the tube to fire. (The ratio, which is discussed in Section 3–2, can be obtained from the grid-control characteristic.)

When the tube fires

$$K = \frac{E_{mp} \sin \phi_1}{E_{mg} \sin (\phi_1 - \theta)}$$

where $E_{mp}$ = maximum value of anode voltage
$E_{mg}$ = maximum value of grid voltage

Solving for $\phi_1$

$$\sin \phi_1 = K \frac{E_{mg}}{E_{mp}} [\sin (\phi_1 - \theta)]$$

$$\sin \phi_1 - K \frac{E_{mg}}{E_{mp}} \sin \phi_1 \cos \theta = -K \frac{E_{mg}}{E_{mp}} \cos \phi_1 \sin \theta$$

$$\frac{\sin \phi_1}{\cos \phi_1} = \frac{-K \left(\dfrac{E_{mg}}{E_{mp}}\right) \sin \theta}{1 - K \left(\dfrac{E_{mg}}{E_{mp}}\right) \cos \theta}$$

$$\tan \phi_1 = \frac{\sin \theta}{- \dfrac{E_{mp}}{K E_{mg}} + \cos \theta} \tag{12–8}$$

EXAMPLE. Assume the following circuit parameters for the rectifier circuit of Fig. 12–21b and solve for the load current.

$E_p = 110$ v (rms value)      $C = 0.468$ microfarads
$E_g = 110$ v (rms value)      $R_L = 50$ ohms
$f = 60$ cps                          $K = -30$
$R = 1,520$ ohms                 $TD = 15$ v

Solution:

$$X_C = \frac{1}{2\pi f C}$$

$$= \frac{1}{2\pi 60 (0.468 \times 10^{-6})}$$

$$= 5,670$$

---

* Although $K$ is not constant, values of current calculated on the assumption that $K$ is constant check reasonably well with experimental values.

Solving for $\theta$,

$$\theta = 2 \tan^{-1} \frac{R}{X_C}$$

$$= 2 \tan^{-1} \frac{1,520}{5,670}$$

$$= 2 \tan^{-1} 0.268$$

$$= 2(15°) = 30°$$

Solving for $\phi_1$,

$$\tan \phi_1 = \frac{\sin \theta}{- \dfrac{E_{mp}}{KE_{m\varrho}} + \cos \theta}$$

$$= \frac{0.5}{0.033 + 0.866}$$

$$= \frac{0.5}{0.899} = 0.556$$

$$\phi_1 = 29°$$

Solving for $\phi_2$,

$$\sin \phi_2 = \frac{TD}{E_m}$$

$$= \tfrac{15}{155}$$

$$= 0.0968$$

$$\phi_2 = 174.5° \text{ *}$$

Substituting limits in Eq. (12-6b) and solving

$$I_{dc} = I_{av} = \frac{1}{2\pi R_L} \int_{29° \text{ or } 0.505 \text{ rad}}^{174.5° \text{ or } 3.04 \text{ rad}} (155 \sin \omega t - 15) d(\omega t)$$

$$= \frac{1}{2\pi 50} [-155.5 \cos \omega t - 15\omega t]_{29° \text{ or } 0.505 \text{ rad}}^{174.5° \text{ or } 3.04 \text{ rad}}$$

$$= \frac{1}{100\pi} [155 - 45.6 + 136 + 7.6]$$

$$= \frac{253}{100\pi} = 0.805 \text{ amp}$$

**12-12. Thyratron Light-Dimming Circuits.** One important use of thyratrons is in the control of alternating current through a load. The dimming of ac-operated lights in large theaters, etc., is a very common application of thyratron control. The basic circuit diagram of a light-dimming arrangement which makes use of a thyratron control circuit and a saturable reactor is illustrated in Fig. 12-25. The lamps in this circuit operate on ac, the magnitude of which can be controlled by varying the firing angle of the

---

* Since the sign of both first and second quadrant angles is positive, mathematically $\phi_2$ can be either 5.5° or 174.5°. By referring to the diagram of Fig. 12-24, however, it can be seen that the second quadrant angle ($\phi_2 = 174.5°$) is the extinction angle.

thyratron. The portion of the cycle over which the thyratron conducts is controlled by a phase-shift circuit similar to the one discussed in Section 12–11.

The reactor is wound so that the fluxes set up by coils 1 and 3 add around the outside circuit and cancel through the center leg. This results in high reactance in series with the lamps and correspondingly low brilliancy. If the thyratron grid circuit is adjusted so the tube will conduct over an

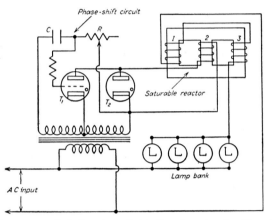

Fig. 12–25. Phase-controlled thyratron light dimming circuit with saturable reactor.

appreciable portion of the cycle, the rectified current through coil 2 will saturate the core of the reactor. The greater the magnitude of the direct current through coil 2 the greater the degree of saturation of the iron core and the less the reactance of coils 1 and 3 which are in series with the lamp load. If the circuit parameters are properly chosen and the phase-shift circuit adjusted so that the thyratron fires for approximately 180° (maximum portion of the cycle over which the tube can be made to fire), the dc through coil 2 will be sufficient to produce almost complete saturation reducing the reactance of coils 1 and 3 to a negligible value and allowing full line voltage to be impressed across the lamps. This will, of course, give maximum lamp brilliancy. On the other hand, when the thyratron conducts only over a very small portion of the cycle the reactance in series with the lamps will be high and the brilliancy low. By varying the phase angle between the grid and plate potentials of the thyratron any desired lamp brilliancy can be readily obtained.

The gas diode $T_2$ is inserted to maintain current through the dc winding of the reactor during the nonconducting period of the gas triode $T_1$. When the current through coil 2 is increasing, the voltage induced in the winding $\left(e = -L \dfrac{di}{dt}\right)$ is in a direction so as to make the anode of $T_1$ negative with respect to the cathode; however, when the current through the coil is de-

FIG. 12–26.  Thyratron-reactor group in basement reactor room of Radio City Music Hall, New York.  (Courtesy General Electric Co.)

creasing, the voltage induced in the coil is in the opposite direction making the anode of $T_2$ positive with respect to the cathode and causing it to conduct.   Conduction will continue until the thyratron begins to conduct again.   Omission of the diode would result in continuous conduction of the thyratron and make it impossible to control the amount of rectified current.

When compared to rheostats as a means of dimming lights, the thyratron-control circuit is far more efficient and makes possible a much finer degree of control over the brilliancy.   The illustration of Fig. 12–26 shows a bank of thyratrons used for lighting control at Radio City Music Hall.

**12–13. Thyratron Control of Ignition Firing.**   As mentioned in Section 3–6, in order to fire an ignitron it is necessary to pass a current through the ignitor circuit for a short period of time.   The time required for ignition of an ignitron is in the neighborhood of 100 microseconds.   In many

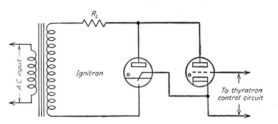

Fig. 12–27.   Ignitron rectifier circuit in which the firing of the ignitron is accomplished by a thyratron.   The firing of the thyratron can be controlled by any conventional method.

applications the ignitor current is supplied by copper-oxide rectifier circuits which are operated by a mechanical relay or switch; however, there are numerous welding applications, etc. which require higher control speed than is obtainable from the most rapid mechanical relays.   In such cases the firing of ignitrons is accomplished by thyratron control circuits.

The simplest type of ignitron firing circuit which makes use of a thyratron is shown in Fig. 12–27.   In this circuit the thyratron is in series with the ignitor and at the same time in parallel with the ignitron across the ac input.   The firing of the thyratron can be controlled by any suitable control circuit.   As soon as the thyratron fires, current exists in the ignitor circuit and at the same time the anode of the ignitron is positive with respect to the mercury pool; thus the ignitron fires.   As soon as the ignitron conducts, the voltage drop across the thyratron and ignitor in series is equal to the voltage drop across the ignitron.   This means that the voltage across the thyratron will be too low to maintain ionization and the thyratron will cease to conduct.   The ignitron will continue to conduct until the end of the first half cycle when the anode voltage drops below the value necessary to maintain conduction.   The ignitron cannot fire again until the thyratron is fired again. Since the thyratron conducts for only a very small portion of each cycle, the over-all efficiency is decreased only very little due to the loss in the ignitor circuit.

**12–14. Thyratron Welding Control Circuits.** Another important application of thyratrons is in connection with the control of current in welding

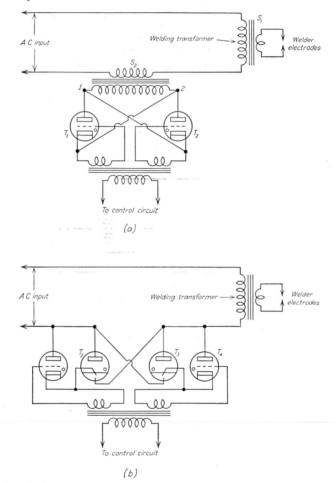

Fig. 12–28. Welding control circuits. (a) Thyratron welding control circuit employing a series transformer. (b) Ignitron welding control unit.

circuits. The schematic circuit diagrams of Fig. 12–28 illustrate two basic thyratron controlled welding circuits. Fig. 12–28a is the circuit of a series transformer type of welding control unit. This circuit makes possible the control of currents much in excess of the rating of the thyratrons by use of a series transformer. The series transformer $S_2$ which is placed in series with the welding transformer $S_1$ is a step-up transformer having its low voltage high current winding in series with the welding circuit and its high voltage low current winding in series with the thyratrons. The thyratrons are connected across the transformer $S_2$ in opposite directions, i.e., thyratron $T_1$ has its anode connected to terminal 1 and its cathode to terminal 2. The anode of thyratron $T_2$ is connected to terminal 2 and its cathode to terminal 1. This means that thyratron $T_1$ can conduct only during the portion of the cycle when terminal 1 is positive and that thyratron $T_2$ can conduct only during the portion of the cycle when terminal 2 is positive; thus the combination will pass alternating current if both tubes are fired during each cycle. If neither tube is conducting, the secondary winding of the transformer will be open, resulting in a very high primary reactance limiting the line current to a negligible value. When alternating voltage is applied to the control circuit each grid will be made alternately positive and negative during each cycle and both tubes will conduct during each cycle, effectively short-circuiting the transformer. With a short-circuit across the secondary the primary will offer negligible reactance to the line current; thus normal voltage will be applied to the welding transformer.

Although the series transformer arrangement of Fig. 12–28a has been used extensively in connection with the control of resistance welding, at present the ignitron control circuit has largely replaced it for this application. The circuit of Fig. 12-28b illustrates the basic circuit of an ignitron welding control unit in which the firing of the ignitrons is controlled by thyratrons. Referring to the circuit of Fig. 12–28b it will be seen that the thyratrons $T_1$ and $T_4$ are connected in series with the ac line in opposite directions (in the same manner as in the case of Fig. 12–28a); therefore, tube $T_1$ fires when the lower side of the ac line is positive and tube $T_2$ fires when the upper side of the ac line is positive. The ignitrons $T_2$ and $T_3$ are connected up in the same manner as the thyratrons so far as the ac line is concerned. The ignitor circuit of ignitron $T_2$ is in series with the plate circuit of thyratron $T_1$ and the ignitor circuit of ignitron $T_3$ is in series with the plate circuit of thyratron $T_4$; therefore when the thyratron $T_1$ fires, it will fire ignitron $T_2$ and similarly, when thyratron $T_4$ fires, ignitron $T_3$ will fire. This means that when ac is applied to the grids of the thyratrons the ignitrons will pass ac. Current will flow through the primary of the welding transformer only so long as the ac control signal is applied to the grids of the thyratrons. This circuit is essentially the same as the circuit of Fig. 12–28a with the exception that the series transformer has been replaced by ignitrons.

## PROBLEMS

**12–1.** Work out a phototube arrangement which might be used to control some process in your particular field of endeavor.

**12–2.** Specify all the circuit parameters (including a suitable tube and voltages) for the time-delay circuit of Fig. 12–13a if the relay is to open one second after switch $S$ is closed. Assume that the relay has a resistance of 1,000 ohms, negligible inductance and requires a current of 5 ma to close.

**12–3.** Give the circuit parameters for the arrangement of Fig. 12–13$b$ if it is necessary that the relay close one second after switch $S$ is opened. Assume the same relay as in Prob. 12–2.

**12–4.** A thyratron, the control characteristic of which is given in Fig. 12–22, is to be utilized as a controlled-grid rectifier. If the rms value of the ac-input voltage is 115 v, the tube drop 15 v and the load resistance 100 ohms, determine the reading of a dc ammeter placed in series with the plate circuit when the dc grid voltage is set at ($a$) $-2$ v and ($b$) $-4$ v.

**12–5.** If the following information is known concerning a thyratron rectifier circuit in which the magnitude of the rectified current is to be controlled by varying the phase angle between plate and grid voltages (Fig. 12–21$b$), determine the magnitude of the rectified current.

| | |
|---|---|
| Tube—Gas triode | $R_L = 100$ ohms |
| $K = -20$ | $R_p = 20,000$ ohms |
| $TD = 15$ v | $R = 700$ ohms |
| $E_g = 120$ v (rms value) | $C = 0.5$ microfarad |
| $E_p = 120$ v (rms value) | $f = 60$ cps |

## BIBLIOGRAPHY

BATCHER, R. R., and MOULIC, W. *The Electronic Control Handbook.* New York: Caldwell-Clements, Inc., 1946, pp. 178–95, 247–63, 286–94.

BENDZ, W. I. *Electronics for Industry.* New York: John Wiley & Sons, Inc., 1947, pp. 355–86.

CHUTE, G. M. *Electronics in Industry.* New York: McGraw-Hill Book Co., Inc., 1946, pp. 15–46, 62–89, 145–70.

———. Fundamentals of Industrial Electronics. General Electric reprint of a series of eight articles which appeared in *Steel*, April 3 to May 22, 1944.

COCKRELL, W. D. *Industrial Electronic Control.* New York: McGraw-Hill Book Co., Inc., 1944, pp. 129–96.

FINK, D. C. *Engineering Electronics.* New York: McGraw-Hill Book Co., Inc., 1938, pp. 306–30.

GULLIKSEN, F. H., and VEDDER, E. H. *Industrial Electronics.* New York: John Wiley and Sons, Inc., 1935, pp. 63–96, 119–21.

HENNEY, KEITH. *Electron Tubes in Industry.* 2nd ed. New York: McGraw-Hill Book Co., Inc., 1937, pp. 119–62, 331–460.

REICH, H. J. *Theory and Applications of Electron Tubes.* 2nd ed. New York: McGraw-Hill Book Co., Inc., 1944, pp. 448–532, 543–51.

RICHTER, WALTHER. *Fundamentals of Industrial Electronic Circuits.* New York: McGraw-Hill Book Co., Inc., 1947, pp. 189–95, 436–67, 502–13.

ROGERS, G. L. Welding Controls. *Electronics.* December, 1942, **15**, 63–7, 174.

RYDER, J. D. *Electronic Engineering Principles.* New York: Prentice-Hall, Inc., 1947, pp. 329–58.

STADUM, C. B. Basic Electronic Circuits for Industrial Functions. *Production Engineering.* February, 1944, **15**, 92–6.

WALKER, R. C., and LANCE, T. M. C. *Photoelectric Cell Applications,* 2nd ed. London: Sir Isaac Pitman & Sons, Ltd., 1935, pp. 22–97.

WESTINGHOUSE ELECTRIC CORPORATION, *Industrial Electronics Reference Book.* New York: John Wiley & Sons, Inc., 1948, pp. 278–89, 361–73, 599–640.

ZWORYKIN, V. K., and RAMBERG, E. G. *Photoelectricity and Its Applications.* New York: John Wiley & Sons, Inc., 1949.

# INDEX OF NAMES

# SUBJECT INDEX